Conserving Life on Earth

The bald eagle, whose population has declined steadily as a result of environmental contamination with DDT and related compounds. (Ralph L. Shook—Courtesy *Questar*)

Conserving Life on Earth

DAVID W. EHRENFELD

NEW YORK OXFORD UNIVERSITY PRESS 1972

Permission to use copyright materials is hereby gratefully acknowledged:

To Brandt & Brandt, Miss Sonia Brownell, and Secker & Warburg for a selection from *Coming Up For Air*, by George Orwell, copyright 1950 by Harcourt, Brace & World, Inc.

To Delacorte Press and Kurt Vonnegut, Jr., for a poem from *Cat's Cradle*, copyright © 1963 by Kurt Vonnegut, Jr.

To The Macmillan Company and Dame Veronica Wedgwood for a selection from *The King's Peace* by C. V. Wedgwood, copyright 1955 by C. V. Wedgwood.

To the American Museum of Natural History for a selection from "The Melan-choly addiction of 'Ol King Cotton" by Robert van den Bosch, *Natural History Magazine*, Dec. 1971, copyright © 1971 by American Museum of Natural History.

To The American Association for the Advancement of Science for Figures 4 and 6 from "Gardens on Swamps," by Pedro Armillas, *Science 174*, 12 Nov. 1971, pp. 654-61. Copyright 1971 by The American Association for the Advancement of Science.

For Joan

Foreword

When I first met David Ehrenfeld he was fresh out of Harvard. He had a good grounding in modern biology, a love of animals, and—to me astonishing in a native-born citizen of Manhattan Island—a strong reverence for wild landscapes. For a while all these things stayed apart in Ehrenfeld; but then one day he came across Ramon Margalef's paper *On Certain Unifying Principles in Ecology,* and from then on it was obvious that he was bound to wind up writing this book.

The subject of the book is "the ecology of conservation." Both nouns in that phrase have undergone marked linguistic evolution. When I was a Boy Scout conservation was mostly plowing along contour lines and never setting the woods afire. Today it has become vastly more complicated. As for "ecology," that originally meant the study of natural biologic organization above the species level. Now, by a recent quantum jump, it has come to mean man's *disruption* of natural organization. It can even mean picking up beer cans—which is all right if it gets the cans picked up. But the original kind of ecologists ought to make haste and find another name for themselves. In his book David Ehrenfeld sets out to show why that old original ecology is really the most complex branch of biologic science and one that requires of anyone who wants to repair the damage we have done a "humility and caution in the face of forces dimly understood."

What Margalef did for Ehrenfeld's conception of ecology was to give it structure and integration by clearly identifying the relation between successional maturity, diversity, and stability in ecosystems. In their huge, somewhat amorphous, but epoch-making book *Principles of Animal Ecology*, Allee, Emerson, Park, Park, and Schmidt made progress in this direction. Later on, in *Fundamentals of Ecology*, Eugene Odum gave boundary to the discipline and made it a tractable classroom subject. But it took Margalef's paper to bring community metabolism people and evolutionary ecologists into the same camp, and thereby to validate an ecosystem concept as more than a figure of speech. To Ehrenfeld, the misunderstanding created by the "dichotomy between the resource and holistic conservation schools" seems the fundamental cause of the dire troubles we are having with our environment. To make sure that other people understood that too was no doubt the main reason he set out to write a book in which the stabilizing force of biological diversity is the principal theme.

If one had to name the main trend of human evolution it would be environmental control. That sounds peculiar when you see the mess we are in today; but really, all the so-called human evolutionary specialties—the straight thighs, free hands, opposable thumb, simian pit, big cerebral cortex—are directly related to the human specialty of striving to dominate rather than be pushed around by the environment. Up to now organic evolution has not produced many animals that are able to control environment to any great extent. Termites do, but their way is to wall themselves off in pitch-dark cities out of which they venture only in tubes, and within which they can live only by absolute surrender of individuality. Man, on the other hand, has set no limits to the space he would control. He has taken charge of the whole ecosphere. And he is ruining it. What Ehrenfeld does in his book is to show some of the ways in which our penchant for environmental control has backfired on us. It is a disturbing story he tells, and being an articulate writer, a broadly versed biologist, and a natural-born environmentalist, he tells it with authority as well as verve. Near the end of the book someone evidently bullied him into coming to grips with a question he would obviously rather had not come up—whether he was optimistic or pessimistic about the future of nature and the human race. Working over that, he makes himself squirm a bit. He finally points out hopefully that "hundred percent pessimists" do not write books about conservation, and then suggests that he has a kind of optimism that comes from the possibility that beneficent supra-rational factors that are by definition unknowable will materialize. In other words, the ecosystem is so complicated that who knows what might happen some day, for better as well as for worse? That is about the best that any objective student of our predicament can say, I suppose; but it is not a whole lot of comfort really, and probably none at all to the great blue whales.

Archie Carr

Gainesville, Florida
June 1972

Preface

In this age of environmental consciousness popular books on the subject of "ecology" abound. There are many books in print on specific environmental problems: books on overpopulation, technology, vanishing species, suburban sprawl, urban decay, and endangered ecosystems. People are beginning to feel overwhelmed and depressed by reading about the awful things that may happen, and guilty about the hundreds of things they are asked to do to forestall calamity. The situation is certainly grave, but we need something more than a random, fragmented approach. I believe that what has been lacking is the perspective that comes with ample scope and that enables people to make balanced decisions and to direct their limited energies with some semblance of rationality and efficiency.

My role in writing this book has been that of an advocate for the natural world. I have examined all of the problems mentioned above, and others, but always in the light of basic ecological theory as we understand it today. With this unifying approach, themes emerge, particularly the notion of lost diversity, and these themes provide the missing perspective.

Because of the nature of the subject matter, my sources have been varied. The reader should not be surprised to find excerpts from the research and writings of demographers, economists, novelists, and landscape architects blended with accounts of the findings of biologists and chemists. The greatest strength of conservation is its potential to serve as a rallying point for people with different kinds of training, in an era when real human communication has been all but supplanted by a variety of unsatisfactory substitutes. I am not fond of the aura of magic and ritual that sets scientists apart from others and often prevents us from relating our work to worldly needs. And I suspect that there are many persons in nonscientific fields who are equally dissatisfied with being held responsible for deciding what to do with a black box that they are never able to open.

One problem peculiar to this kind of book is the increasing remoteness of fundamental biology—of animals and plants, of biological functions and biological events—from the lives of an urban populace. In order to want to conserve something, one has first to know about it and appreciate it; and the number of people who are intimately familiar with natural landscapes outside the city and with wild species other than rats and pigeons grows proportionately smaller every day. Few of us have followed a biological community through a full-year cycle of life and death; few of us know when the grunions are supposed to arrive or when the blackberries ripen; and few of us have had any contact with any of the environments in which the human species evolved and to which it remains obscurely committed by physiological cycles of daily, lunar, or seasonal periodicity, by metabolic adjustment, and by psychological associations of great complexity. Thus, writing about biological conservation in the 1970s is a little like advertising color television on black-and-white screens: one can assert, persuasively, how beautiful and rich the colors are, but acceptance of the idea is still an act of faith on the part of the inexperienced audience. Here I can only hope that this book provokes some people into seeing for themselves what all the shouting is about.

Two criticisms of conservation are now increasingly part of what may be called, for lack of a better word, a "backlash." Conservation has been labelled "elitist" and "pastoral," both terms being used disapprovingly. I have tried to answer these important criticisms in the following pages, both directly and indirectly. Such charges are best met with facts and a detailed appreciation of the world situation—the whole book is thus an answer, but whole books make unwieldy arguments. Therefore it may be useful to condense my response to the two criticisms in a few brief sentences here.

To those who do not appreciate the interdependence of all life on earth, conservation does appear elitist, since most of the earth's peoples seem to have nothing of their own to conserve. Some people who carry the analysis no further than this give vent to their legitimate feelings of outrage and distress in the not-so-legitimate assertions that pollution is nonexistent, over-population is a state of mind, the loss of wilderness is exaggerated, and the extinction of species is both "natural" and irrelevant. I cannot help thinking, when I hear such opinions, of the dread Orwellian world of 1984, in which war is peace, freedom slavery, and ignorance strength. The injustice of this approach, apart from its ostrich-like denial of reality, is that it is itself a concession to a perverted and ego-serving form of elitism. If clean air and water, diverse and peaceful landscapes, and the enjoyment of wildlife are accessible only to the few, the solution is surely not to damn everyone by eliminating them altogether, but rather to conserve the life of earth while working for redress of the human inequalities that now plague us. Some insist that lasting conservation is not possible without widespread political and social change. This may be true, but in the interim, lacking the power of creation, we must preserve what we have. That is what this book is about.

At Barnard College I teach a course on conservation. This year, one of my students wrote her term paper on "Third World Attitudes Towards Conservation." It was based on conversations she had had with friends and interviews with strangers in the black and Puerto Rican ghettos of Manhattan. Understandably, none of her subjects had the time, opportunity, or desire to be conservationists. But some knew that there were severe problems with the environment and felt that these problems were part of *their* problem, an aspect of their oppression. My student encountered the belief that China, a political promised land for many of the ghetto residents, was the only country to cope successfully with environmental deterioration. The truth of this belief is not the issue here; what is important is that the conservation of the natural world can be considered elitist only by those who have abandoned all hope of human happiness. Socio-political reform and conservation cannot be competing interests if either is to succeed. Opposing conservation because it is an activity of the privileged is a good example of cutting off your nose to spite your face.

The issue of pastoralism, being more explicitly dealt with in the book, needs less attention here. If by pastoralism the technologically oriented opponents of conservation mean the life of paleolithic cavemen or the illusory quest for the noble savagery of Rousseau, they are right in their objection. But few of us seek that kind of personal existence. What the technophiles are really afraid of is the kind of pastoralism that subordinates technology to human needs—picking and choosing only those items among the inventions and processes of modern existence that enhance rather than degrade the life and surroundings of man. In our century, technology, while seeming to unite men with its advanced techniques of communication, has fostered a kind of personal loneliness and isolation that has come to be a hallmark of industrialized, "developed" countries. Today, the unthinking pursuit of technology is increasing the extent of that personal loneliness by means of a devastating reduction in natural diversity. No one need be ashamed of a pastoralism that rejects this irrational but seductive "progress."

I am grateful to the following people for suggestions, references, and assistance that made this revised and expanded edition possible: E. H. Buckley, Ray C. Erickson, Sir O. H. Frankel, Hugh Iltis, Michael Levandowsky, Matthew Meselson, Roger Payne, Vincent Roth, Ross Sandler, Joseph Sax, James Schmid, David Seymour, A. P. Vayda, A. H. Westing, E. O. J. Westphal, and Charles F. Wurster. Since I did not always follow their advice, the responsibility for errors of fact or judgment is entirely mine.

Ellen Flynn applied her terrifying critical faculties to the writing, whenever asked; and Patricia Richards obtained many useful references that I might have been too lazy to find for myself. Arlene Jacobs did her customarily superb job of typing-editing on less than short notice. My editors at Oxford, James Raimes, Joyce Berry, and Stephanie Golden, worked wonders with the evolving manuscript, and somehow made the process pleasant besides. Don Schumacher, at Holt, Rinehart and Winston, was as helpful and competent as with the preceding edition.

René Dubos was the first to suggest that the original textbook, *Biological Conservation*, should be turned into a book for the general public. His enthusiasm has been most encouraging; I hope the result meets his expectations. My most unqualified supporters have been my parents; if I have often taken this support for granted it does not mean that it went unappreciated.

As Dickens wrote in *Pickwick Papers*, "There are dark shadows on the earth, but its lights are stronger in the contrast." By "lights" he meant particular people, friends and acquaintances no doubt, whose personal qualities found their way into his fictional characters. I, too, have been fortunate in knowing people like this: the Carrs, Archie and Margie, whose friendship and teaching made me a conservationist and introduced me to a world that was worthy of respect and love; and Joan, my wife, whose conversations inspired and whose knowledge improved this book, and whose presence leaves no doubt in my mind that writing it was worthwhile.

Northvale, New Jersey   D.W.E.
June 1972

Contents

In the discussions held by the General Assembly at its twenty-third session it was emphasized that for the first time in the history of mankind, there is arising a crisis of world-wide proportions involving developed and developing countries alike—the crisis of the human environment. Portents of this crisis have long been apparent—in the explosive growth of human populations, in the poor integration of a powerful and efficient technology with environmental requirements, in the deterioration of agricultural lands, in the unplanned extension of urban areas, in the decrease of available space and the growing danger of extinction of many forms of animal and plant life. It is becoming apparent that if current trends continue, the future of life on earth could be endangered. It is urgent, therefore, to focus world attention on those problems which threaten humanity in an environment that permits the realization of the highest human aspirations, and on the action necessary to deal with them.

Report of the Secretary-General
United Nations Economic and Social Council
47th Session, May 26, 1969

But it seems that the wind is setting East, and the withering of all woods may be drawing near.

J. R. R. TOLKIEN, *The Lord of the Rings*

Conserving Life on Earth

1
Introduction

The subject of this book is best described as the ecology of conservation. The definition of ecology, as the study of the relationships among living organisms and their environments, will be illustrated by numerous examples later on, and can wait. Not so with conservation. By conservation I mean not just the preservation, for the immediate future, of man and his current roster of natural possessions, but the conservation of the world's natural communities, with their myriad member species of animals and plants, in some semblance of health and with the means and vigor for perpetual self-renewal. This is *not* just a book about an *impending* "crisis": too many people, too little space, foul air, food, power, resources—expected to strike a mortal blow within the next five to thirty years. Like the Beast in the Jungle, in Henry James' great short story of that name, the central problem we must recognize and confront is not a faceless terror of the future; it is here among us, unseen but scarcely hidden to those who look, and it has been with us quite some time. For now, we must be content to call the Beast the loss of irreplaceable diversity.

Diversity can of course refer to many things besides the components of the natural world. Those who have been saddened to watch Paris, London, Boston, and San Francisco grow daily more similar to New

York will appreciate this. Indeed the parallel and relatively recent loss of diversity in many areas touching on human life leads one to believe that the same cause operates for all. Although the biological aspects of conservation are stressed in the following pages, this is not done at the expense of its social and aesthetic aspects. Few of man's activities can claim so successful a fusion between science and the other branches of human study and perception; the success, in turn, of any book on conservation will depend on the degree to which its author is willing to deal with the full sweep and extent of the problem.

Conservation is a broad topic; there is no guarantee that people—including conservationists—are talking about the same thing when they refer to it. The central premise of this book is that a comprehensive sample of existing animal and plant species and natural communities should be preserved, not just for the sensible humanistic reasons of maintaining ecological stability and for man's enjoyment, but also because of the vague but growing feeling that the wholly anthropocentric perspective is not always the wisest and best. We cannot totally degrade the natural world and still retain the hope of some day discerning and assuming our rightful place in it.

Failure to conserve life forms is outright theft, irrevocable theft, since once species and communities have been obliterated they cannot be reconstituted, regardless of whether future generations of men should want to have them again. All species are potential Humpty Dumpties: the processes of evolution, as we know them, will not put them together again on this planet once they are destroyed. Nor does the possibility of genetic manipulation offer any promise; even if the means were at hand, one could not reconstruct *de novo* something for which no models or descriptions exist. Indeed all of the communities and most of the species that have vanished to date have disappeared with their stories untold or badly told. We know virtually nothing, we are beginning to realize, about the ecology of the American great plains; and now that we have some of the tools and theories available for community analysis, there is not enough of these boundless plains left intact to give us an understanding of their original condition and functions. Similarly, we are informed that the Australian thylacine, or mar-

Garbage dump, McMurdo Sound, Antarctica. (*The New York Times*)

supial wolf, the only large marsupial carnivore to survive to modern times, hopped on its hind legs, kangaroolike, when frightened, but we are not likely to learn much else about this bizarre and unique creature, since it is nearly extinct in its final retreats in the wilds of western Tasmania.

There are numerous valid aesthetic and practical reasons for supporting the conservation of species and communities, but this spectre of irreversibility is the most powerful of all. We have been privileged to witness some of the finest examples of the great bursts of evolutionary development that took place during the last two hundred million

5

years. We have seen, *alive,* giant tortoises, giraffes, elephants, orchids, bees, cockatoos, crocodiles, redwoods, orangutans, walruses, whales, cloud forests, and coral reefs—fabulous creations that would enliven any mythology if they were not real. Our immediate descendants will be unable to see living representatives of some members of this list, and no one should blame future generations if they consider our personal accounts and recollections an inadequate substitute for living specimens—nor will their loss be less if they do not know that such things once existed.

Most persons are only vaguely aware of the magnitude of the threat to wildlife and of the present urgency of the situation. It is tempting to cling to the childhood fantasy that there still exist vast areas where wilderness and wild creatures flourish unmenaced, faraway places with strange-sounding names: Sarawak, the Osa Peninsula, the Ross Shelf, the Dismal Swamp. But it is no coincidence that wherever one goes, the unspoiled places are generally somewhere else. The largest relatively blank area left on the land part of the map of the earth is the Amazon basin, containing extensive rain forests and a monumental river system that collects nearly a fifth of the world's free-flowing fresh water. Yet even here, where the best atlases show frequent gaps of more than a hundred miles without a named human habitation, widespread changes have occurred in recent years. Biologists traveling in the far interior reaches of the Amazon system, more than 1500 miles from the river mouth, report that extensive areas of rain forest, which present an unbroken green canopy to the airborne observer, show marked depletion of wildlife when viewed from the ground. In such areas the forest sounds are now mostly insect noises, while once-common mammals, large birds, and large reptiles are scarce or absent.

It may be some time, however, before most of the fauna and flora of the Amazon basin are irretrievably lost; other regions present far more immediate problems. Lake Erie, with an area of 9940 square miles, has been biologically altered almost beyond recognition. Only time, in the absence of pollution, might bring back a vestige of its original plant, fish, and invertebrate populations. Experts estimate that Lake Michigan, twice as large as Erie and much deeper, might be relatively clean in a thousand years if all pollution were stopped now. The Amazon basin and Lake Erie define the lower and upper limits of the disaster that now confronts all wild environments on earth. Between these limits, facing a multitude of both recognizable and obscure threats to their continued existence, are all other places that still have at least a part of their natural flora and fauna intact.

Although the word "conservation" implies a series of static holding maneuvers, this is scarcely the policy intended by conservationists, even if it were possible. Modern conservation, regardless of the scale of activities, must deal with a large number of variables that differ widely from situation to situation. A completely flexible position is necessary, as is the case whenever a considerable amount of advance planning and a delayed feedback are involved. Thus conservation policy ranges from a complete laissez-faire style of protection for some wilderness areas and sanctuaries to nearly complete management and manipulation of others.

Specific conservation strategy is variable, but the broad aim of conservation (as the word is used in this book) can be stated. The aim is not to prevent changes from taking place—ecosystems and species will change even without the actions of man. It is, rather, to ensure that nothing in the existing natural order is permitted to become permanently lost as the result of man's activities except in the most unusual and carefully examined circumstances. G. L. Kesteven, an Australian conservationist, has stated it clearly: "There should be no further modification of, or interference with, water, air, soil, substrate, rock, [organism] or biotope unless the immediate and necessary benefits of that modification are accompanied by long-term benefits." One might add that the burden of proof should fall on those seeking to modify the environment.

Most humans find natural surroundings pleasant, which is hardly surprising, since this is the setting in which our species evolved and to which we are genetically attuned. It can be argued that even our most artificial environments, our cities, are most successful in satisfying their inhabitants when they begin to approach and mimic the complexity and variety of a natural ecosystem such as a mixed hardwood forest and its intricate organization of components in space and time. We are paying increasing though still inadequate attention to the planning of future cities; it will be equally important to give imaginative and careful consideration to the problem of finding a way to maintain some natural areas with indigenous species in a mechanized and densely populated world. There is no way to predict whether such areas will serve as models, museums, or refuges, but one thing is quite certain: if our descendants tire of having wild places and wild creatures coexisting with them, they will have as little trouble getting rid of them as we do now.

The most urgent needs of conservation lie in the realm of education. The cause itself has been well publicized by energetic individuals, by private conservation organizations, and by some public agencies. Good intentions are legion, and new proposals backed by people willing to contribute time and money are appearing with increasing frequency and regularity. But many of these schemes are unrealistic; some are of marginal utility and may block more worthwhile programs, and a few would actually damage the things they seek to protect. Far too often conservationists find themselves on opposite sides of practical issues even though they agree on the long-range goal. The preservation of the coastal redwood forests, discussed later, is a case in point. Education will not solve all such difficulties, but it will help.

Unfortunately, improvement through education is a slow process, and the problems are already at hand. By every conceivable measure the rate of wildlife disappearance is increasing rapidly. One can plot the number of species that become extinct per year, the reduction in population size for given species, or the loss of wild and semiwild terrain—each tells the same story. Perhaps it is too late to do anything other than save a few odd bits and pieces of the landscape; nevertheless the possibility of achieving more than that makes the effort imperative.

One dictionary provides the following primary definition for the word "resource": "a source of supply, support, or aid, especially one held in reserve." If we expand this slightly to include the idea of a resource as unconverted or raw wealth, we arrive at the concept that forms the core of the philosophy of the most common variety of conservation that has been practiced in the twentieth century. A resource has value or utility, and there is enough of it to satisfy at least some of the anticipated future demand. Therefore, if one is concerned about taking action to conserve resources, there is no need to give high priority to things that have little tangible value or that appear to be present in inexhaustible supply. The majority of conservation efforts have been resource-oriented; this has meant that, until recently, certain selected elements of our flora and fauna and certain selected parts of our unsettled territory have been the subjects of intensive, often governmentally supported, conservation efforts, while the rest of our wildlife and natural communities have been left unattended or entrusted to private conservation organizations.

For example, where forests have been seen as a resource during the past century, they have been accorded official protection; the United States had, by 1963, some 154 national forests comprising 284,000 square miles of virgin and second growth timber (but only one-twentieth of this is fully protected as "wilderness"*). At the same time, only 1400 of 21,000 miles of ocean shoreline (exclusive of Hawaii and Alaska) had been reserved for public recreation, and only a very small fraction of this had been set aside as wild. The prairies have fared worse, despite the romantic place they occupy in American history and popular fiction. Virgin grasslands have little "value" as a resource, nor do they make popular national parks. Swamps and wetlands have been similarly despised in the resource context, receiving scant attention unless they happen to be surrounded by other land that is protected. Even in the Everglades National Park the swamp and marsh habitat has been allowed to deteriorate as a consequence of constant and badly planned interference with the natural drainage system.

The idea of conserving primarily those parts of the natural world that have been assigned a certain value as resources implies what has been described by the geographer Clarence Glacken as an "extrac-

---

* The effectiveness of this protection is another matter. See Chapter 7 for a discussion of "multiple use."

tive" relationship with nature. In this kind of relationship man sets himself apart from his environment and is often at odds with it. The components of the environment (at least those few of which we are aware) are treated as if they are assets or liabilities of a business, and can be maximized or minimized according to arbitrary goals and requirements. The damages that result from this philosophy are not easily perceived, but they are very real. They all share a common causative element: that the natural world has its own functions and relationships which exist regardless of the external, artificial value system of men.

The most obvious problems with the resource approach are first, that values change from time to time, unpredictably and according to the turn of innumerable independent events. Thus what is worthless today may be prized tomorrow, but too late. A hundred years ago only Thoreau and a very few others valued solitude in nature enough to warn that it was threatened. Today, how many millions would enjoy an abundance of quiet places—stream banks, woods, meadows, farms —in and near all parts of cities and towns, had such places been valued enough to have been saved when land was cheap? Second, even if values did not change, the complexity of nature makes our assignations of them inaccurate and terribly incomplete. We call healthy timber a resource but think nothing of forest tree diversity or the effects of pesticides on soil organisms; yet in the intricacies of the natural world these things and a thousand others are parts of the same whole.

There are less obvious difficulties in conserving only "resources." In a resource-based economy of the modern type, the value of a natural product or a natural amenity is abstracted from its ecological role in nature and becomes part of an entirely separate system with a different focus, the system based on human demand. But the dictates of a world market are largely disconnected from and unrelated to local (and global) facts of ecology—from the realities of nature. The extractive society, for all its pleasures and opportunities, is a construct: we ignore ecological warning signals because we have placed ourselves beyond ecology; it is culturally alien to the system. When a resource becomes scarce its price goes up; if one thinks about it, this is neither an effective nor an appropriate means of conservation. Finally, and not unrelated, is the problem of the physical remoteness of advanced, technological (extractive) societies from the origins of their resources. Ultimately, we cannot escape the natural world, but we create the illusion of doing so by escaping locally, by imposing compartments on an indivisible and integrated system. In this way, the unregulated consumption of seafood in the Soviet Union results in the exhaustion of fish populations along the Atlantic coasts of Canada and the northeastern United States. Since there are other fishing grounds, it is an "American" problem for the moment. More than ever before, complex happenings may affect the lives and destinies of people without their being able to do anything about it, often without their even knowing anything about it.

One of the themes of this book is that it is dangerous and self-defeating to advance the saving of present-day resources as the main rationale for conservation. Although it may take time to wean the majority of the public from this superficially attractive notion, conservationists at least should know better. There is another kind of conservation, which for want of a simpler term I call "holistic." This conservation acknowledges both the complexity of ecological relationships and the high degree of connectedness binding together the biological world, the atmosphere, the surface of the earth, the fresh and salt waters, and the artifacts of human civilization. The basic perception of these facts can be scientific, aesthetic, or religious in nature, but the end result is the same: a humility and caution in the face of great forces dimly understood. This common denominator is the strength of holistic conservation. Who knows the world so well that he can say that the scientific, "objective" reasons for saving alligators are ultimately more important than the emotional, "subjective" ones? The former are heavily emphasized in this book, but only because the latter are gained by personal acquaintance, not by reading intellectual expositions. Holistic conservation, then, is a way of looking at the natural world first as a functional whole (insofar as this is possible), then using the knowledge and impressions thus gained in determining what specific things must be done. It is a way of reconciling the needs of men with the requirements for stability of the natural world.

> *Agriculture and its science is so imperfect here [in America] that one can travel several days and learn almost nothing about the land, neither from the English, nor from the Swedes, Germans, Dutch, and French, except that from their gross mistakes and heedlessness of the future, one finds opportunities every day of making all sorts of observations, and of growing wise by their errors. In a word, the grain fields, the meadows, the forests, and the cattle, are treated with equal carelessness; and the characteristics of the English nation, so well-skilled in these branches of husbandry, are scarcely recognizable here. We can hardly be more hostile toward our woods in Sweden and Finland than they are here; their eyes are fixed upon the present gain, and they are blind to the future. . . .*
>
> PER KALM, *En Resa til Norra America* (1753-61)

Historically, the dichotomy between the resource and holistic schools is greatest in the United States, where it has mirrored existing national tensions, and where the rapidly vanishing frontier has offered grand scope for conservation activities. It is possible to trace the existence of conservationists and conservation ideas back to the early days of the colonial administration of North America. In 1681, William Penn decreed that for every five acres cleared of forest, one acre of timber should be set aside; even earlier conservation ordinances are on record. However, most seem to have had the same fate—they were largely ignored; not until the second half of the nineteenth century did any popular conservationist sentiment arise. The intellectual base for this sentiment came in the form of a massive and surprisingly readable tome published during the closing years of the Civil War, entitled *Man and Nature* (later, *The Earth as Modified by Human Action*). Its author was George P. Marsh, whose previous works had dealt with the origins of the English language.

In *Man and Nature* Marsh provided extensive documentation for his theme, the relatively unexplored idea that man was in the process of making global and often permanent changes in "the balance of nature." His examples included the digging of canals, the removal of seaside dunes, the draining of swamps, the introduction of exotic animals and plants, and the destruction of forests. He examined the consequences of these actions at length, and in so doing showed that he anticipated many of our modern ideas about ecosystems. Some section headings in his chapter "The Woods" are: "Electrical Influence of Trees," "Chemical Influence of the Forest," "Trees as Conductors of Heat," "Influence of Forests on the Humidity of the Air and the Earth," "Its Influence on the Flow of Springs," "Protection against the Fall of Rocks and Avalanches by Trees," and so forth. Marsh's insistence that man's activities were having a profound effect on nature was most timely because he had behind him the full weight of nineteenth-century philosophy, which preached that man had been endowed by God with dignity and power. It is appropriate that he chose a quotation from a sermon by Horace Bushnell for the inscription on the title page of *Man and Nature:* "Not all the winds, and storms, and earthquakes, and seas, and seasons of the world, have done so much to revolutionize the earth as Man, the power of an endless life, has done since the day he came forth upon it, and received dominion over it."

Having presented his argument that man was changing nature, Marsh went a step farther in a significant departure from the Judeo-Christian doctrine that God made man master of nature. He wrote:

> The equation of animal and vegetable life is too complicated a problem for human intelligence to solve, and we can never know how wide a circle of disturbance we produce in the harmonies of nature when we throw the smallest pebble into the ocean of organic life. This much we seem authorized to conclude . . . the law of self-preservation requires us to restore the equilibrium, by either directly returning the weight abstracted from one scale, or removing a corresponding quantity from the other. In other words, destruction must be either repaired by reproduction, or compensated by new destruction in an opposite quarter.

The intellectual origins of the conservation movement are here, plainly stated. When man altered his natural surroundings, the results were frequently unforeseen and unpleasant. This was a situation that the disturbers were obliged to correct, either by protecting the disturbed environment and allowing ecological processes to effect restoration insofar as possible, or by following the more dangerous but sometimes necessary course of redressing the balance through additional alteration and management.

Marsh was responsible for establishing the broad features of the conservation idea, but he did not determine specific policies. This was done during the last decades of the nineteenth century and the first decade of the twentieth, and it was during this time that conservationists found themselves split into the two groups described above, one of which was to dominate conservation efforts. Although many persons in the United States were associated with the conservation movement during this period, two men best represent the opposing points of view; they were Gifford Pinchot, America's first professional forester and later chief of what was to become the United States Forestry Service, and John Muir, naturalist, author, and founder of the Sierra Club.

In 1910, in a book entitled *The Fight for Conservation,* Pinchot defined what he meant by the word "conservation," which he had coined several years earlier. "The first principle of conservation is development, the use of the natural resources now existing on this continent for the benefit of the people who live here now. . . . In the second place conservation stands for the prevention of waste . . . there is a third principle. It is this: The natural resources must be developed and preserved for the benefit of the many, and not merely for the profit of a few." Like Marsh before him, Pinchot was in accord with his times. His first principle of conservation said nothing to damp the exuberance of a country just beginning to become aware of its power, and the second and third principles blended nicely with the muckraking, trust-busting, outraged public spirit of the early 1900s.

Muir was a generation older than Pinchot, although their careers overlapped at a critical time. In 1908 Secretary of the Interior James R. Garfield granted a permit to the city of San Francisco to dam the Hetch-Hetchy Valley in Yosemite National Park and turn it into a

Gifford Pinchot and John Muir with Theodore Roosevelt in Yosemite, 1903. Pinchot is standing in the center, rear; Roosevelt and Muir (with a long beard) are in front of him. The tree is the "Grizzly Giant." (Le Conte— Courtesy Sierra Club)

city reservoir. Muir, whose writing had prompted the creation of the park in the first place, had written earlier,

> Any fool can destroy trees. They cannot run away; and if they could, they would still be destroyed. . . . It took more than three thousand years to make some of the trees in these western woods —trees that are still standing in perfect strength and beauty, waving and singing in the mighty forests of the Sierra. . . . God has cared for these trees, saved them from drought, disease, avalanches, and a thousand straining, leveling tempests and floods; but He cannot save them from fools—Only Uncle Sam can do that.

15

The Hetch-Hetchy Valley as it looked in 1894. Ribbon Falls is seen in the background. Large trees in the foreground are oaks. (LeConte—Courtesy Sierra Club)

Acting on this belief, he appealed to his friend President Theodore Roosevelt, but Roosevelt's term of office expired with the matter unresolved. In 1911 the Advisory Board of Army Engineers revealed the true issue in its report on the Hetch-Hetchy proposal: "The Board is of the opinion that there are several sources of water supply that could be obtained and used by the City of San Francisco. . . . From any one of these sources the water is sufficient in quantity and is, or can be made suitable in quality, while the engineering difficulties are not insurmountable. The determining factor is principally one of cost." Pinchot supported this viewpoint, which was consistent with his resource-oriented philosophy of conservation. He urged San Francisco

16

The Hetch-Hetchy Valley in 1955. Upper end of the reservoir at low water; numerous tree stumps are visible. (Philip Hyde—Courtesy Sierra Club)

to "make provision for a water supply from the Yosemite National Park. . . . I will stand ready to render any assistance in my power." The kind of cost accounting that was favored by Muir, an accounting based on present and future aesthetic intangibles more than short-term material considerations, was rejected not only by Pinchot but also by Congress, which legislated the damming of Hetch-Hetchy several months before Muir's death in 1914.

To Pinchot, conservation meant the development and wise use of our material natural resources: forests, agricultural land, water, and mineral reserves. To him belongs much of the credit for establishing strong governmental agencies to promote conservation, and also the credit for placing millions of acres of forest land in the system of National Forests, which was largely of his design.

During the first half of the twentieth century the conservation of material resources was advanced on a number of fronts. Sport fish and game management had widespread public support and many successes. Few of the threatened species in the United States have ever been major game animals. The Bureau of Sport Fisheries and Wildlife's deer census showed a twenty-eight-fold increase in the national deer population during the interval from 1890 to 1963. The Migratory Treaty (1916) and subsequent Migratory Bird Treaty Act (1918) were aimed primarily at game birds that regularly crossed the United States-Canadian border, but offered protection to other species as well. Commercial and sport fishermen have been aided by extensive research on the physiology, behavior, population biology, and ecology of various species of salmon, trout, bass, and other edible fish. The Fur Seal Treaty of 1911, signed by Japan, Russia, Great Britain, and the United States, was the first international agreement to protect a marine resource. The Soil Erosion Service of the Department of the Interior (in 1935 it became the Soil Conservation Service of the Department of Agriculture) initiated thousands of projects to prevent the recurrence of the dust bowls that were common during the Great Depression; these projects included the establishment of soil conservation districts and the creation of the Shelterbelt program, in which thousands of miles of tree windbreaks were planted in the plains states. Finally, many areas were designated as national parks and monuments, most of them in wilderness regions of great beauty, and most highly suited for recreation such as camping, hiking, boating, and fishing.

At the height of the hard-fought campaign to save America's material natural resources, there was a technical advance in biological conservation practice that was of great significance. George Marsh had written about two ways of restoring natural "harmony": the first was primarily protection; the second involved protection plus additional planned interference with biological and nonbiological parts of the ecosystem to achieve a desired result. The latter method was both hazardous and difficult to apply, and it was not until 1933, when Aldo Leopold, a pioneer in game management, published a book entitled *Game Management* that the second of Marsh's two approaches to conservation became really practical. Leopold studied the interrelationships among wild animals and their habitats and described the conditions that would produce a surplus of game animals which could be harvested by man without endangering the breeding stock. Leopold's conclusions were independently confirmed by a growing number of American and British field ecologists and conservationists, including F. Fraser Darling, who spent two years in the Scottish Highlands observing the native red deer. In his classic account of his findings, *A Herd of Red Deer*, Darling wrote, "A constant mistake in Scotland has been the equal toll [by hunting] of stags and hinds [females]. There should be a kill of twice as many hinds as stags [as an effective population control measure], and the overall kill should be a fifth of the whole stock. The hind stock should be kept young, except for a few leaders, and, therefore, highly productive, and stocking should be below capacity, say 1 to 60 acres." Closely reasoned and well-documented game management plans such as this were the response to Leopold's contention that simple protection, without active management, for a community that was already unbalanced by loss of predator species could result in drastic overpopulation of deer and other game, with attendant weakening of individual animals.

During the time when Pinchot's style of conservation was making its greatest gains (roughly during the first half of the twentieth century), the preservation of communities and species that were not considered prime material resources in their original form was left, by default, to private organizations with limited resources, such as the Sierra Club and the Audubon Society. As indicated, the natural communities that suffered most were swamps and wetlands, river estuaries, bays, offshore marine habitats, coastal beach and dune communities, inland waters, grasslands, deserts, and the island patches of semiwild land that once were a characteristic feature of American suburbs. Species that were especially affected included the fishes that spawn in estuaries and coastal waters, nonsport freshwater fishes (particularly those in the Southwest, in the Great Lakes, and in heavily polluted rivers), predatory birds and mammals, trees that grow slowly, species requiring solitude or unspoiled habitat during some phase of their life cycles, species like small song birds displaced by imported competitors or parasites, and many others.

By 1960 it had become apparent that the traditional policies of conservation were inadequate to meet conservation needs. Muir's conservation philosophy had been largely disregarded because the thing he prized, unspoiled wildness, had little cash value as a natural resource. However, during the 1960s, under the twin pressures of a rapidly expanding population and heavy industrialization, the seemingly inexhaustible open space began to shrink at an alarming rate. As wilderness areas dwindled in number and size, the once intangible value of the remaining areas and the creatures they contained became suddenly quite real. This change in the status of natural communities and species encouraged a possible working agreement between the Muir and Pinchot schools of conservation. Conservationists are in the wrong field if they compromise too readily; but the finding of common ground is not much of a compromise. If the Muir and Pinchot philosophies are ever to be reconciled it must be now, when the followers of Pinchot can admit that most "resources" haven't been identified yet, and the followers of Muir can confess that they haven't always been effective in getting things done. Then both schools will agree that it is the better part of wisdom to conserve existing diversity and

postpone the arguments about theory until later.* Nor should the resource conservationists delude themselves into going it alone: the
victories of Pinchot, as the condition of the U.S. National Forests will
bear witness, have turned sour through the years.

Perhaps none of this will seem very practical; but it has always been
a mistake to be practical first and thoughtfully farsighted later. Hopefully the reader will find enough of both qualities blended in the
following pages. This seems the only way to achieve a dynamic and
viable conservation.

The dictionary provides the following definition for the word "conservation": "preservation from loss, injury, decay or waste." It is
derived from the Latin verb *conservare*, "to preserve." As one might
guess, this stem is the same as for the word "conservative," but the
similarity does not end there. Traditionally most conservationists have
been middle-aged or elderly, they have belonged to the middle or upper
classes, and have been political conservatives as well as conservationists. They are accustomed to the idea of preserving assets. Conservation and conservatism have gone well together, and to the extent that
this has furthered conservation, it is probably a good thing.

But what about the Left and the poorer nations? Surely no policy of
such importance as conservation can afford to become political and
thereby automatically alienate masses of people for reasons not ger-
mane to the central cause. Yet the Left and the poorer nations have
up to now been in a bind with respect to conservation. On the one
hand, they can recognize the value of a healthful and healthy environment—on the other, they associate open space and unspoiled environments with the privileged, and they see conservation as just another
in the long line of ingenious schemes to preserve the inequitable *status
quo*. This is particularly true in the Third World countries, many of
which have taken a hard line against pollution control and other fea-

* The fight against the Cross-Florida Barge Canal (see Chapter 4) is a good
example.

tures of conservation policy. At the Conference on Asian Environments held at Ann Arbor, Michigan, in June 1971, Hamilton Shirley Amerasinghe, Ceylon's ambassador to the United Nations, remarked: "All developing countries are aware of the risks, but they would be quite prepared to accept from the developed countries even 100 percent of their gross national pollution if thereby they could diversify their economies through industrialization."

The facts presented in this book should enable the reader to decide whether the developing countries have accurately appraised the risks of which Amerasinghe spoke. The future of technologic-industrial progress is discussed in the last chapter; here we can only look at the political implications of conservation in a more theoretical way. If we observe the two kinds of conservation, it becomes obvious that the *resource* variety makes conservation a political issue and unpalatable to the Left by associating it with the idea of property, while holistic conservation is relatively free of this association.*

Again, the goal of achieving a viable and dynamic conservation with the support of both conservative and nonconservative interests demands the finding of a common ground. Surely we can dispense with neither philosophy. We need the practicality of the resource conservationists, who say, "The world is ours and serves our needs, guard it carefully." We need, perhaps even more, the apolitical vision of the holistic conservationists, who say, "We are part of a larger scheme, and it is a sad commentary on our species if, knowing better, we behave like pigs in a cathedral." Perhaps in the politics as well as in the procedure of conservation, reconciliation will arise from sheer necessity.

Throughout most of this book the conservation of communities and that of species are treated separately. This facilitates the organization of a great deal of diverse material in a relatively simple and rational

---

* The issue is more complex in the Third World Countries, but here, too, resources have often been owned or exploited by foreign, developed countries.

way. It is, however, artificial, as any categorization is bound to be. All natural communities are composed of species; all species are members of some community. Therefore, although it may be useful for the purpose of understanding to have the conservation puzzle separated into its component parts, it is essential that at some point the reader perform the necessary integration so that a coherent picture of the whole subject will emerge.

The scope of this book is limited to biological conservation, the conservation of flora and fauna. One could stretch a point to include soils; this has not been done, nor is the conservation of water (as distinct from aquatic habitats), minerals, or commercial lumber reserves discussed. Although the topics are necessarily limited, the geographic compass of the book is not; the need for conservation is global. Its manifestations vary from place to place, depending on a multitude of local circumstances; nevertheless, with study, patterns can be discerned. For this reason, I have tried not to be too parochial in my coverage and discussions, wherever possible drawing examples and quoting ecologists and conservationists from many parts of the world.

2
How Natural Communities
Are Threatened:
Ecology and Man-Made Change

Plants and animals are not sprinkled haphazardly over the surface of the earth; each species has a geographical range and occupies restricted portions of the territory within that range. The primary environmental determinants of the distribution of species are geology and climate, accounting for variables such as soil type, topography, yearly temperature profile, and rainfall. To say that particular plants and animals will be found where conditions are right for them is a truism, but there is a less obvious corollary: plants and animals are rarely found in all places where conditions are presumably right for them. The European starling (*Sturnus vulgaris*) was not found in the United States prior to 1890; yet after its introduction by man it adapted remarkably well, spreading from New York's Central Park to the West Coast, Mexico, and Alaska in sixty years. Evidently the starling was not a resident of a large part of the earth that constituted an ideal habitat for it. Charles S. Elton has written: "When one was a child, this circumstance was very simply summed up in books about animals. The tiger lives in India. The wallaby lives in Australia. The hippopotamus lives in Africa." To the geologic and climatic determinants we must therefore add the biological determinant of dispersive power and the determinant of history. The area where a plant or animal naturally occurs is related to the place where it evolved and its movements since that time.

24

One major determinant of species distribution that remains to be mentioned is the distribution of other species. Biologists have long been aware that the distribution of animals is greatly dependent on that of plants; the dependence of plants on plants, of plants on animals, and of animals on animals is equally well documented. This dependence is not simply a matter of parasitism. Relationships between species may be subtly constructed in space and time. Tobacco grows well in fields that have previously been covered with wild ragweed. Amazon parrots nest in the hollows of diseased or dead trees; the two hundred remaining Puerto Rican parrots *(Amazona vittata)* may not now find enough of these trees in their protected area in the Espiritu Santo Valley to maintain the species. Baby burrowing owls frighten away potential predators by imitating the warning buzz of a rattlesnake. Every type of animal and plant in a region is linked with all others in an evolved meshwork of immense complexity. Some are less dependent than others on the biological integrity of the region—there are always a few adaptable species that persist after most of their neighbors have gone—but all are involved with each other to some degree.

This kind of assemblage of plants and animals sharing a common environment and a degree of common history, and operating as a highly interrelated unit, is known as a community. (A community in its total physical environment is referred to as an ecosystem.) Similar environments may generate similar-looking communities in different places (the rain forests of Panama resemble the rain forests of equatorial Africa), but the elements of these similar communities are rarely the same species. Although it is literally quite true that no square inch of the earth's surface is exactly like any other square inch in climate, topography, and soil type, nevertheless we find that the number of major kinds of communities is small. A particular community is most easily characterized by its most typical members, indicator species that are rarely found in other communities in the vicinity. The indicator species for the formerly predominant community of north-central Indiana are sugar maple and beech trees and the small woodland salamander, *Plethodon cinereus.* Ecologists often group similar terrestrial communities together in broad categories, described for convenience by their vegetation type. In one widely accepted classification scheme these categories are known as biomes and include desert, grassland, savanna, and forest, in order of increasing rainfall.

From the standpoint of conservation the most important thing about communities is that their growth and maturation involve a series of metamorphoses. Each stage is a different community; only a few of the former species remain when a new community replaces the old. The metamorphic process, whose study was pioneered in the United States by H. C. Cowles and F. E. Clements, is referred to as succession. The total assemblage of communities that occupy a given region during succession is known as a sere. The final stage of a sere, which in theory will remain until some major geologic or climatic change takes place, is called the climax community. If the climax is representative of the virgin flora and fauna of its climatic region, it is a climatic climax; if it is different because of some local peculiarity in the physical environment, such as atypical soil or unusually frequent fires, it is an edaphic climax. The complexity of the sere varies from place to place; seral stages in tropical climates with high yearly rainfall contain the largest number of species interlinked in the most complex way. This "horizontal" increase in community complexity as the equator is approached is often paralleled by a similar increase along the time axis, with the climax community containing more elements more intricately related than in earlier seral stages.

It is probably climatic mildness and regularity that accounts in part for the multitude of species in the tropical rain forest, where each square mile contains hundreds of different sorts of trees, but it is probably another and different kind of phenomenon that accounts for the relative complexity of climax communities when compared to their predecessors. The only thing that changes in time is the biological matrix. A climax beech and sugar maple community does not spring full-blown from the bare earth, but arises (in one particular sequence) in the shelter of a red oak and white oak forest, which may have arisen from a black oak grove derived in turn from a jack pine forest, itself preceded by cottonwood. The maturation of each seral stage prior to the climax provides conditions unfavorable for growth of the young of its own species, but favorable for the young of the community to follow. In another kind of succession, we find that many species of southern pines sprout and grow readily in open fields, but pine seedlings cannot compete with oak and magnolia in a mature pine forest. The maturation of pines thus has the curious result of ensuring that the pine forest will be replaced with oak and magnolia (and other broad-leafed trees). This may be the climax stage in this case—a complex mixture of shade-tolerant trees and their associated animals, *whose individuals can replace themselves as they age and die.*

Additional ecological topics will be considered in their conservation context, but ecology itself is too extensive to be covered in detail here. In particular, the idea that one climatic zone ordinarily has only one climatic climax community is an oversimplification, made only for the sake of brevity.

Community Diversity and Stability

Since the beginning of the post–World War II era, a powerful but controversial theory has been gaining headway among ecologists who study communities and ecosystems. The theory has had formidable champions, most notably the renowned Spanish marine biologist and mathematical ecologist Ramon Margalef and an American colleague, Eugene Odum, whose pioneering textbooks have consistently set the pattern for the education of the next and most crucial generation of ecologists. The theory is composed of two parts, each with its own set of exceptions and conditions. The first is that community "maturation" or succession is characterized by an increase in species diversity, with a concomitant increase in the "complexity" of the community, e.g. an increase not only in the species elements but in the number and kinds of relationships among them. The second part is as easy to state but harder to comprehend: that the increase in diversity and complexity leads to an increase in "stability" of the entire ecosystem of which the community is a part. Before elaborating, we can avoid much of the controversy that surrounds this theory by stating exactly what is meant by "stability" in this case.

The problem with discussing stability in reference to ecosystems is that there are several kinds of stability and various ways of measuring them. What is referred to here is a self-protection conferred by the community as a whole, and permitting its survival. The existence of *all* the species as an interrelated, integrated unit makes possible the existence of the component individuals in an otherwise inhospitable world. This meaning of stability is, therefore, best evaluated not in terms of immediate effects, such as amelioration of local climate or the stabilizing of population fluctuations, but, as the ecologist Frederick Smith and others have stated, in terms of the end result—the permanence or persistence of the community itself.

At first glance this is a circular kind of argument, and so it might be if mature* or climax communities came directly and suddenly into being. It is succession, however, that demonstrates the sense of the idea, with the increasing complexity of each seral stage paving the way for the next. The reader may wonder where the individuals of each stage come from when conditions become favorable for their growth. The answer is that over any large region with a single type of general climate and landform all stages of the sere exist at once. Local fires, storm damage, floods, earth slides, plant pests and diseases, and the activities of man help create a patchwork where early, intermediate, and late stages of succession are geographically intermingled and close enough for the transfer of seeds and the movement of animals across ecological boundaries. If disturbances are few, climax and mature successional communities will predominate; it is possible, however, for man to create sufficient disruption over a wide enough area to make it virtually impossible for the climax or anything remotely like it to return during historical time.

The idea that increasing diversity promotes stability helps, in turn, to explain why succession occurs. Odum has stated it in this way:

> . . . the mature community with its greater diversity, larger organic structure, and balanced energy flows is often able to buffer the physical environment to a greater extent than the young [early] community, which, however, is often the more

* "Mature" does not refer to the age of particular individuals but to the community itself, which is in a late successional stage.

productive [in terms of plant growth]. Thus, the achievement of
a measure of stability or homeostasis . . . in a fluctuating physical
environment may well be the primary purpose (that is, the survival value) of ecological succession when viewed from the evolutionary standpoint.

In other words, contemporary succession is a kind of continuous
replay of evolution. The *types* of plants and animals that make up the
mature community, be it tropical forest, prairie grassland, or Arctic
tundra, owe their existence not only to the fellow members of their
own community but to the many species that preceded them in that
place. This leads directly to another aspect of the theory—one of great
importance to conservationists.

Margalef, in 1963, attempted to identify and list the characteristics
that distinguish members of a mature community from those of an
early stage of succession. We can summarize his most relevant conclusions as follows: in a mature community, species are "specialists,"
fitting into a narrow and sharply defined niche in terms of feeding
behavior, reproductive behavior, activity patterns, shelter requirements, and the like. They usually maintain relatively small but stable
population sizes, surviving in the midst of many similar species by
virtue of their peculiar adaptations. Having evolved a highly defined
way of life in the world, they keep their competitive position by
doing what they do very well, and by deviating little from this one life
style (the ivory-billed woodpecker described in Chapter 9, is a case in
point). Overall, one could describe the typical inhabitant of a climax
community as rigid and inflexible, and very much at a loss outside its
own community. Although every community has its exceptions, they
do not invalidate the general description.

One example of these attributes is well known to many amateur and
professional gardeners. The native American beech (*Fagus grandifolia*)
is magnificent as an ornamental tree; its smooth silver-gray bark and
low-branching growth form make it particularly attractive in the
winter against a background of snow. People who want beeches around
their houses, but lack them, may not find them as easy to transplant
and raise as most other species; those fortunate enough to have
mature beeches may well have inherited the survivors or descendants

of survivors from the days when their land was a beech woods. The beech is a true climax forest tree in the northeastern United States, and it depends on its community in subtle ways. When transplanted from its natural environment, especially to city lawns, it is likely to die. Experienced tree surgeons and nurserymen believe that such trees have a much better chance of surviving if earth from a beech forest is mixed with the soil in their new location, providing soil fungi that are somehow necessary for the proper functioning of the tree roots in absorbing nutrients. Even so, a transplanted beech is not the safest of landscaping investments. The beech may be a particularly finicky kind of tree, but it still illustrates Margalef's point well.

The characteristic members of "immature" or early seral stages are quite different in nature. They are adapted to life in an unsheltered, unpredictable environment; that is to say, they are flexible and adaptable in their behavior and growth requirements. Characteristically, they eat or utilize a variety of foods and maintain their competitive advantage of out-reproducing other species. Their population sizes may fluctuate wildly, and the separate individuals of a single population may differ widely from one another in habits and appearance. Most of the pests, the vermin, the bad parasites, and the weeds belong to this group—it is their nature to exploit disrupted habitats.

For conservationists, the implications of the diversity-stability relationship are urgent and numerous. The built-in stability of mature climax communities is often sufficient to overcome ordinary challenges to their integrity, but, as Marsh long ago pointed out, man is not an ordinary challenge. When enough stress is imparted to a mature community it reaches its "elastic limit" (a term I have borrowed from physics) and, like a rubber band, abruptly snaps. When such a community disintegrates, many of the component species, as predicted, are unable to adapt to the new conditions and are lost. Like worms on asphalt, they are out of their element. New species, a motley (and not entirely bad) assortment from the early stages of a variety of seres— the Norway rats, the aphids, the red-winged blackbirds, the ragweeds, and many others, possibly including the plagues and poxes—invade promptly. Man's hitherto clumsy attempts to fight off the invaders often have disrupted still other communities, with additional unexpected and unhappy side-effects. Other reasons for keeping mature communities include maintenance of regional climate, soil, landform, and other ecosystem features; also the preservation of organisms of unknown and possibly incalculable value to man and the biosphere, organisms that will survive only in their evolved communities.

It follows that the natural communities that are both the most threatened and the most desirable to preserve are frequently the late successional and climax communities. The climax community comes into being in the shadow and protection of the penultimate seral stage; its own structure and functions maintain it, and it is climax because no other assemblage of species can replace it. If its structure is lost to the bulldozer, insecticide, or defoliant, the only way to get it back is via the lengthy process of succession, if at all. Climax communities cannot be planted or stocked; the variables to take into account are innumerable. Since the course of' a sere is reckoned in hundreds or thousands of years, the loss of a mature community is as permanent, on the time scale of human civilizations, as the extinction of a species.

Fragile Ecosystems

In describing communities and ecosystems, there is a common tendency to generalize too much, in order to simplify complex processes. The only harm in this in a book on conservation is that it obscures the essential fact that some ecosystems are more fragile than others and can tolerate very little tampering by man. Although there are usually special and unique features of particular ecosystems that make them either fragile or resilient, at least two characteristics of all fragile ecosystems can be identified. Their biological communities regenerate very slowly or their successions are easily deflected from the normal course by disruption; and the size of the minimal functional unit, the smallest subdivision of the ecosystem that will survive without much input, is very large.

There will be plenty of illustrations of these principles in the pages to follow, but a few examples may be helpful now. Opponents of the proposed trans-Alaskan pipeline have described the Arctic tundra with its permafrost as one of the world's most fragile ecosystems. It is still possible, they point out, to find the tracks of bulldozers or trucks that travelled *once* over the permafrost more than thirty years ago. The ruts may actually get deeper with time because of freezing and thawing processes. No geophysical or biological changes have obliterated or smoothed these scars in a third of a century. Arctic life is more finely tuned than the engine of a racing car; it is preoccupied with the Arctic climate and not capable of dealing with other stresses, too. The tundra ecologists have also shown that the survival of the animal life is dependent upon free movement of one of the simple food chain's major herbivores, the migratory caribou. Experience in Swedish Lapland with the closely related reindeer has demonstrated, according to ecologist D. R. Klein, that: "Reindeer have strong traditions for migrating along specific routes, and realignment of these routes is extremely difficult. . . . Fences have proved very useful and have created a minimum of problems when they are used in conjunction with traditional patterns of movement. . . . In many [other] instances they have proven virtually unworkable because of the reluctance of the reindeer to be 'forced' into dense herds in unfamiliar terrain."

The tundra ecosystem will cease to exist if it is partitioned—by pipelines or by fences—except parallel to natural corridors and barriers such as river valleys and mountain chains. Unlike the Netherlands or the state of New Jersey, it cannot be arbitrarily subdivided without experiencing a change for the worse in all its parts.

Although different from the Arctic tundra in most respects, mountainous ecosystems are similarly fragile. In the Appalachian region of the eastern United States, and recently in the northwest Canadian Rocky Mountains, strip mining has devastated or is threatening areas of vast size. In these cases, the regrowth of the forest community is slowed or prevented altogether by the self-accelerating forces of erosion. Moreover, it is impossible to damage part of a mountain without affecting the plants and animals both above and below the stripped area and in the valley as well. An entire watershed can show the effects of a mining operation that covers only a few acres.

An aerial view of a coal strip-mining area in Kentucky, 1966. The barren gullies and eroded ridges are unfit for human use and will not be recolonized by the native vegetation for many decades. (Billy David and the *Louisville-Courier Journal*—Courtesy U.S. Bureau of Mines)

Perhaps the most fragile ecosystems of all, even more than tundra, are the deserts and desert grasslands. They are also among the least understood. Again the problem is that the community is so preoccupied with the climate, with the extremes of temperature and the lack of water, that there is scarcely any latitude to resist man. In the desert plants are widely spaced and animals are mostly underground, at least during the day. To the layman, damage comparable to the worst strip mining in West Virginia may pass unnoticed. But it is just as long-lasting. In an ecosystem where it may take fifty years for a bush to grow one foot, and where the soil has been organized with painful slowness into a hidden, vital network of roots, tunnels, chambers, and granaries, any alteration of drainage patterns, lowering of the water table, or bulldozing can put an end to the desert community.

A healthy desert seems devoid of time; in remote places in Arizona

33

The sacred cave of Pinacate, Sonora, Mexico, *ca.* 1909. Note the two Ocotillo plants (in rectangles, right and left), the prickly pear (in rectangle, center), and the large cactus at the right. From Carl Lumholtz, *New Trails in Mexico*, New York, 1912.

and northern Mexico arrowheads and bits of pottery shine dully on the same surfaces where they were dropped centuries ago, and appropriately small changes wrought in the landscape by the vanished Indians may look, to the fortunate and observant traveler who finds them, as if they were fresh that day. "Civilized" man recklessly introduces time into desert ecosystems; the life of the desert cannot stand the pace and falls by the wayside. It will not return in our age. Again, the minimum functional unit of a desert ecosystem is large, being organized around widely spaced, temporary ponds and streams, and having few surface relief features to interrupt the continuity of the land. In this respect, the desert and its apparent opposite, the tropical rain forest, are quite similar. In the rain forest, where there are hundreds of species of trees per square mile and where individuals of the same species are widely

The sacred cave of Pinacate, 1962. This photograph was taken from a different angle, but the photographer believes that the two Ocotillo plants and the prickly pear are the same ones shown in the photograph taken fifty-three years earlier. (The cactus shown on the right in the earlier photograph is gone.) This observation agrees with many others on the persistence of desert shrubs. (Courtesy Vincent Roth)

Ritual circle on old Cocopa Indian trail, Baja California, Mexico, 1962. This trail was probably used until the latter half of the nineteenth century by Indians traveling through this remote desert to the Sierra Juarez in search of piñon nuts. A century later the abandoned trail still looks freshly made. (Courtesy Vincent Roth)

separated, a representative and functional section of the ecosystem has to be huge indeed.

Finally, it may be helpful to mention, for contrast, an example of a relatively sturdy ecosystem. The forests of New England and the Middle Atlantic states have in a sense been preadapted to coexist with all but the most destructive of men. As might be expected, their structure is such that fairly representative woods communities may survive in patches of a few dozen acres each. The northeastern forest also recovers rapidly. People are often surprised to learn that in this era of overpopulation and pollution the forests are reclaiming abandoned pastures and farms all over New England.

Population and Technology

It is no longer necessary to provide a gentle and reticent exposition of the problems associated with a rapidly increasing population. As the biologist Garrett Hardin has pointed out, nobody dies of "overpopulation" the way people die of starvation, of natural disasters (such as floods) whose effects are aggravated by crowding, or of gunshot wounds in urban slums. But even though the word "overpopulation" never appears on a death certificate, it lingers unspoken in the minds of all but the dullest of the funeral guests. Already, fresh water, food, and space have been depleted in some places; unless present trends are altered, these prerequisites for life will soon be available in sufficient quantities only in a few fortunate enclaves in a sea of poverty. Agricultural researchers, urban planners, sociologists, and psychologists seem to agree on only one thing: overcrowding is bad, and the human crowd is increasing so rapidly that new problems arise faster than old ones are being solved. Conservationists, as might be expected, are generally at the heart of the population control movement. All kinds of conservationists find themselves involved: expanding human populations consume food, commodities, and space at a rate that frightens resource conservationists; expanding populations also destroy habitats and communities and overcrowd the fragile parks and wilderness areas at a rate that frightens holistic conservationists.

The correlation between population expansion and loss of resources appears to be simple and direct, and it would seem that the resource conservationist should have no trouble in testing it. The extent of real and potential resources can be estimated, and this, if combined with the predicted rate of consumption, should in many cases give a good measure of the effect of increasing population. Such technical predictions, however, may fall short of usefulness. Thus, W. R. Schmitt a food and population expert, in a discussion of the planetary food potential in a world that may contain thirty billion people by the twenty-second century, claims: "Technically, the long-range prospects for adequate nutrition are excellent—other factors than the food supply will likely control the size of the human population. . . ." But Schmitt also points out: "Socioeconomic restraints control food production before physical factors do, because the potential of each major mode— agriculture, silviculture [forest culture], aquaculture, and microbial culture—in terms of the production of organic matter, is greater than the requirements of three billion people, or even of the 30 billion projected for the future. Yet, food shortages exist." Evidently, in this branch of conservation (resource conservation) the effects of population increase, although of major importance, are neither simple nor readily predictable. Many times in this century we have seen populations starve while mountains of food were available on the other side of a political boundary. Other supporting examples may be found in the areas of mineral, fuel, and water resources, where the imponderables mentioned above, plus the prospects of improved technologies and development of the embryonic field of reclamation of raw materials from processed goods, make it difficult to assess the impact of increased demand.

If the effects of population increase on resources are hard to predict, what about the effects on natural communities? Natural communities, like people, don't die of human overpopulation: the immediate cause may be a new shopping center, an industrial complex, an expressway, an agricultural clearing, excessive clearcutting in a forest, or a war; but without the oppressive force of human overpopulation propelling them forward, few of these causes of destruction would have the

momentum that they now command. But again, the role of overpopulation is not easy to understand. It is possible, for example, to demonstrate that the growth of human societies has been accompanied by a
parallel increase in the cultivation and settlement of land, with dis-
placement of natural communities as the result. But the effects of the
human population increase are not so simple or direct as the mere
taking and modification of land in accordance with the number of
people there are to support. For example, a glance at a world population
map will reveal that Europe is one of the most uniformly densely populated areas, with 100 to 150 persons per square mile in most places.
Central America, on the other hand, averages less than 100 persons
per square mile, and for many regions the figure is near zero. Yet the
European population lived, until very recently, in relative balance with
the remnants of a flora and fauna that were never rich to begin with;
a series of fairly stable seminatural communities was established, and
in a number of national parks, primarily in Hungary, Czechoslovakia,
Poland, and the Soviet Union, one can still see representative forests,
marshlands, and alpine communities, some containing wild boar,
wolves, and bears. In contrast, despite the lower population density,
ecosystems are in turmoil throughout Central America; as yet there
are few stable seminatural communities, and almost no national parks
in the broad sense of the term as used in Africa, Europe, and North
America. There are still many undamaged areas remaining in Central
America, proportionally many more than in Europe, but they are disappearing rapidly, with no indication that a European style of compromise conservation will be worked out. With one or two exceptions,
Central American countries have demonstrated little effective concern
for conservation practices.

Perhaps the density of population is no more important than other
parameters, such as the rate of population increase (Central America
has one of the highest rates in the world; Europe, the lowest), cultural
history, and population movements. In Japan, with an average population density of 700 persons per square mile, alpine roses, sika deer, and
the aggressive Asiatic black bear can be found in the timberline com-

Mount Okan in Akan National Park, Hokkaido, Japan. (Courtesy Japan National Tourist Organization)

munity of the Akan National Park in the eastern part of the large island of Hokkaido. It is true that most Japanese national parks incorporate man-made features like Shinto shrines, Buddhist temples, towns, and occasionally industrial areas. But, this should not be unexpected: their cultural, religious, and social institutions and low rate of population increase in recent years enabled the Japanese to evolve a prosperous society that was somehow partly integrated into the natural landscape rather than at war with it. (Recent visitors to Japan claim that this fabled integration and harmony has largely gone up in the smoke of postwar hyperindustralization.) It may be worth mentioning that if the earth's population reaches thirty billion, the population density on

40

all potentially inhabitable land will average a little more than 700 persons per square mile. Unfortunately, unless present indications prove false, there is little likelihood that much of this area will be even as liveable as Japan is now.

There is a tendency in industrialized countries to assume that excess population growth is somehow more fundamental than technology in the genesis of environmental problems. Yet, virtually no evidence supports this belief, and some experts are beginning to argue that if anything is at the root of our difficulties, it is the growth and transformation of technology that have occurred in the past quarter of a century.

Foremost among these advocates is Barry Commoner, who, with his colleagues Michael Corr and Paul Stamler, recently wrote that "the predominant factor in our industrial society's increased environmental degradation is neither population nor affluence, but the increasing environmental impact per unit of production due to technological changes." Commoner points out that from 1946 to 1968, while the population of the United States increased 43 percent, increases in various pollution indices ranged from 200 to 1000 percent. In terms of the per capita production (and therefore consumption) of food, clothing, and shelter, traditional measures of "affluence," there was during this same period no increase at all. Meanwhile, total electric power production increased more than 600 percent. The reason for the discrepancy involves the nature of technology itself. Mass production efficiency demands the uniformity of synthetic materials, which are designed and made to suit the requirements of production machinery first, the consumer a poor second, and the environment last or not at all. The system operates as a closed loop, with no opportunity for environmental information to feed back and modify the direction or speed of technology. As if a blind and deaf man were driving a fast car, the onrush of approaching traffic cannot affect the foot that pushes the accelerator.

Throughout the United States and in other industrialized countries with a variety of political systems there exists a curious assortment of monumental engineering projects whose purpose is obscure: combined water conservation–hydroelectric dams, which waste vast quantities of water through seepage and evaporation, which impair water quality through silting, and which produce relatively expensive electric power; flood-control dams on rivers that rarely flood; new, shallow-draft barge canals not needed in the space age; and rural superhighways that carry barely enough traffic to crowd a bicycle path. Most of these projects have no clear connection with the needs of an expanding population; they are built in areas of extremely low population density, provide surprisingly few permanent jobs, and produce a service that is usually but one of several economically feasible alternatives. In a different but related category are what might be called the "superfluous" industries: these may convert sweet, slightly yellowish sugar into sweet white sugar at considerable cost to the consumer; slightly alter perfectly serviceable molecules (drugs are a prime example), creating "new" products; or produce marginally useful products and then create a market for them, as is the case with many varieties of cosmetics, household "aids," packaged goods, and even books. Although these industries often meet genuine consumer demand, they too cannot be considered a result of population increase.

These forms of modern technology appear to some extent to operate independently of the feedback controls that regulate industrial production in modern capitalist and communist economies. In short, they are hard to turn off—even part way. One reason, at least in the case of the heavy construction industry, must be the enormous inventory of expensive and specialized equipment like power shovels and bulldozers. In 1964, before the Vietnamese war began seriously to distort economic indicators, shipments of selected types of construction machinery monitored by the U.S. Department of Commerce were valued at $2256 million. Another less tangible reason is the natural desire of people who possess highly developed skills to use them. Presumably, an undammed river gorge, an unpaved mountain ridge, or the chance to make a sudsier cleanser are professional opportunities to engineers, regardless of the actual merit of the plans. Yet despite these factors weighing against change, it is not clear, at least to this author, why alternatives to slow-down have been so little explored. Surely in urban reconstruction there exist challenges equal to the damming of the Grand Canyon. The repair and renovation of existing highways in congested zones is primitive, slow, and unimaginative; modern engineering has passed it by. But even the simple and cheap expedient of consultation with ecologists and other biologists during the initial project planning stage is unusual; more frequently they are summoned later to repair the damage. Few persons who have experienced the benefits of technology would wish to do without all of them, but it has become painfully obvious that technology is not an unmixed blessing.

The pressures generated by the growth of population and of technology are not always easy to distinguish, but it is necessary, if practical solutions are to be found, to remember that population alone is not at the root of all conservation problems. Every conservation problem is unique, so the search for underlying causes of a disturbance is rarely routine. Certain classes of factors that threaten natural communities do recur, however. Population and technology, the prime factors, are usually identifiable somewhere in the picture, and it will be left to the reader to make what will sometimes be an indirect connection.

Landscape Alteration

Many activities that affect ecosystems involve direct destruction of the physical and biotic habitat. In the past, the clearing of land for cultivation was responsible for most landscape alteration. This process has now largely ceased; in some places it has been actually reversed. Ireland, Japan, Sweden, and Switzerland now have a smaller land area under cultivation than in previous years. The Soviet Union, according to L. R. Brown, "is reportedly abandoning some of the land brought under cultivation during the expansion into the 'virgin-lands' area in the late 1950's." By 1966, one-seventh of all cropland in the United States was idle, primarily because of governmental restrictions. This unused acreage has subsequently been substantially reduced in response to world food shortages and declining grain reserves. The most populous countries, India and China, are cultivating nearly all of their suitable land: India planned to expand its farmland area less than two percent between 1966 and 1971. Of the major types of biotic community that are seriously threatened by agricultural expansion at this time, perhaps the most important are the low-lying coastal deserts found on most continents and the tropical rain forests of the Amazon basin, Africa, and Southeast Asia.

If fertilized and irrigated, deserts can prove very productive; the limiting factor is fresh water, and it will remain so until (and if) desalinization of sea water becomes economically practical—possibly around 1980. The use of plastic films to retard evaporation during crop-raising is also in an experimental phase, with promising small-scale results already obtained in the Arabian desert. Crop-raising poses less of a threat to most deserts, however, than do over-grazing and other forms of exploitation.

Tropical rain forests currently present more of a problem; although there is no guarantee that they will ever be amenable to large-scale clearing for agriculture (see p. 258), they are constantly being exploited for this purpose. Despite the lush appearance of tropical rain forests, their soils are usually poor and thin and are often undergoing a natural process known as laterization, in which certain minerals in the topsoil are dissolved out, and along with organic materials leach (percolate) downward. Most of the remaining organic material is oxidized. If the forest is left intact this laterization has no serious effect, but clearing, with erosion of the thin topsoil, exposes a layer of aluminum and iron oxides, which can form a hard, impermeable red crust called *laterite*. Once formed, this crust appears to be relatively permanent, and will support only an edaphic climax vegetation of widely spaced, low, herblike shrubs. In addition to the danger of producing laterite soils, deforestation can modify climate: plant biogeographer P. Dansereau cites examples in which removal of native vegetation may have caused a local warming trend in parts of Brazil, Africa, and Ohio. In Central and South America, the traditional Indian agricultural methods still seem better suited to the local environment than many "modern" techniques. Small patches of rain forest are partly cleared, and several different

Multiple-crop agriculture in the Simbai Valley, New Guinea. Altitude 3700 feet. The broad-leafed plants are bananas, but most of the other plants in this deceptive tangle of vegetation have a use as food or medicine. This garden has been newly cleared and planted. (Courtesy Roy A. Rappaport)

45

types of crop are planted, as if in imitation of the original diverse community. Thus banana plants may be used to shade several dozen other vegetable crops all mixed together. After a few years, the clearing is abandoned and secondary succession begins. In contrast, the large banana plantations initially produce a more marketable fruit, but experience in Central America has shown that prolonged use of the land for growing bananas may favor the growth of banana parasites as well. Extensive plantation holdings and even cities have been deserted, and the biotic and economic future of these areas is uncertain.

Another agricultural threat to natural communities may come as a surprise to those who regard it as an unmixed blessing. It is called the "Green Revolution," and its real meaning for the future of earth and man has not yet been revealed to those of us who lack the gift of prophecy. If one takes the press releases and early newspaper accounts at face value, the Green Revolution means more food for mankind, and nothing more. It means IR8, IR20, and IR22 "miracle" rices; it means T-cytoplasm corn; and it means Mexican semidwarf wheat. It has meant in just a few short years an increase in grain production in countries such as West Pakistan and India of from ten to eighty percent (depending on whose figures one believes), a welcome increase regardless of the magnitude. It meant a Nobel Peace Prize for N. E. Borlaug, a pioneering wheat geneticist.

What else does it mean? Before examining this question we must look more carefully at what the Green Revolution means in biological terms. The development of miracle rice is typical. According to D. S. Athwal, of the International Rice Research Institute in the Philippines,

> The traditional tall-growing varieties of rice and wheat had been selected over the centuries for their ability to grow rapidly in initial stages, to compete well with weeds, and to give modest yields with minimum care under conditions of low soil fertility. . . . But when modern methods of production are used with tall varieties, the results are discouraging. The application of high levels of fertilizer (especially nitrogen) makes these varieties grow excessively tall, and they lodge (fall over). . . . The earlier the plants lodge, the greater the loss in yield.

The Green Revolution scientists wanted rice (and wheat) that would respond to both massive applications of fertilizer and mechanical cultivation by increasing grain yield without growing tall, and produce a short, stiff straw that would lend itself to mechanical harvesting.

These properties, now all present in miracle rice, were not and could not be created by scientists. They existed prior to the 1960s but were scattered widely among many hundreds of local strains of rice known to agriculture. What the Institute scientists did was collect, for controlled cross-breeding, the most promising types, many of which had originally been brought from mainland China to Taiwan. Among these last was a variety known as Woo-gen, a plant of normal size which, either by mutation or by incorporation of new genes from other mainland stocks, gave rise to a dwarf rice plant. In Athwal's words, this plant "was [probably] selected and propagated by some enterprising farmer before the turn of the century." The result was a dwarf strain known as Dee-geo-woo-gen, one of the parent strains of the first miracle rice plant. Other desirable properties besides small size and fertilizer response, including improved grain quality and disease resistance, are continuously being incorporated into the miracle rice stocks by selective breeding.

The various seed grains developed by Green Revolution scientists have been introduced throughout the world and are very popular, especially in places where international programs or local resources have provided fertilizer and equipment to help in the tillage and harvesting. Where these agricultural aids have been available the new grains have provided the expected bumper crops, and the successes have been well-publicized. Nearly drowned out, however, in the din of jubilation and self-congratulation have been the voices of a few, possibly sour ecologists who have looked beyond the first triumph and been frightened by what they have seen.

The potential problems generated by the Green Revolution fall into two categories, lesser and greater. In connection with the lesser problems, W. Paddock, a population expert, has raised several difficult questions: first, should we produce more food *before* we have controlled the population explosion, and thus risk making that explosion worse and in the long run more destructive of human life? Second, is the Green Revolution really capable of maintaining its early momentum, or is the main production increase, which was largely the result of improved fertilizer response, now a thing of the past?

The first question is mainly a moral and ethical one, which the reader must examine for himself. For the second, only a few hints are available. Certainly it is true that improvements in plant stocks cannot go much beyond the gene resources, such as Dee-geo-woo-gen, currently available but widely scattered. This places a firm limit on the magnitude of the improvements that can yet be made. Any comparable future breakthroughs must now exist in the world in living plants, and it is indeed difficult to imagine what they might be. It has often been suggested that we will be able to "manufacture" genes as they are needed in the future. We cannot, however, invent genes for miraculous properties and introduce them into plants; even if our genetic science should take us that far some day, we are likely to know much too little about evolution to hope that a complex organism, finely honed by millions of years of natural selection, would function properly with our crude additions. It was once remarked by the biologist Ernst Mayr that the offspring of a thrush, given the wings of a hawk by some sudden, simple mutation, would probably not be able to fly at all. It would lack all of the innumerable supporting adaptations of hawk structure, physiology, and balanced gene interactions.

Other matters pertaining to Paddock's second question are even more troublesome. Continuous, heavy applications of fertilizer are apt to leave salts in the soil, especially when there are problems with irrigation and drainage. This is believed to have been a cause of the decline of Babylon (and many subsequent civilizations); who now would think of the wastelands of the Tigris and Euphrates valleys as a garden of paradise? It is already a serious matter in the valley of the Rhine and in California's Imperial Valley, the latter possibly the richest agricultural land in the western hemisphere. Poisonous nitrites from fertilizer are finding their way into baby foods and grocery produce in increasingly toxic concentrations. Equally worrisome are the insecticides that are staunchly defended by the champions of the Green

Revolution. Pesticide "addiction" with growing ineffectiveness, and the harmful side effects of these chemicals on natural communities are discussed later in the chapter, as are herbicides, widely used for weed control.

Another "lesser" problem, beyond the scope of this book, is the question of exploitation and imperialism. The money of industrial nations has fostered the Green Revolution for the "developing nations." But the Green Revolution is nothing without massive infusions of capital for fertilizer, agricultural machinery, and insecticides. To what extent do we limit the future independence of poor nations by the self-perpetuating indebtedness that accompanies this gift? Furthermore, will the millions of agricultural laborers who constitute India's one visible resource understand the virtues of being displaced by mechanization? These may be loaded questions, but still they deserve debate until the issues become more clearly defined.

Serious as all these matters are, they recede into the background in the face of what I have called the "greater" problem. It has already been pointed out that the Green Revolution depends on the pre-existence of a wide diversity of plant types. This diversity has been fostered and nurtured by agricultural man since neolithic times, but ultimately it arose from and is renewed by the natural community. The great tragedy of the Green Revolution as currently pursued is that it tends to destroy the very diversity that it and the world need to survive and prosper. This destruction is effected in two ways: first, through the deleterious side effects of the various chemicals now applied to agricultural land throughout the world; second, through the widespread acceptance of the miracle grains themselves, with the consequence that farmers all over the world are abandoning the personal strains of rice and wheat that have been in their families for generations or centuries. As miracle crops replace or outproduce existing plantings, they herald the spread of a deadly agricultural uniformity, while an irreplaceable wealth of food crop diversity vanishes in their path. The more the Green Revolution succeeds, the more it fails—under these conditions nobody wins.

Only recently has this danger been appreciated—with one or two exceptions. In 1938, Carl O. Sauer, a geographer and historian of agriculture, wrote, "Commercial corn-growing . . . utilizes only two subspecies of maize and of them only a small part of the range of genes that have been fixed by primitive plant breeding. Yet the qualities on which we have standardized for present-day commercial corn growing may not be the same that will be desired a century from now." (It took less than a third of a century for Sauer's uncanny prediction to start coming true.) He continued:

> Of the great varietal range of upland cotton only a very few enter into the commercial forms. The extension of cotton in the United States, Egypt, and India has resulted in its disappearance over much of its primitive area of cultivation in Mexico and Central America, where the full range of varietal forms was developed. Yet these primitive forms hold by far the greater range of plant breeding possibilities for future, as yet unrecognized needs. Some years ago we secured from southern Mexico seeds of a type of cotton called Acala, which made possible the current development of cotton-growing in the San Joaquin Valley. Had the plant explorer missed this particular spot in the State of Chiapas or come a few years later, we might not have a successful cotton industry in California. No one knows how many domestic varieties of cotton survive or have been lost.

Despite the critical significance of this type of thinking for the contemporary world, today only a handful of knowledgeable men appreciate it. One is the Australian plant geneticist Sir Otto H. Frankel. His examples sound ominously familiar:

> The hills of Eastern Galilee in Israel abound with a great diversity of wild wheat, barley, oats and Aegilops,* among rocks and ancient trees, where the rough terrain creates a natural sanctuary. The "wild orchards" of Anatolia, consisting of wild pears, apples, plums, pistachio, on rocky slopes at the edges of cultivation, were similarly preserved for hundreds, or more probably thousands of years, being used as stock for grafting of cultivated forms. . . . Aerial application of fertilizer and seed could presumably trans-

---

* [A wild grass related to wheat.]

The "Horns of Hattin," Galilee, Israel. (Courtesy Israel Government Tourist Office)

form the Galilean hills into more productive pastures, with certain destruction for gene pools bridging the millennia.* The bulldozer is reputed to be dealing with the wild orchards.

As Frankel points out, the small cultivated plots of local or family strains of crop plants are even more vulnerable to the Green Revolution than the totally wild varieties, although both are endangered and both are essential. Hugh Iltis, an American botanist, has described the way in which wild and cultivated native strains of the same plant can interact, with benefit to man.

According to Iltis, in the Lake Titicaca region of Peru, the native Indians have cultivated potatoes for at least two to three thousand years. From generation to generation, family groups have developed their own strains of potato, frequently unique to their small plots of land. More than a *thousand* different potato types have been reported from the Lake Titicaca Basin and Huanuco Province to the north. Recently, a number of aid agencies have urged the replacement of these native potato stocks with a handful of standardized high-production strains. Many of the old types have already been lost—others are decreasing rapidly. Iltis fears that several undesirable results of this "progress" may occur. The local potato varieties have evolved, with the help of man, from bitter, inedible, native plants, and some still cross with the fifty or sixty wild types, producing weedy hybrids which many agriculturists would like to eliminate. However, as Iltis points out, "these weedy strains act as a genetic bridge by which a tremendous amount of variety can be transferred from the wild, useless, bitter, uneatable kinds to the cultivated ones; introducing disease resistance and high protein content." It is obvious that hundreds of different cultivated potato strains with opportunities for gene exchange with dozens of wild types offer a far greater barrier to the spread of epidemic plant diseases than do the few genetically isolated and over-domesticated varieties that are replacing them. Furthermore, the North American potatoes, with less than one percent protein content, are

* [This is only an example. Frankel states that the hills of Galilee are now protected, except from light grazing. Few other governments have been so careful with their plant resources.]

clearly less valuable in the Peruvian diet than the local potatoes, which may have four times as much protein.

In Iltis' words, *"There is only one way to preserve a species* [or variety], and that is by *preserving a sufficiently large population in its native habitat,* a habitat complete with its own particular climate, its own particular soils, its own particular pollinating insects." Small botanical garden collections or even seed cold-storage units could never preserve more than a fraction of the existing wild plant diversity, although they may be adequate to maintain a good working collection of domestic crop plants.

Dozens of other species or strains are now imperiled by the Green Revolution, from the unique strains of African rice to wild fruit trees of the Malayan and Amazon rain forests; most will never even be reported as missing when they go. The first great surveys and censuses of the diversity of cultivated crops were made by the famous Russian geneticist and plant geographer N. I. Vavilov, starting in the 1920s. His work has continued at the U.S.S.R.'s Vavilov Institute of Plant Industry and elsewhere. Most recently, efforts to identify for subsequent protection the remaining environments containing diverse strains of wild or cultivated plants have been coordinated by FAO in collaboration with a committee of the International Biological Program. The magnitude of the task is overwhelming; and the outside interest in it—even among biologists—is far too scanty.

One other part of this problem has to do with the idea that the species diversity and durability of living systems are related. As this principle pertains to agriculture, it is especially obvious in tropical rain forests, but the Green Revolution has extended the hazard to temperate zone agriculture as well. In March 1971, an article appeared in *Science* entitled "The Southern Corn Leaf Blight Epidemic," followed a few weeks later by a dramatic headline in the *New York Times:* "Corn Blight: A Triumph of Genetics Threatens Disaster." The story, in brief, is as follows. Hybrid T-cytoplasm corn is a product of the Green Revolution. It incorporates a genetic change that makes its production much more economical by eliminating the need for the costly hand-labor de-tasseling operation. Consequently it has replaced nearly all other hybrid corn grown in the United States. Until 1970, the economic benefits of this crop were so great that no one except a few Philippine scientists gave much thought to Sauer's early warnings about the dangers of the low diversity of commercial corn varieties. In 1961 agricultural scientists A. C. Mercado, Jr., and R. M. Lantican reported, on the basis of experience in the Philippines, that T-cytoplasm corn seemed especially susceptible to infection by new mutant forms of the fungus *Helminthosporium*. Their paper, published in a Philippine agricultural journal, was largely overlooked in the United States. In the meantime, most of the U.S. corn was being converted to the T-cytoplasm type; the *Helminthosporium* leaf blight was in the country, but had been causing no serious problems. Then, according to agronomist L. A. Tatum, "Southern corn leaf blight underwent a dramatic transformation from a disease of quite minor status to one of almost catastrophic dimensions in a single season." In 1970, after years of comparative obscurity, *Helminthosporium* suddenly moved into the corn belt and destroyed more than fifteen percent of the year's crop, an economic loss of at least a billion dollars. The start of the 1971 season saw farmers scrambling to obtain the older N-cytoplasm seed, which was in extremely short supply, and plant breeders desperately trying to find *Helminthosporium*-resistant stocks for breeding.

In an article entitled "Man-Made Plant Diseases," plant pathologist C. E. Yarwood writes, "In general, the succulent, fast growing commercial varieties of crops are more susceptible to pathogens than their wild ancestors. The crossing of susceptible commercial varieties with resistant wild species is a standard method of breeding for disease resistance." In addition, monoculture, the planting of large tracts with one kind of food plant or commercial tree, fosters disease by facilitating the epidemic spread of disease organisms from one plant to the next. Wild and cultivated diversity is the principal hope for solving these problems, but diversity is fast disappearing. Green Revolution scientists expect to keep one step ahead of crop diseases by continuous breeding programs; where the breeding stock is to come from in an efficient, monocultured earth they do not say.

We cannot afford to end all monocultures, especially for grain crops such as wheat, and no one wants to curtail the Green Revolution activity of plant breeding. But it is essential that there be great restraint and control in the former case and far-sightedness in the latter. Governments will probably have to subsidize diversity in crop plantings and agricultural techniques (including small farms and hand labor) so that diversity can compete with the blind, destructive efficiency of monoculture. Plants that are inordinately dependent on fertilizers, herbicides, and insecticides have no place in truly modern farming; like ineradicable weeds, they are crowding out the life and future of human agriculture. The counter-argument about "feeding the starving millions" is a cruel hoax—what will the agronomists of the twenty-first century feed their starving millions? Only those willing to watch their children eat processed algae in a joyless and moribund world could be content with the present course of agricultural technology.

The value of biological diversity is one of the main themes of this book. Diversity is unique in that it is equally prized, though for different reasons, by both the resource and holistic schools of conservation. In this gray age of anthropomorphic machines and mechanomorphic people, of hard facts, of quantification and efficiency, people tend to place a higher value on the resource arguments. The other kind of conservation is hard to explain or justify in writing, at least to those who haven't already experienced and felt the meaning of diversity. It gets fewer words in this book, but it is not less important. Those for whom the brief descriptions of Frankel's Galilean hillsides or Iltis' Andean potato farms aroused something personal and internal, like sudden memories of pleasant days long forgotten, will understand.

Although unrelated to the increase of croplands, another landscape-altering process is causing the deterioration of rain-forest and other tropical communities and soils on a truly national scale. This is "defoliation," which has been practiced extensively by the American military in Vietnam. The scope of the devastation is beyond comprehension and

Defoliated mangroves, South Vietnam. There is no evidence of regrowth several years after the spraying. Some dead trees have been cut for wood. (Matthew Meselson—Herbicide Assessment Commission, AAAS)

unprecedented in world history. To say that every ecosystem in Vietnam, major and minor, has been seriously altered or wrecked beyond hope of repair, is to make a safe and conservative statement.

The first method of defoliation employed by the U.S. forces was chemical. Approximately thirteen to fourteen million pounds of 2,4-D and 2,4,5-T (di- and trichlorophenoxyacetic acids), the entire production of these chemicals in the United States during 1967 and 1968, plus other compounds such as the arsenic-containing cacodylic acid, were sprayed on the Vietnamese rain forests in these two years alone. The result, especially in the vital coastal mangrove forests, was the death of most forest trees as well as any rubber or fruit trees in the

Bomb craters in coastal forest, Gia Dinh Province, South Vietnam, August 1971. From 1500 feet. (A. H. Westing)

general vicinity of the spraying. The forests (except for the mangrove community, which remains barren and empty) are rapidly being replaced by early successional invaders, ineradicable and worthless plants including bamboo and the fifteen-to-twenty-foot *Imperata* grass, which hide guerillas as well as did the previous forest. Many defoliated zones are so extensive that succession may be permanently arrested at this early stage for lack of recolonizing seeds and animals of the mature communities. In one small incident near Saigon, a single forest fire destroyed nearly 100,000 acres of heavily treated woods. Living rain forests do not ordinarily burn.

Chemical defoliants kill fish and needed soil organisms. They are

57

toxic to man if ingested with food in large doses and are suspected of causing an increase in birth defects among children whose mothers were exposed to the chemicals while pregnant. With the increasing scientific protest in the United States, the use of chemical defoliants has been slightly curtailed, but the gap is now being filled by bombs and giant bulldozers.

According to ecologists Arthur H. Westing and E. W. Pfeiffer, who have made detailed studies of the damage in Vietnam, there are more than 10 million bomb craters pitting the countryside; they may be twenty feet deep and are often filled with mosquito-breeding fresh water. A new and increasingly popular bomb, the "daisy-cutter," second only to nuclear weapons in power, clears a space the size of a football field and kills or injures all wildlife in a surrounding area of more than 1700 acres. Even the worms in the earth of the central two acres are reportedly killed by the shock wave. The primary purpose of this bomb is to clear instant helicopter landing fields in the jungle, but it is also used against other targets.

The bulldozers, twenty tons in weight, are fitted with an eleven-foot wide "Rome plow" blade and a three-foot tree-splitting lance, plus fourteen extra tons of armor. Westing reports that military estimates place bulldozed forests at 750,000 acres by 1971, with stripping continuing at the rate of more than a thousand acres a day. By 1970, at least 126,000 acres of prime timberland accessible to lumbering was included in this total. Some of the destruction is actually done for pleasure and to occupy leisure time. Thus, Westing writes, "one can now find a U.S. First Infantry Division emblem, covering some 1500 acres, carved into the landscape about 25 miles northwest of Saigon. . . ."

In all, chemical defoliants, bombs, and bulldozers have obliterated more than three million acres of Vietnamese forest and have affected every other kind of ecosystem. Pfeiffer estimates that bomb craters alone occupy a combined area of at least 325,000 acres. In the ruined forests, the *Imperata* grass and bamboos thrive. Laterite crust formation in some of the eroded soils may be yet to come. Cratered areas are dangerous to use for agriculture because of unexploded bombs and mines and millions of metal fragments that cut the feet of water buffalos. In some places the craters make planting impractical anyway. Shrapnel embedded deep in the wood renders the fallen and splintered trees useless for lumber.

Not all deliberate defoliation has occurred in Vietnam. Chemical defoliants have been used (and largely abandoned) to eliminate deciduous "weed" trees in Swedish forests. They are commonly employed in agriculture and brush control in the Soviet Union, where they are sprayed from airplanes. In 1970, the Soviets treated 86,500,000 acres with herbicides, an increase of 16,100,000 acres over 1969. Herbicides are similarly used in the United States. Nevertheless, when one thinks of defoliation one still thinks of Vietnam, henceforth the symbol of ecological vandalism and desolation.

During the first part of this century, urbanization actually meant the recovery of rural land as the population migrated to the centers of widely spaced cities. This is no longer true. Two factors now affect the fate of land adjacent to urban areas: first, the steady increase in city population caused by continued migration and high birth rates; and second, the increase in per capita requirement of land. It is expected, for example, that between 1965 and 2000 the average town dweller in France will have doubled his living space. Because the population will also double, the total urban area of France will quadruple in one generation. Under this kind of pressure, neighboring cities coalesce. A single urban area will soon stretch from Amsterdam south to Paris and along the Rhine to Köln (Cologne) and the Ruhr. Similar urban-suburban regions have developed in the United States along the shore of Lake Erie and along the Atlantic Coast from Boston to Washington. Urban land area in the United States is expected to increase from 21 million acres in 1960 to 45 million acres by the end of the century.

Since three-fifths of the total land in the United States is privately owned, any comprehensive planning of urban spread must be accompanied by the advance purchase of property by the government or by strict regulation of land use. This has not generally been done, and these functions have been delegated to local governments (whose authority to plan derives from the police power of the states), with the federal government keeping only loose control over the financing of housing construction. Although there has been an increased tendency toward formation of regional associations for metropolitan planning, it is not likely that the alteration of exurban communities will be either orderly or coordinated in the future. Nevertheless, several interdisciplinary groups are planning for a more extensive reorganization of urban structure than has yet been attempted anywhere. Athelstan Spilhaus has said: "The overgrown urban complex must be selectively dismantled and dispersed if we are to cure the ills of the megalopolis." He suggests that when the population of the earth reaches 15 billion, around A.D. 2068, it could be housed in 60,000 cities, each with a population of a quarter million and each surrounded by sixty-four square miles of "open land." Global plans of this sort take no notice of ecological or any other kind of diversity; fortunately, the chances of their implementation are zero. There are many other plans for model cities, including a few like Disney World's model city in central Florida, which have gone beyond the planning stage. Aside from pollution control, these model cities often seem to be no better designed to coexist with their regional ecosystems than do existing cities, and are possibly much worse. Here, as in other land-using ventures, it is imperative that ecologists and local residents be given a major role in formulating initial plans. With this kind of cooperation, the result can be a livable and pleasant community well integrated with its environment, as in the case of Tapiola, Finland, and a very few other new towns.

One effect of rapid urbanization in the United States (and in all other countries) will be enormous harm to natural and semi-natural communities, including those most accessible to the bulk of the population. The areal expansion of cities does not necessarily mean the loss of natural communities; much of the surrounding land is already semi-urbanized, containing dilapidated buildings and weedy, treeless lots. There are, however, some surprisingly intact areas near even the largest cities. Regulations against hunting and overnight camping in densely populated suburban regions have had the effect of protecting bird and small mammal populations. For example, New Jersey's Great Swamp, an

The Passaic River in New Jersey's Great Swamp. (Annan Photo Features)

61

Jamaica Bay Wildlife Sanctuary, New York City. This biologically diverse and enormous wetland park is entirely within the city limits of New York. Its 9151 acres include 6283 of water and 2868 of land. A subtle combination of man-made features such as ponds, dikes, and selected plantings of vegetation, plus natural mud flats and salt marsh make Jamaica Bay especially attractive to birds. (Horst Schäfer—Photo Trends)

exceptionally rich biotic community, is less than thirty miles from the center of the world's largest metropolitan area. Central Park, in Manhattan, is not exactly a natural community, but 101 species of birds have been seen there on a single day. The Cornell Laboratory of Ornithology lists two hundred places in Greater New York City where many varieties of birds may be found. At the Jamaica Bay Wildlife Refuge, within the New York City limits and accessible by subway, a number of large, showy birds have started to breed for the first time in this century, despite the noise of arriving and departing jets at Kennedy International Airport a few hundred yards away. These species include the glossy ibis, Louisiana heron, and snowy egret, and an assortment of migratory ducks that ordinarily breed in the western prairie regions. Unfortunately, in most large cities the wildlife that remains is usually a testimonial not to far-sighted planning but to human oversight and to the stability of certain natural communities. Even in the New York area, which does not lack conservationists, the beautiful Hempstead Plains have been filled with grotesque and dismal suburban developments. The Great Swamp is coveted by airport builders, despite its status as a National Wildlife Refuge, and in Central Park air pollution is finally driving away species of song birds that were able to survive all other challenges presented by more than ten generations of New Yorkers.

In urban areas, public and private land acquisition patterns are based on property valuation and on neighborhood factors; long-range conservation projections to maintain city vitality are shunted aside by the pressure of these immediate economic demands. A prime example of profit-making at the expense of both an important ecosystem and a city itself is the filling of the Tampa and San Francisco bays. In addition to scenic beauty, which in each case is the major attribute of the surrounding city, the bays are strategic spawning areas for a host of marine animals, including game fish. San Francisco Bay is the most important stopping place for migratory birds on the Pacific Flyway. According to the U.S. Fish and Wildlife Service, approximately one million water fowl winter on the bay; there may be as many as 30,000 per mile along the tidal flats, and from half to three-quarters of all water birds migrating along the Pacific Coast depend on this habitat.

Surprisingly, much of the floor of both bays is privately owned: a fifth of San Francisco Bay, including a large part of the biologically rich offshore region, is in the hands of developers and speculators; another fourth is owned by local governments whose major concern is to increase their taxable lands by filling in the bay. Already fifteen to twenty percent of Tampa Bay and one-third of San Francisco Bay have been filled in. Since some of the fill comes from dredging in other parts of the bay, the damage is even greater than the figures indicate. The bottom of Tampa Bay was referred to by one official of

Boca Ciega Bay, Tampa, Florida, in 1949 (above) and 1969 (below). (Bob Graeber—Airflite)

the Interior Department as a "biological desert." Only part of the fill material is obtained by dredging, however; the remainder is garbage. At one time at least thirty-two garbage disposal sites jutted out into San Francisco Bay. If the bay becomes seventy percent filled (this much of it is less than twelve feet deep and therefore fillable), some meteorologists predict a sharp rise in summer temperatures and a drastic increase in smog. Geologists worry about the effects of earthquakes on buildings constructed on the unstable land fill. The narrow, polluted tidal creek that will remain will still be spanned by the Golden Gate and Bay bridges—a monumentally unfunny joke on the future residents of the cities of San Francisco, Berkeley, and Oakland, and on the rest of humanity. (Citizens' action groups have done much to halt the indiscriminate filling of San Francisco Bay, but occasional clandestine operations still occur, including one recently discovered—and stopped —at San Francisco International Airport.)

The ecological and aesthetic damage done by the dredgers and fillers has aroused enough opposition to generate some political action. In Florida, the city of Sarasota is holding its present bulkhead line at the mean high-water mark. No commercial developing will be allowed beyond this line. Florida's Brevard, Martin, and Palm Beach counties, which are urbanizing rapidly, have passed moratoriums on the sale and dredging of submerged lands. Florida's Randell Act now requires "biological and ecological surveys" of submerged land before the state will consider issuing permits for it to be dredged, filled, or sold. Important as this pioneer law is, William Partington, a noted Florida conservationist, has pointed out that it has a number of biological defects. For one, the term "ecological surveys" is not well defined; consequently these surveys are not performed. Second, the Florida Game and Fresh Water Fish Commission is not asked to evaluate the effects of estuarine development on air-breathing vertebrates that do not actually live in the water, although many such mammals, birds, and reptiles depend on an undamaged marine habitat for food and, indirectly, for shelter. Finally, the biological value of land areas above the mean high-water mark is not usually considered, but the mangrove swamps, buttonwoods, or marsh grasses of this zone are an integral part of the coastal ecosystem, regulating the flow of nutrients, the movement of soil, and the growth of invertebrates and microorganisms important to the adjacent waters.

The second and third points underscore the importance of an ecological concept that must be understood by the concerned public before conservation can become fully effective, namely: an essential structural unity among ecosystems gives them their distinctive character; disturb it and what remains is merely a loose assortment of those animals and plants that may manage to survive under less-than-optimum conditions. We would not think of preserving an historical mansion without its roof or colonnade or grounds. It is strange, then, that we can try to keep some south Florida coastal waters intact, but fail to preserve the intricate tangle of mangroves that hold the soil, catch organic debris, provide asylum for young fish and invertebrates, and harbor the nests of roseate spoonbills, herons, and ibises. The question of where one ecosystem stops and the next begins, therefore, becomes crucial. Obviously, any demarcation line will be somewhat artificial, yet such decisions can and must be made. For practical purposes, we can assume that the littoral community of the south Florida Gulf Coast "stops" above the line of salt-tolerant plants that defines the farthest reach of storm tidewater and salt spray.

Neither agricultural nor urban expansion is altering the landscape of industrialized countries more profoundly than an assortment of massive engineering ventures that usually fall under the heading of "public works" and include dams, flood control projects, and highways. These enterprises are justified by their proponents in terms of urban and agricultural needs, but in considerable measure are pork-barrel projects that utilize an enormous inventory of heavy construction machinery, and provide work for a large number of highly trained engineers and the extensive organizations that back them up in both government and private industry. In the United States, the principal governmental agencies engaging in this kind of activity are the Army Corps of Engineers, the Bureau of Reclamation, and the Bureau of Public Roads.

Mangroves in Everglades National Park, Florida. The tangle of roots holds the soil in the shifting, tidal waters and offers shelter for fish hatchlings and invertebrate animals. On the more northerly coasts of the eastern United States and Western Europe, the *Spartina* grass of salt marshes performs a similar function. (Jack E. Boucher—Courtesy National Park Service)

These agencies (and many private corporations, especially power companies) have had great impact on the land, and the net result is difficult to assess. Certainly they are neither the monsters of the popular conservation literature nor the shining knights of the technology-oriented press. They perform a large number of essential services, but they also make dreadful mistakes, which have caused unnecessary, widespread alteration of the landscape.

Over the years, the "earth movers" have advanced a philosophy that might be crudely summarized as "progress through technology and change." From an ecological point of view, the least appealing aspect of this philosophy is a tendency to minimize both the importance of existing ecosystems and the consequences of their destruction. From the beginning of the twentieth-century technological upsurge in the United States, this tendency has been incorporated in a quasi-scientific dialogue with social, economic, and political ramifications. Because the fundamental controversy has undergone little change during the past seventy-five years, it may be useful to reach back to the scientific literature of the first quarter of this century and uncover a debate that has long been buried. Marsh had raised the spectre of wholesale changes in climate and stream flow occuring as the result of removal of forest cover in watersheds. In 1909, Lt. Col. H. M. Chittenden, of the Army Corps of Engineers, denied Marsh's conclusions in a lengthy paper, "Forests and Reservoirs in Their Relations to Stream Flow, with Particular Reference to Navigable Rivers"; in 1927, Chittenden was answered in turn by Raphael Zon, director of the Lakes States Forest Experiment Station of the U.S. Forest Service, in a monograph titled *Forests and Water in the Light of Scientific Investigation.*

Chittenden based his argument concerning forests and stream flow on two bizarre claims: first, that snow accumulates to a lesser degree in forests than in open spaces and melts more quickly in the former; second, that it is not the cutting of forests but the subsequent cultivation of the cleared land that permits erosion by altering its waterholding and run-off properties. Even this supposed loss of topsoil through cultivation he regarded as beneficial because it "builds up deltas and surely, though slowly, extends the habitable area of the globe." Zon's conclusions were in direct opposition: "Among the factors, such as climate and the regularity of stream flow, the forest plays an important part, especially on impermeable soils. The mean low stages as well as the moderately high stages in the rivers depend upon the extent of forest cover on the watersheds. The forest tends to equalize the flow throughout the year by making the low stages higher and the high stages lower."

The bulk of the Chittenden paper is taken up by a "Discussion" section; a number of the twenty-three discussants were highly critical of Chittenden's conclusions. The remarks of one participant, Gifford Pinchot, reveal the intensity of the debate:

> . . . Colonel Chittenden's fundamental conception as to the forest floor and its influence is mistaken. His idea that records in the United States do not show an increase in the frequency of floods and low waters is mistaken. His idea that the critical point to be considered is flood heights, and not flood frequencies is mistaken. And his conception of forestry . . . is so fundamentally mistaken that the speaker might discuss it at far greater length without exhausting the mistakes."

Taken as a whole, the Chittenden paper suffers from the lack of a list of verifiable references and from an approach that makes little use of the fundamental scientific concept of the "control," specifically from a paucity of data comparing stream flow in forested and deforested watersheds in the same climatic region and at the same time. Because of drastic yearly fluctuations in rainfall and temperature, analysis of the same river system for a few years before and after deforestation is not meaningful for the small number of documented examples that Chittenden considers.

In addition to employing the necessary controls, Zon used an analytic approach that is far more amenable to scientific test; he recorded separately "the influence of the forest upon each of the different factors affecting stream flow, and the final effect of the forest upon stream flow is deduced from the combined effect on all the factors. While less direct, this method lends itself more readily to experimentation. . . ."

The Yukon Flats, August 1962. (U.S. Fish and Wildlife Service)

Zon's bibliography, in which he cites more than a thousand scientific papers, is a virtually complete review of the literature up to that time. Since 1927 there has been little serious disagreement with Zon's major conclusions, whereas Chittenden's paper illustrates the danger of advancing unsupported scientific arguments as an *ex post facto* justification of nonscientific policy.

Since the time of Chittenden the tactics of the Corps of Engineers and other public works agencies in the United States and elsewhere have not changed a bit. There is still a "scientific" justification for every project, supported by scientists and consultants in the pay of the agency. Increasingly in the 1970s, these clumsy and heavy-handed arguments have fallen apart in an embarrassing way in court, under the pressure generated by environmental lawyers and their volunteer expert scientific witnesses.

One of the best examples of a "make-work" scheme that will have disastrous effects on an ecosystem of great international value is the proposed Rampart Canyon Dam on the Yukon River. (At the time of

70

this writing, the Corps of Engineers had not received authorization or funds for this controversial project.) If built, the dam will flood 10,500 square miles, obliterating 400 miles of the Yukon River and more than 12,000 miles of its tributaries, as well as the 36,000 lakes and ponds of the Yukon Flats. The Yukon Flats ecosystem has been described by ecologists A. Starker Leopold and Justin W. Leonard:

> The Yukon Flats are a complex admixture of lakes, ponds and sloughs, coniferous and hardwood timber, willow brush and muskeg, with tundra on some elevated ridges. Viewed from a low-flying airplane, the intermixing of types on the Flats, it becomes quite clear, is maintained in considerable part by action of the meandering and braided channels of the Yukon River and some of its principal tributaries.
>
> The Yukon is a restless river, constantly undercutting banks on the outsweep of meanders and depositing new bars on the inner curves. Oxbow sloughs are left in the wake of the migrating channels, and in time these develop marshy borders favorable for waterfowl, muskrats and beavers.
>
> Newly deposited sandbars soon develop fresh young stands of willow that constitute excellent winter forage for moose. The willow stands advance slowly through successional stages of aspen or cottonwood to spruce forest, and the sloughs fill gradually with organic matter and the silt of spring floods. But sooner or later transient channels of the river migrate back through the forest, again initiating the processes of succession. It is this dynamic process of self-renewal that maintains such varied and productive wildlife habitat on the Yukon floodplain.

The dam would substitute for this natural community a large, monotonous, relatively sterile lake, useless as a breeding site for ducks and geese, and unsuitable as a habitat for the mammals of the region, including more than 10,000 moose, two caribou herds, minks, beavers, otters, martens, wolverines, weasels, lynx, and red foxes. A salmon run that provides 800,000 fish per year for the local inhabitants would be lost. The total waterfowl breeding land that would be inundated amounts to 6.9 million acres, accounting for 1.5 million ducks and 12,500 geese annually. Boating and fishing in the new lake, which will have little scenic value, are likely to be impaired by countless snags—remnants of the old forests—that will remain on the bottom for many decades.

The economic arguments against the dam are also strong. It would create few jobs, and any industry it might attract would be highly automated. It would produce far more electricity than the projected needs of the population and industry of Alaska during the next half-century, and its surplus power would probably be too expensive to compete with locally produced nuclear power on the U.S. Pacific Coast, 2000 miles away. In addition, there are a number of excellent untapped sources of power near the population centers of Alaska; and finally, the construction cost estimate of $1.3 billion, if previous Corps of Engineers estimates are any indication, is very conservative. In short, the best that can be said about the Rampart project is that Rampart Canyon is an unoccupied dam site that presents some challenging engineering problems.

Besides electric power, another common justification for rural engineering projects is the appealing phrase, "water conservation and flood control." Perhaps the most grisly example of compounded errors and ecological mismanagement in the United States is the vast series of canals, levees, dikes, and spillways that comprise the Central and Southern Florida Flood Control District. That part of Florida south of Lake Okeechobee is the only part of the continental United States that has a nearly subtropical climate, and its dominant biological community, the Everglades, is so complex that its most important biotic relationships are only beginning to be understood. The Everglades were formed and molded by the moderate climate and, equally important, by the high summer rainfall and run-off from Lake Okeechobee. When Lake Okeechobee overflowed, the waters crept south in a broad, shallow sheet, supporting what has aptly been called a "river" of tall sawgrass, and forming teardrop-shaped islands that became covered with a variety of trees, including mahogany, palms, and a number of other tropical species. Southwest of the lake was an extensive region of cypress swamp whose quiet waters were dyed black by organic acids leached from the trees. In the south, sawgrass gradually gave

The Everglades, "River of Grass." (Courtesy Florida News Bureau)

way to mangrove, and fresh water to brackish, in an area that was a remarkably rich spawning ground for fish and invertebrates. The list of animal species was long (and still is), befitting such a highly developed ecosystem. The most representative member of the local fauna was the alligator, but a host of other animals—ranging from the panther to the snail-eating Everglades kite to the loggerhead sea turtles nesting at Cape Sable—were integrated into the Everglades community.

As was pointed out earlier, a mature ecosystem confers environmental stability on its member species; indeed the stability of these communities goes a long way towards explaining why they have evolved. But even though mature ecosystems can locally damp the effects of normal environmental fluctuations, the specializations of their individual species make the community particularly susceptible to extreme environmental changes. In the words of Margalef, "Succession can build history only when the environment is stable. In the case of a changing environment, the selected ecosystem will be composed of species with a high reproductive rate and lower special requirements. Such an ecosystem is less diverse and less complex. . . ."

Eighty years of ill-conceived tampering with the water system of south Florida has resulted in such violent environmental fluctuations that the predicted disintegration of the mature Everglades ecosystem has begun to occur. An early attempt to drain the glades for agricultural development culminated in the Tamiami Canal, opened in 1928, running from the Gulf of Mexico to the Atlantic Ocean. It intercepts much of the southward flow of water from Lake Okeechobee. In 1949, one year after the Everglades National Park was dedicated, the Central and Southern Florida Flood Control District replaced the old Everglades Drainage District as the state authority that was to manage the increasingly intricate water diversion system built by the Corps of Engineers. Three "conservation areas" were created between Lake Okeechobee and the Park; these further ensured that the Park could receive no water unless authorized by the Corps or the Flood Control District. Moreover, the water is now delivered by canals, not by slow, steady seepage through the river of grass. The complexity of the arti-

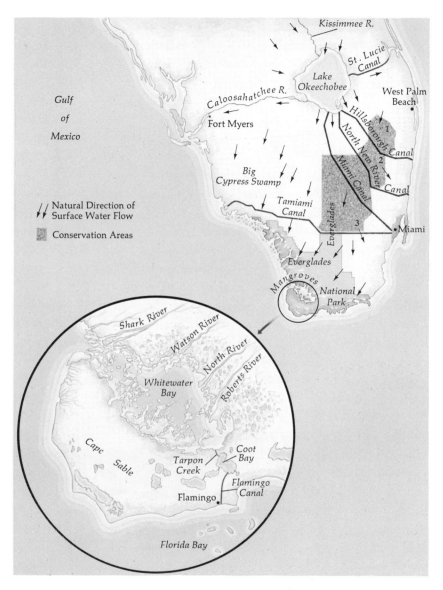

The Florida Everglades.

ficial system now in operation (many of the canals were built in response to agricultural, real estate, and industrial pressures and do not even meet sound water management criteria) makes it difficult to control; consequently the conditions in the conservation areas, especially Area 3 (see map, p. 75), fluctuate wildly between flood and drought, while the Park rarely has enough water. Floridians have been treated to the spectacle of millions of fish stranded in parched mud holes and thousands of dead herons and egrets, while a few miles north the Corps of Engineers released "surplus" fresh water into the Atlantic Ocean. Between 1961 and 1967, the wood ibis, North America's only stork, had one successful nesting season.

Although the Flood Control District and Corps of Engineers have become somewhat more sensitive to the needs of the Park, it remains to be seen whether their unwieldy system can ever be tuned finely enough to restore the delicate balance of Everglades ecology. Meanwhile, other factors threaten the ecosystem. On August 11, 1969, the *New York Times* reported that construction had begun on a thirty-nine-square-mile jetport in Big Cypress Swamp, which provides thirty-eight percent of the water flowing into Everglades Park. Initial construction grants by the U.S. Department of Transportation were made without prior consultation with the Department of the Interior. At this writing, further construction on the jetport has been prohibited, but the existing training runway is still in use. In other areas, unregulated suburban residential and industrial expansion has caused intrusion of salt water via canals and via seepage into the depleted underground aquifers (reservoirs). Ironically, the Flamingo Canal, built by the Corps under Park authorization to increase visitor access to the Park, was not provided with protective locks, and the saline waters of Florida Bay have flowed into and wrecked Coot Bay and the surrounding area, killing the water plants *Chara* and *Naiad*, which once fed a nesting waterfowl population of several hundred thousand birds. Caught as they are between the twin pressures of a million visitors a year and alteration of the surrounding landscape, there is serious doubt whether the Everglades will survive in the original unique form that made them worthy of perpetual preservation.

Deer in the Everglades during a high-water period in 1966. (Charles Trainor
—*Miami News*)

The Land Ethic

There are innumerable factors that alter landscapes and thus threaten
ecosystems and natural communities. "Modern" lumbering operations
that substitute monotonous and potentially highly vulnerable stands of
a single species of fast-growing tree for the forest ecosystem, inappropriately placed highways, strip-mining operations, the building of un-
needed gas stations for real estate speculation and tax relief, and many
other questionable procedures deserve more detailed examination. Aldo
Leopold, in his essay "The Land Ethic" in *A Sand County Almanac*,
summed up the problem that currently confronts nearly all countries
and societies in the world:

77

Dried-up creek in the Everglades during a drought in 1967. (Charles Trainor
—*Miami News*)

There is as yet no ethic dealing with man's relation to land and to the animals and plants which grow upon it. . . . The land relation is still strictly economic, entailing privileges but not obligations. . . . All ethics so far evolved rest upon a single premise: that the individual is a member of a community of interdependent parts. His instincts prompt him to compete for his place in that community, but his ethics prompt him also to co-operate (perhaps in order that there may be a place to compete for).

In the years since Leopold's death there has been scant progress toward his goal of a meaningful and binding land ethic.

3

How Natural Communities
Are Threatened:
Pollution, Industrial Accidents,
and Species Manipulations

Pollution is perhaps the best-publicized of the various threats to ecosystems and natural communities, but the subject is so broad and
objectives so diverse that little common ground for discussion exists,
even among conservationists. In this book the two points of view
adopted should help clarify the biological aspects of the problem.

First, uncritical appeals for "an end to pollution" are of limited
value. Granted, all pollution is bad—but some kinds of pollution are
worse, and therefore a list of priorities must be established. This list
can be made according to the following criteria: the extent, degree, and
type of damage caused by the particular pollution; an estimate of the
relative effectiveness of methods of stopping the pollution versus
methods of treating after the fact; and last, the existence of reasonable
alternatives to pollution and economically feasible control methods
(this implies that some sources of pollution will have to be allowed
to continue operating, at least for the present, and that some commercial and noncommercial enterprises must cease operations).

Second, pollution must be judged according to its ecological effects;
chemical and other nonbiological quality standards and monitoring
systems should be used to supplement rather than supersede biological

evidence of damage. When chemical tests show permissible concentrations of pollutants, but biological indicators show signs of pollution damage, then there is indisputable pollution. Biological indicators are often more sensitive to pollution than other assay methods; and furthermore it is the ecosystem with which we are ultimately concerned, not chemical tables of maximum permissible concentrations listed in parts per million.*

Pollution may affect water, air, and soil; insofar as they are separable, our understanding of these categories decreases in the order listed. The effects of pollution on natural aquatic communities will therefore receive the most attention in the following pages. There are many aspects of water pollution: natural pollutants; oxygen-consuming wastes; suspended solids; poisons, including cumulative food chain toxins (pesticides, for example); agents of eutrophication; radioactive wastes; thermal pollutants; salt; oil; detergents; and chemicals whose exact composition and source are unknown.

Water Pollution

People who think of ecosystems as being maintained by static balance rather than by a dynamic interplay of active processes may have trouble imagining that there can be pollution in the absence of man— yet it occurs often. H. B. N. Hynes describes a number of examples in his excellent book, *The Biology of Polluted Waters*. In one case, where fish and invertebrate populations were adversely affected by a toxic substance diffusing out of spruce and red cedar needles that had fallen in the water, Hynes remarks, "Had any mine or factory existed in the area it is probable that its effluent would have been the first suspect, and the investigation might not have been pursued further." The leaves of deciduous hardwoods can also cause pollution, especially at times of low stream flow. It has been shown that leaves falling in ponds and streams during autumn can block light transmission, inter-

---

* There are many possible examples, such as the one described in *Nature in Focus* (1970), a bulletin of the Council of Europe: "In the Netherlands, endive, lucerne, clover, buckwheat and barley are used to detect sulphur dioxide, and gladioli and fresias [sic] for hydrofluoric acid."

fere with oxygen exchange at the water's surface and, most important, cause depletion of dissolved oxygen as they decay. At the time of peak contamination with leaves, fish kills were observed in an otherwise unpolluted stream; in addition to a very low oxygen concentration, levels of iron, manganese, bicarbonate, and acidity were significantly altered. One major difference, however, between natural and man-made pollutants is that the former are all biodegradable, usually in a short period of time, and they are among the normal components of ecosystems. In this respect, "pollutant" may be an inappropriate word for these substances. There is also a distinction in magnitude: natural pollution is a miniscule fraction of the total amount.

Despite its common occurrence, natural pollution is minor compared with the pollution caused by man. Of the many forms this can take, one of the most destructive and most prevalent is pollution by wastes whose consumption by chemical or bacterial oxidation lowers the oxygen concentration of the water. Most of these wastes are organic and consist of raw sewage and industrial effluents such as those from food-processing plants; but some, like sulfites from pulp and paper mills and ferrous salts from acid mine drainage, are inorganic. In rivers, deoxygenation reaches a peak a short distance downstream from the pollutant outfall, coincident with the disappearance of the normal flora and fauna and the appearance of large populations of a few species of organisms that can live successfully without much oxygen. These include the familiar white "sewage fungus" (actually a bacterium, *Sphaerotilus natans*), bacteria that produce noxious gases, and invertebrates like the bacteria-eating protozoan *Paramecium putrinum* and the small red sludge worm *Tubifex tubifex*, well-known to aquarium fanciers as a food for tropical fish. As expected in communities subjected to extreme fluctuations of environmental conditions, the number of member species is low, but populations of the few adaptable species are likely to be enormous. Fish, of course, can be killed by low oxygen concentrations, but if the area of deoxygenation is not extensive, they are more likely to migrate. Toxins and low oxygen concentrations often act synergistically (they are mutually reinforcing) on fish. It is unusual for deoxygenation to occur without other signs of pollution.

Because lakes and rivers may be deoxygenated in several ways, it is sometimes important to be able to measure the actual amount of oxygen-consuming wastes in the water. The BOD (Biochemical Oxygen Demand) test was devised for this purpose; it is supposed to measure deoxygenating pollutants indirectly. In theory and practice it is simple: the oxygen saturation of a sample of water is measured (a known quantity of oxygen may be added) and the water is then sealed in a light- and airtight container kept at 20° C. (68° F.). After a given period the oxygen saturation of the sample is measured again and the difference between the two readings is taken as a measure of the oxygen-consuming material originally present in the water. Unfortunately, the results of this test, which are the summation of hundreds of different chemical events, are easy to misinterpret; for example, the presence of a poison that lowers the rate of bacterial decomposition of organic matter will give a misleadingly low BOD. Even if the results are accurate, some persons still make the mistake of considering a very low BOD as a sign of clean water, although the test does not measure concentrations of phosphates, nitrates, and other substances that may cause serious pollution. The BOD is not a comprehensive test for pollutants, but is adequate for monitoring certain controlled waters like the effluents of sewage plants.

Analyses of the flora and fauna are the most sensitive tests for pollution in complex natural communities. In the United States, Ruth Patrick, an expert on the ecology of fresh waters, has developed a pollution monitoring system based in part on the population sizes and diversity of a variety of indicator species of diatoms, single-celled organisms commonly found in both fresh and salt water. Such observations must be made over a long period of time to discern local trends, since individual bodies of water are likely to exhibit unique biological responses to all but the most extreme pollution. To confuse matters further, the community of a polluted lake in Michigan may resemble the community of an unspoiled lake in Georgia. Thus the word "pollution" must be used with reference to a regional norm.

Throughout the temperate latitudes it is especially important to look for the effects of deoxygenation in the summertime because the higher the temperature of water, the less oxygen it can contain, and because chemical deoxygenation proceeds at higher rates with higher temperatures. Measurements should also be made at night, when plants are consuming oxygen but not producing it via photosynthesis.

Suspended solids in lakes and streams are produced by soil erosion in watersheds, mine slurries, china clay quarries, factories where root crops are washed, and other contributors. Even if chemically inert, such wastes may damage ecosystems by clouding water so that game fish and other animals that depend on vision while hunting are unable to find prey; by settling on and killing rooted bottom plants and bottom animals (including salmon and trout eggs); by reducing light transmission needed for photosynthesis; and by drastically altering depth and flow rate because of silting. Suspended solids are becoming an increasingly severe problem in suburban streams that drain areas where construction has exposed the soil. M. F. Katzer and J. W. Pollack, who studied Mill Creek (near Washington, D.C.) during a storm, report that at the beginning of the storm the concentration of suspended solids was approximately 11.5 milligrams per liter; one hour later the concentration of solids at the same point was 13,000 milligrams per liter. When suspended solids are of industrial origin they are generally easy to trace because of the contrast between the turbidity of the effluent and the relative clarity of the waters upstream from the pollution's source.

Poisons are usually considered to be substances that interfere directly with the essential metabolic chemistry of organisms and are effective in small doses. These doses may be spread over long periods in the case of "cumulative" poisons like arsenics and many pesticides. Poisons vary in their selectivity, but the responses of animals and plants are rarely "all or none"—rather they are related to a difference in toxicity thresholds. The *Handbook of Poisoning* (R. H. Dreisbach, Lange Publications) lists hundreds of common poisons, and new industrial processes are adding so many obscure ones to the list that all the challenge has gone out of murder mystery writing. The industrial poisons released into the environment now number in the many tens of thousands. Any of these could find its way into an aquatic ecosystem, and most of them have probably done so at one time or another; so any remarks about the effects of poisons on biotic communities are bound to be generalizations riddled with exceptions.

Nevertheless, some generalizations about poisons are important. To paraphrase Hynes:

Toxicity is dependent upon many environmental factors, particularly temperature, oxygen content, acidity, and calcium concentration in the water. The behavior, under natural conditions, of animals also affects their exposure and susceptibility to poisons. Their ecological relationships do likewise. *Therefore, toxicity experiments performed in the laboratory may have little predictive value when applied to real pollution situations.*

Although fish are repelled by some poisons, others, such as dilute solutions of ammonia or phenol, can attract them.

All but the most extreme cases of poisoning usually leave a few resistant members of susceptible species, and if the resistance is genetically transmissible and the poisoning is continued at the same level, resistant populations may develop. This phenomenon has played havoc with the users and abusers of antibiotics and pesticides. No hospital is now without its own special strains of penicillin-resistant *Staphylococcus;* and insecticide resistance has appeared in every major group of insect pests. In Central America, malaria is common wherever continual agricultural spraying has caused the selection of DDT-resistant *Anopheles* mosquitoes.

Poisons rarely affect all species in a habitat; the few species that remain, now free from the danger of predation by those affected, may reach enormous population sizes and may otherwise behave like members of an "immature" community.

All members of an aquatic community—not just fish—must be

examined for the effects of poisons. In one example cited by Hynes, populations of the stonefly *Leuctra* and the alga *Lemanea* clearly demonstrated the effects of ammonia and cyanide poisoning from a mildly polluted effluent, although neither local fish populations nor chemical tests indicated the presence of these toxic compounds. Just as there are freshwater pollution faunas containing organisms like *Tubifex*, so there are a variety of clean-water faunas with stonefly nymphs, caddis worms, and other forms intolerant of pollution.

The effects of some cumulative poisons are subject to biological amplification. A nonlethal dose of DDT insecticide ingested by a filter-feeding plankter (member of the plankton, small marine animal and plant life) will be deposited in its fatty tissues. When the plankter is eaten by a predatory fish, the DDT will be stored in the fatty tissues of the fish. During its lifetime the fish will consume much plankton; and nearly all the fat-soluble DDT from the plankton will remain in its fatty tissues. The fish thus becomes a kind of insecticide trap, accumulating concentrations of DDT much higher than those found in its prey. The story repeats itself when the fish is eaten in turn by an osprey, pelican, eagle, or other bird of prey. Although DDT accumulates in the same way in the fatty tissues of man (and is suspected on the basis of incomplete evidence, to cause nervous system changes, mutations, and cancer), its biological effects on man are less well understood than among predatory birds. A similar kind of biological amplification may occur with mercury. In one food chain, methylmercury fungicides used on seed grain can accumulate in the grain grown from these seeds. If this grain is eaten by chickens, organic mercury will collect in the whites of their eggs, and if the eggs are eaten by man, the mercury will accumulate in the brain, kidney, and other tissues, or, in pregnant women, may be transferred across the placenta to the fetus. In another food chain involving man, mercury-containing industrial wastes can be concentrated in the muscle of fish and in shellfish. Since 1953, more than a hundred people in two small villages in Japan have been killed or severely disabled by this kind of mercury poisoning.

Of the various poisons that have become a global problem, none exert so broad a spectrum of environmental damage over so great an

Ospreys with chick, Mexico. The decline of populations is directly related to the concentration of DDT and related compounds in the food of this fish-eating hawk. (Jen and Des Bartlett—Bruce Coleman, Inc.)

area as the chlorinated hydrocarbon pesticides, including DDT and its long-lived toxic derivatives, DDD and DDE. These compounds can truly be described as "community poisons" because of their distribution, their persistence in air, water, and soil, and the range of their effects not only upon virtually all animals and many plants, but also upon the interactions among them.

DDT represents this family of poisons, which also includes non-insecticides such as the PCB's (polychlorinated biphenyls), the waste products of plastics and plastic manufacture.* Perhaps the first thing to understand about DDT is that it is impossible to keep it in one place. It enters the air by evaporation, in combination with water vapor, and by clinging to tiny wind-borne particles of soil or dust. Although not very soluble in water, it is easily carried in water as a suspension (like milk of magnesia) or again adsorbed to particles of dirt. Since it is fat soluble, and since all living organisms other than viruses contain fat, it is carried from place to place, often in high concentrations, by floating or swimming aquatic life. H. Nicholson has pointed out: "Even animals far removed from areas where pesticides are known to have been used may have chlorinated hydrocarbon insecticide residues in their tissues." He cites two Antarctic species, the Adelie penguin and the crab-eating seal, both of which feed on small crustaceans and now contain measurable amounts of DDT residues. The story is similar everywhere. C. F. Wurster and D. B. Wingate state, "Residues of DDT . . . averaging 6.44 parts per million in eggs and chicks of the carnivorous Bermuda petrel indicate widespread contamination of an oceanic food chain that is remote from applications of DDT. Reproduction by the petrel has declined during the last ten years [1958-68] at the annual rate of 3.25 per cent; if the decline continues, reproduction will fail completely by 1978." Carnivorous land birds are also affected. The peregrine falcon (duck hawk), which once could be seen catching pigeons among the skyscrapers of Manhattan, has almost disappeared from its vast range—it no longer is believed to nest successfully anywhere in eastern North America. The bald eagle, national symbol of

* Some other well-known insecticides in the DDT family are Aldrin, Chlordane, Dieldrin, Endrin, Lindane, Mirex, and Toxaphene.

Peregrine falcon—a young female. These duck hawks, known for their great speed of flight, are no longer reproducing over much of their once-great range. (Conway-Scala)

the United States, is similarly endangered despite massive protection efforts.

In addition to its fat solubility (which leads to the biological amplification described above), its mobility, and its persistence, DDT is characterized by an enormous range of poisonous effects in many species; only some can be given here. It causes a change in the calcium metabolism of birds, making them produce thin-shelled eggs that break upon incubation. PCB's have recently been suspected of causing birth defects

89

such as winglessness, cross-bill, and abnormal feather development in terns and other fish-eating birds. This has not yet been proven. DDT is a nerve poison—indeed this is its primary effect on its target insects —but it is not selective; almost any animal with a nervous system is potentially subject to DDT-induced nervous disturbances. DDT is known to modify the function of liver enzymes in such a way that the balance of certain sex hormones is upset. In some birds this appears to interfere with normal reproductive behavior.

The various chlorinated hydrocarbons are toxic to fish in a number of ways. Subtle effects are particularly important: for example, salmon and brook trout exposed to a few parts per billion of DDT lose their resistance to temperature change and are killed by exposure to cold water, particularly if the fish are poorly fed, as they often are in nature. Also, each year, newly hatched fish die in great numbers because of the DDT and related compounds that are concentrated in the fatty egg yolk that nourishes them during the first days of life. Another effect of DDT is interference with photosynthesis in some species of marine algae. Although this is not likely to alter the world supply of oxygen (mostly derived from photosynthesis by marine algae), it could have a disrupting influence on marine communities that depend on these single-celled plants for food.

Finally, there are the possible effects of DDT on man, some of which were mentioned above, and some of which can be inferred from the other effects described. None has been demonstrated conclusively, but our physiological processes, our enzymes and hormones, are so similar to those of the rats and birds that have been studied that it would be very surprising if we proved totally immune to these community poisons. (The world is greatly in the debt of the late Rachel Carson, whose prophetic and much-maligned book *Silent Spring* first aroused both scientists and the public to the enormous dangers of the persistent insecticides; and we are similarly indebted to Charles F. Wurster, who has carried her work forward with a brilliant fusion of good science and true public spirit.)

If DDT and its chemical relatives are so bad, why do we keep on using them? There seem to be at least four reasons for this peculiar self-destructiveness. The first, control of malaria and other diseases, is frequently invoked by the pesticide champions as the major reason for continuing the aerial spraying and massive worldwide application of DDT. Yet the record hardly bears this out. If anything, indiscriminate use of DDT, after initial apparent successes, is beginning to make malaria worse in all but a few special cases. For example, in Central America, local areas where DDT is used in heavy crop-spraying programs have seen the emergence of highly resistant strains of mosquito. Malaria in these regions is coming back, unlike those places where insecticides are being used sparingly and primarily inside houses. This is also true in Vietnam. DDT has been most successful in Ceylon, a comparatively small and isolated island, and in Greece, whose dry climate makes insect control unusually easy. Even here, more discriminating use of less persistent insecticides would very likely be sufficient.

Second, as an integral part of the Green Revolution, DDT is supposedly needed to maintain world food production in the face of damage by insect pests. Here, too, the record is sadly at odds with the hysterical threats and claims of the chemical promoters. The reason for the discrepancy between promise and performance is twofold: first, the emergence of widespread insecticide resistance among virtually all insect pest groups; second, an ecological phenomenon known as "Volterra's principle." In 1926, the great Italian ecologist Vito Volterra concluded, on the basis of equations he had formulated to describe the interactions of predators and their prey, that moderate destruction of both predator and prey populations would afterwards allow a great rebound increase in prey population size, but would further decrease the number of predators. This surprising mathematical result is based on the nature of the interaction, in which, among other things, a simultaneous reduction in both predator and prey populations means fewer enemies and more food per capita for the surviving prey, but lower food density for the remaining predators. The ecologists MacArthur and Connell provide an example in their book on population biology:

> A remarkable confirmation [of Volterra's principle] came from the cottony cushion scale insect . . . which, when accidentally introduced from Australia in 1868, threatened to destroy the

American citrus industry. Thereupon its natural Australian predator, a ladybird beetle, was introduced and took hold immediately,
reducing the scale to a low level. When DDT was discovered to
kill scale insects, it was applied by the orchardists in the hope
of further reducing the scale insects. However, in agreement with
Volterra's principle, the effect was an increase of the scale insect
[because of the wiping out of the ladybirds]!

And they conclude, "This shows the danger of tampering with those
aspects of nature that are not understood."

With the emergence of DDT-resistant insect pests and the manifestations of Volterra's principle, insecticide users often find themselves addicted, like heroin addicts, to ever-increasing doses of their
deadly chemicals. Robert van den Bosch, an expert on pest control, has
described the classic case in an article in *Natural History* magazine.

The Cañete is one of a number of Peruvian coastal valleys that
are self-contained agroecosystems. Major cotton production in
this valley began in the 1920s. Until the late 1940s cotton
growers controlled a limited pest insect complex with old-
fashioned insecticides such as calcium arsenate and nicotine
sulphate. Then the growers, opting for modern pest control,
shifted to the new synthetic organic insecticides, mainly DDT,
benzene hexachloride (BHC), and toxaphere. During the first
years, the modern pesticides effectively killed insect pests. Striking increases in yields were recorded. Because of the success, the
growers spread a virtual blanket of insecticides over the valley.

But the miracle was short-lived. Some of the pest species began
to develop resistance to the insecticides. Old pests became increasingly destructive and new ones appeared. By 1952, BHC was
no longer effective against the cotton aphid, and by 1954, toxaphene failed to control one of the leafworms. Quickly a general
pattern of resistance to organochlorine insecticides developed.
The growers turned to the deadly organophosphates. But the
pests, which had doubled in number, rapidly developed resistance
to these too. The growers had to increase dosages and shorten
treatment intervals. By the 1955-56 season, insect resistance to
the organophosphates was general, the pests were rampant, and
the crop suffered severe losses. The yield for the 1955-56 season
was one of the lowest ever recorded in the valley.

Fortunately the Peruvian growers realized their mistake and broke the addiction cycle by abandoning the "modern" insecticides and switching to the combination strategy of using simpler, less toxic chemicals in small doses, different farming practices, and restoration of the predators of the insect pests. Cotton yields soon reached record highs and stayed that way. In the United States, cotton growers have not behaved so intelligently or responsibly. Following heavy and fantastically expensive insecticide spraying in the Imperial Valley of California, the only tangible result was the destruction of tens of thousands of valuable honeybee colonies. Van den Bosch describes the Imperial Valley after spraying as "an enormous insectary from which millions of insects boiled out over the countryside, infecting adjacent crops." With the existing modern and potential methods of "biological control" of pest insects, including the planting of decoy crops, the release of millions of sterilized males during breeding season, the use of tiny quantities of specific pest insect hormones to interfere with their life cycles, the introduction of other insects as predators, and the controlled release of pest parasites, there is no longer any justification— if there ever was—for big insecticide programs.

The third reason for continued use of these pesticides is that in the United States, insecticides mean big money. Insecticide sales to the cotton industry alone exceed $100 million annually. The Mirex campaign against the fire ant (a totally ineradicable insect that may not even be a pest) was to cost the government $200 million until it was reduced by pressure from conservation and scientific groups. U.S. insecticides are sold in huge quantities around the world. Chemical corporations that manufacture insecticides provide grants and expense accounts to some agricultural scientists, and they fund programs at schools of agriculture. According to the *New York Times* (November 26, 1971), a press conference at which Green Revolution scientist N. E. Borlaug supported the use of DDT was "arranged" by the Montrose Chemical Corporation, the world's largest DDT manufacturer. It seems fair to say that in the United States, most of the pressure and publicity in favor of chemical insecticides is ultimately ascribable to the profit motive.

In the Soviet Union, where the folly is of equal magnitude, different causative forces may be operating. Although the same kinds of chemical insecticides are widely used, Philip R. Pryde, who has reviewed the Soviet literature on pesticides, writes, "Bureaucratic expedience and inertia, rather than an entrenched agrochemical lobby, appear to be the main causes of the continued Soviet reliance on chemical controls [including herbicides]." Public and scientific opposition appears to be mounting, as in the United States and Europe; and Pryde reports that Soviet publication of *Silent Spring* was recommended at one pesticide symposium.

Finally, there is the factor of consumer demand. As Western man has grown more citified he has at times developed an outlandish response to some elementary facts of nature. The hysterical fear of insects in and around the home is one such response. The use of Lindane and DDVP vaporizers or anti-pest strips, especially in kitchens, dining rooms, nurseries, or bedrooms and the constant spraying or "bug bombing" of anything that moves on more than four legs is environmentally irresponsible and probably hazardous to human health. Fly swatters are cheap, nonpolluting, and effective, but most people in our hypermechanized society prefer to kill insects with the biological equivalent of a Sherman tank. Perhaps the dispensation of death-by-aerosol gives them a sense of power.

The unrealistic demand, especially strong in the United States, for perfect and unblemished fruit and vegetables is the other component of the consumers' economic reward to the pesticide manufacturers. It contributes to the high price of food while adding to the burden of agricultural and wild communities; there is no long-term benefit to anyone.

It is as easy to disrupt communities by promoting growth as by retarding it. The addition of free nutrients to an ecosystem may have a number of unbalancing effects. If the nutrients (that is, fertilizer, phosphate from detergents, or organic wastes) are added rapidly and achieve high concentrations, the integrity of the community will be destroyed and a few opportunistic species, evolutionarily geared to take advantage of the bonanza, will predominate. If the addition of nutrients is relatively slow, the community may gradually become more complex, and its species composition will change. This latter process mimics the phenomenon of eutrophication, a naturally occurring feature of succession in aquatic communities. For theoretical reasons it is important to distinguish between these two types of pollution with nutrients, but in practical situations it is common to find examples that do not fit clearly into either category.

Oligotrophy and eutrophy are at the opposite ends of an ecological scale. An oligotrophic body of water is clear, often with a stone or gravel bottom; there is little nutrient turnover, and the biotic community is simple, with short food chains. A eutrophic body of water is turbid, with a muddy bottom; both the water and the bottom are rich in nutrients and organic debris, and the biotic community is complex, with many species related by involved food chains and webs. The manifestations of these conditions are different, however, in rivers and in lakes. In rivers, the transition from oligotrophy to eutrophy is spatial and occurs as clear, cold mountain streams, flowing rapidly over boulders, merge and gradually give way to the slow-moving, silt-depositing rivers that are characteristic of delta regions. Nutrient pollution can seriously affect rivers, but the damage is usually transitory if the source of pollution is eliminated.

In lakes and ponds a slow succession from oligotrophy to eutrophy often occurs in time under natural conditions and is usually irreversible. Lakes trap nutrients: evaporation and overflow prevent the water level from increasing continuously, but dissolved nutrients are left behind by evaporation and are fixed in the bodies of plants and animals, and particulate matter settles and is retained even in the case of overflow. The resulting rich community of plankton, crustaceans, fish, and other creatures, which is the hallmark of eutrophication, is merely a prelude to the eventual filling in of the lake. This takes place in all lakes, and depending on depth and size normally takes thousands or millions of years. The Great African Rift, a gigantic gash in the earth's crust that runs from equatorial Africa northward beyond the Dead Sea, contains a number of deep lakes of great antiquity, including Nyasa, which is so old that an extraordinary evolutionary species diversification of fish has taken place within it, producing nearly two hundred native species. Few lakes are so durable.

Pollution with nutrients can accelerate eutrophication and aging of lakes, and this has a number of unpleasant consequences. First, only biologists and small children enjoy wading in the organic ooze of a eutrophic lake. The majority of the public prefers to swim in the crystal-clear, sand-bottomed, oligotrophic waters of a young, unpolluted lake. Second, the fish of oligotrophic waters, the trout of Lake Superior and the *omble chevalier* of Lake Lucerne, taste better than fish from eutrophic lakes, such edible but unpretentious types as perch, roach, and bream. Third, eutrophication, when caused by pollution, is rarely as uncomplicated as a straightforward increase in number of species; there are periodic sudden increases in the populations of some organisms, sometimes followed by massive die-offs. When this occurs, beaches are littered with tons of foul-smelling algae or, as in the case of Lake Michigan, with great piles of a little herringlike fish called the alewife.

In addition to organic carbon sources, polluted effluents may contain other growth-promoting substances such as phosphates, nitrates, trace minerals, and even vitamins. As we have seen, a waste treatment plant may produce an effluent with a very low BOD that still contains large amounts of inorganic phosphate and nitrate. Detergents, fertilizers, and many industrial products are prime sources of these substances. As much as eighty percent of the nitrogen and seventy-five percent of the phosphorus added to surface waters in the United States now comes from man-generated sources. The biologist F. A. Ferguson has reported that excessive algal growth may occur if "the average concentration of inorganic nitrogen exceeds 0.3 p.p.m. [parts per million] and the inorganic [soluble] phosphorus content exceeds 0.01 p.p.m. . . . However, some waters containing as much as 0.05 p.p.m. soluble phosphorus do not support excess algal growths." This last figure confirms, at least in broad detail, a principle first given by Liebig in 1840, known since as "Liebig's Law of the Minimum." This states, roughly, that growth will

Dead alewives on a Chicago lakefront beach. (Pete Peters—*Chicago Sun-Times*)

be limited by the concentration of any factor(s) present in minimum amount, regardless of the concentration of other necessary factors. In other words, excessive phosphate will not produce an algal bloom if something else is present only in growth-limiting concentration. The limiting nutrient may vary from place to place, for reasons that are poorly understood. This accounts, in part, for the complexity of the whole problem of eutrophication. Recently, detergent manufacturers have taken refuge behind Liebig's Law, claiming that the phosphate from detergents is not always the limiting nutrient, and therefore that it is not responsible for eutrophication. Although the few examples that they usually supply are quite reasonable, this interpretation is a distortion of reality, because phosphate is still the limiting nutrient for many, possibly most, natural bodies of water, and is certainly a major cause of eutrophication. Furthermore, as the ecologists G. E. Hutchinson and Ruth Patrick have pointed out, phosphate is a chemical needed for growth of all plants and animals; we are now using up the limited world reserves at a rate thousands of times faster than we used to, and much of it is ending up in the deep oceans where it may be beyond recovery.

Most of the Great Lakes, with the partial exception of Lake Huron and Lake Superior, which are bordered by relatively small populations, have been subjected to both rapid and gradual pollution. Lake Erie is in the worst condition, with much of its water completely deoxygenated; but even here, where the catch of blue pike dropped from 18,-857,000 pounds in 1956 to less than 500 pounds in 1965, the numbers of sheepshead, carp, yellow perch, and smelt are increasing—at least temporarily. In Lake Michigan it is estimated that 85 to 95 percent of the total weight of fish is composed of alewives. Conservationist J. Chiapetta writes that a small fishing boat can net five to six tons of these little fish in two six-minute runs. Surprisingly, most of the pollution of southern Lake Michigan is caused by industry, not by the city of Chicago, which discharges its treated waste into the Mississippi River system via the Chicago River Canal and the Illinois River. According to Chiapetta, the Inland Steel Company alone dumps 480 million gallons of heavily contaminated waste water into Lake Michigan each day, and this company accounts for only a fraction of the waste produced by industry in the city of East Chicago, Indiana. If any serious waste control is ever put into effect in this region, we can expect a sharp reduction in the concentrations of poisons like cyanide and phenol that are released into the lake, but nutrients may be more difficult to control. Thus eutrophication will probably continue at an accelerated rate for a long time. In the case of Lake Erie there is at least the satisfaction of knowing that not only does the lake flush quickly, but also that it would have disappeared after another 25,000 years anyway; but not even these small consolations apply to the much deeper Lake Michigan.

Contamination with radioactive fallout and waste, especially the latter, is becoming increasingly important, but it is still rather difficult to evaluate the dangers in a comprehensive way. Although radiation can undoubtedly cause damage to ecosystems, there are so many ways to administer radiation and radioactive materials, and so many different communities to study, that it is hard to see how conclusions of any generality could be obtained experimentally, except in the case of massive doses of radiation.* Indeed, most studies of radiation damage concern particular species, usually man, whose slow rate of maturation and long lifespan render him susceptible to the genetic and other

---

* A major study of the effects of radiation on an entire natural community was conducted by the ecologist Howard T. Odum and scores of scientific collaborators in a rain forest in Puerto Rico. The project was supported by the U.S. Atomic Energy Commission and the results have been published in a single gigantic volume. In this case, the main interest seems to have been to learn more about the ecological system of the rain forest by watching its responses to disturbance; the radiation was a means to an end. The radiation dose was thus very large compared with that provided by most existing levels of pollution with radioactive wastes. In generalizing about the effects of radiation on organisms other than man, one can do little more than point out that some species of plants and animals are much more susceptible to certain kinds of radiation damage than others. We can only hope that this sort of information will never become critically important in evaluating damage to natural communities.

bodily changes that accompany prolonged, low-level radiation. Ecological methods may be used, as in studies of food-chain amplification of radioactive waste concentrations, but here it is the fate of the radioactive material, not the community, that is of prime concern. We tend to be interested in strontium-90 and iodine-131 because man is at the end of the short food chains that concentrate them. On the other hand, it is probably safe to say that nobody has ever given a thought to the potential consequences of contamination with vanadium-49, since most of it that might enter biological systems would end up in the green, blue, and orange blood corpuscles of certain sedate and unobtrusive marine animals called tunicates.

The major present or potential sources of radioactive pollution are nuclear explosions that produce fallout; accidents at atomic power and other nuclear installations; radioisotope production and mining operations; isotope disposal sites; nuclear power plants; and research laboratories, including medical and biochemical facilities, which release radioactive wastes into the air and sewage. Despite the test ban treaty, nuclear explosions are not a thing of the past. Sheer bureaucratic momentum prevented the cancellation of the United States' dangerous and useless "Cannikan" nuclear test in the Aleutian Islands in 1971. Typically, a national wildlife refuge was considered an acceptable site for the explosion, and a thousand dead sea otters, an endangered species, was a negligible price to pay for a "successful" blast. Public outcry in the United States has made it unlikely that this sort of folly will be easily repeated, but there is no guarantee that the French or Chinese will not duplicate the American mistakes. Deserts and remote islands, which are considered expedient by the sort of people who play with nuclear weapons, have suffered the most from nuclear testing in the "postwar" era. If the plans to use nuclear explosions to blast canals and harbors ever materialize, we will have to add new habitats to the list.

Radioactive pollution is a cause of direct concern to man through the human health hazards it poses. All the sources mentioned, except for research laboratory effluents, whose effects, if any, are unknown, have become controversial subjects in recent years. At the moment, these sources of environmental radiation do not appear to threaten any natural communities or species, but these words are not written to give the reader a sense of security. Nobody cares about a slight increase in the mutation rate or about the development of a few excess cancers in wild animal populations. It could hardly upset any known ecological system or wipe out any known species. Natural selection quickly does away with the unfit. Mutation and cancer among our family and neighbors is a different matter, and rightfully so. The death or disease of a few persons in Colorado or Utah unlucky enough to live in houses whose concrete foundations were made with sand from uranium mine dumps will not affect U.S. census figures more than a trifling amount. Nevertheless they are important. Radiation may thus be the only example in this book of a form of pollution that can gravely affect man without causing prior or simultaneous environmental damage.

Although the direct effect of environmental radiation on man is not discussed here, a few words follow for the reader who wants to pursue the matter elsewhere. In evaluating the effects of radiation, there are always several questions to be asked. First, has the exposure been to the chemical source of the radiation, or to the radiation alone?* If the answer is the latter, then it becomes a matter of determining radiation type, exposure time, intensity and pattern of exposure, and the effects of this combination. If, however, the contact is with the chemical *source* of the radiation, then additional questions are needed. What is the chemical compound that contains the radioisotope (for example, carbon-14 contained in carbon dioxide)? Is it ingested or absorbed through the skin, and is it incorporated in body tissues? What is its half-life? Is it ultimately likely to be excreted or retained? Can it find its way into DNA, the stable genetic material of genes and chromosomes? All these questions are simply stated, but they are not simple. Seldom are they asked; less often are they answered. For man, the study of the effect of radioactive pollutants has fallen dismally

---

* "Radiation" includes gamma rays, beta particles, X-rays, alpha particles, neutrons, etc.

behind the technology that spawns them. In this case, we are the first among our fellow creatures to suffer.

The excess heat produced by nuclear power stations is one of their major forms of pollution. *Environmental Science and Technology* (1968) reports that, according to power industry estimates, by 1980 "approximately 20 percent of all the fresh water runoff in the United States will be used for cooling purposes." Conventional power plants, gas works, and other industrial facilities also produce thermal pollution. The direct effects of heat on aquatic ecosystems are variable, but can be readily imagined. Most aquatic creatures exist at or near water temperature; changes in water temperature affect both their activity and their energy requirements. Oxygen requirements also change. If the temperature rises, oxygen consumption increases, but oxygen solubility in water declines. Many organisms have a narrow range of temperature tolerance. At some point a lethal temperature is reached; this varies according to rate of change of temperature, species of animal or plant, and physiological condition of the individual. Since a rise in temperature of 10°C. (18°F.) is sufficient to double the rate of many chemical reactions, it can readily be understood why even a small amount of thermal pollution is sufficient to disrupt the organization of aquatic communities. Furthermore, studies at the Sandy Hook Marine Laboratory in New Jersey have indicated that small, nonlethal increases in temperature may affect the behavior of such important fish as flounder and mullet. This could conceivably reduce their fitness and survival in a natural environment subject to thermal pollution.

Thermal pollution also damages ecosystems indirectly. Most important, it aggravates the effects of poisons and accelerates deoxygenating processes, thus converting what might have been mild pollution into a more serious situation. Also, many companies chlorinate water before it enters their cooling systems, in order to prevent the growth of bacteria that could clog pipes. If this is done incorrectly, free chlorine, a highly toxic substance, may be released in the effluent. Even if this does not occur, chlorine will react with certain sulfur-containing compounds (thiocyanates) in the water (especially common in gas-works effluents) to produce a deadly poison, cyanogen chloride, plus acid. Also the bacteria, small plants, and animals killed by the effects of thermal pollution form dead organic matter, which further increases the BOD.

Inorganic salts of many kinds are among the major constituents of industrial pollution. They arise primarily from acid-base neutralization processes, which are among the most common types of reactions used by industry. Enormous quantities of waste salts are produced. Apart from the separate chemical effects of the different salts, they all alter the salt and water balance of freshwater organisms. Tolerances to salt vary widely within the animal and plant kingdoms; freshwater fish are often more resistant than the invertebrates or plants that may constitute their food. If salt-polluted water is used for irrigation, the productivity of the land will decline; this has happened in parts of the Rhine Valley. Another cause of salt pollution is saltwater intrusion, which occurs when coastal freshwater aquifers are overdrawn, as happened in the Everglades. Finally, desalinization plants are producing increasing amounts of sodium chloride (common salt). When this form of freshwater production becomes more widespread, the supply of sodium chloride will exceed commercial demand and disposal of the surplus may be a problem. The ocean seems to be the most logical place to put it, but if this is done haphazardly, zones of hypersaline water may disrupt marine communities.

Oil on water is an increasing sign of global pollution. Oil-soaked, dying water birds are becoming a commonplace feature of most beaches, even in areas remote from population centers. In the case of oil, a little pollution goes a long way; one gallon is sufficient to cover approximately four acres of water. Industry contributes a substantial share of oil pollution, but the private citizen in highly developed countries is equally responsible. Each year Americans leave 350 million gallons of used motor oil in service stations; those few persons who think about it probably assume that "something is done about it," and they are right. Unfortunately, the re-refining of used motor oil is no longer very profitable, so when enough oil accumulates it is usually poured into the municipal sewer system, and hence finds its way into the nearest lake or stream.

Detergents are among the few pollutants that advertise their presence from a distance: mountains of white foam floating down a river can mean little else; the green smelly algal scum that covers lakes and some rivers is another sign. Yet apart from eutrophication, the actual impact of detergents on ecosystems is hard to pinpoint. Hynes claims that when the rate of oxygen uptake by rivers is low, detergents will lower it still more, but he admits that the relationship between oxygen uptake and detergent concentration is not simple. Biochemists and microbiologists are well aware that fairly high concentrations of detergent will kill cells by dissolving away part of the cell membrane. But what about low concentrations of detergents? There is some evidence that detergents act like heat and some poisons, reducing the capability of certain fish to cope with low oxygen concentrations. Hynes also suggests that the eggs of parasitic worms may be dispersed from sewage works in detergent foam blown off the tops of activated sludge tanks. Any detergent threat to man, however, is likely to be indirect, via his natural communities, and not through toxic effects.

Two principal chemical classes of detergents were widely used after World War II. The first, known as alkyl benzene sulfonate (ABS), resists breakdown during sewage treatment and persists for long periods of time afterward. The second group is linear alkylsulfonate (LAS), called "biodegradable" detergents, although the term is a misnomer because the difference between the two classes is not absolute but merely one of rate of decomposition. Largely because of mounting public reaction to detergent foam in drinking water, lakes, and streams, the detergent industries in a number of countries have converted from ABS to LAS production. England converted in 1962, West Germany and Hungary in 1964, and the United States in 1965. W. T. Sullivan and R. L. Evans reported that detergent concentration in the Illinois River fell 61 percent during the year following the introduction of LAS detergents, despite an increase in detergent use. But this encouraging news does not end the detergent story. The biodegradation of LAS detergents can have two other deleterious effects. It can increase the short-term BOD (Sullivan and Evans state, however, that the use of LAS has not lowered dissolved oxygen in the Illinois River); and more important, the biological breakdown of the detergent molecules releases large quantities of eutrophication-promoting phosphates (280 million pounds per year in the United States).

Faced with pressure to effect yet another conversion, the detergent manufacturers experimented briefly with caustic soda and with a compound called NTA (nitrilotriacetic acid), which lacks phosphates but probably has other dangerous environmental side effects, especially in waters already polluted with lead. Both, however, were banned in the United States by the Surgeon General, because of possible hazards to human health. Returning to phosphates, which it had never really abandoned, the industry hardened its position. But the phosphate problem has not gone away. The best substitute at the moment appears to be a combination of old-fashioned soap and washing soda (not caustic soda), which can do everything important that detergents can do—except make exorbitant profits for detergent companies. Those sturdy souls who have resisted the tide and have steadfastly used soap powders and washing soda in their washing machines for the past quarter-century will no doubt wonder what all the fuss is about.

The proliferation of new and sometimes secret chemical processes and new products has caused a host of new pollutants to enter our waters. Some are difficult to identify and trace. Obviously, no detailed statement can be made about them except to say that they are indeed there and may be dangerous. Research on them is understandably rare. In one paper, medical researchers S. S. Epstein and F. B. Taylor reported that organic chemicals of unknown origin were detected in drinking water by means of a test involving the one-celled animal *Paramecium*, which reacted to these chemicals as it does to substances that produce cancer in mammals.

We have discussed types of pollution, not bodies of water. Yet the reader has probably realized that the oceans, containing most of the water on earth, have received far less attention than they deserve. Most flowing fresh waters come to rest in the oceans, and they bring their pollutants with them. As Wesley Marx wrote in *The Frail Ocean*, "The ocean dies invisibly. Neither bold tree stumps nor harsh gullies alert us to the danger." The oceans are large, but not infinite. We know now that the most remote parts of the oceans show visible signs of pollution. We know that poisons such as DDT have spread from the equator to the poles. We know that ocean currents can compartmental-ize the waters so that expected dilutions of pollutants do not take place while they are being carried around the globe. We know that the ocean is polluted directly in massive doses and every day: sewage wastes dumped by barge have created a dead sea off the New York–New Jersey coast; drums of insecticide and other chemical wastes are con-veniently disposed of in the North Sea. We know these things, but the really important biology and chemistry of ocean ecosystems and ocean pollution are still unknown. In the United States, where governmental studies and regulation of ocean pollution were recently transferred to the Department of Commerce, an exploitative and promotional agency, little hope remains that we will learn what we need to know without the heavy-handed prompting of ecological disaster.

Air Pollution

The fact that this book devotes so few words to soil and air pollution does not mean that they are less important, but rather that less is known of the responses of natural communities or species to these kinds of pollution. Most of the air pollution literature deals with man, with species whose physiology is similar to that of man, or with agricultural crops and animals (see table, pp. 108-10). For example, the agricultural researcher D. C. MacLean and his co-workers studied the effects of acute exposures of gaseous hydrogen fluoride (HF) and nitrogen dioxide on six species of citrus and fourteen species of ornamental plants common to central Florida. They found a wide spectrum of sensitivity to the two atmospheric poisons, both of which are common industrial air pollutants in that area. Several gladiolus varieties have been reported to be sensitive to as little as one part per billion of HF after six to seven days of exposure; while MacLean and associates found that Carissa plants could survive as much as eight parts per million for four hours with only moderate damage. They also found that loss of leaves in young citrus plants was largely independent of HF concentration over the range tested (0.5–10 parts per million). The pattern of damage was quite different for chronic low-level exposures, with yellowing and subsequent death occurring in immature tissues. Considering these findings, the reader can appreciate the difficulty of evaluating the effects of complex and fluctuating mixtures of air pollutants on an entire community of plants and animals, even though it is obvious that there is bound to be damage.

One general effect of air pollution on ecosystems is sufficiently well known to cause anxiety among ecologists and other environmental scientists. This is called the "greenhouse effect." Nearly all of the earth's total energy input comes from the sun. It reaches us primarily in the form of visible light, since the ozone in our atmosphere absorbs most of the ultraviolet solar radiation, and the atmospheric water vapor absorbs much of the incoming infrared radiation. Approximately one-third of the incoming energy is reflected back into space, so the total energy taken up at the surface of the earth is the total incoming energy minus the losses from atmospheric absorption and from reflection. Most of this remaining light energy is absorbed by inanimate matter and re-radiated as heat. A small amount of the light energy falling on the surface of the earth is absorbed by plants. This supports all life; it is eventually also largely re-radiated as heat generated by metabolic processes and decay.

During the past century the extensive use of fossil fuels has caused

Some effects of specific air pollutants on domestic animals*

Pollutant	Source	Animals Affected	Nature of Effect
Smoke	Asphalt plants, coal burning, etc.	Cattle and sheep	Loss of appetite, vomiting, enlarged liver, kidney hemorrhage, death
		Chickens	Half of normal egg production, hemorrhage of internal organs, death
		Insects and insect-eating birds	Reduction in population of insects, followed by reduction in insect-eating birds
Ammonia	Chicken farms, industry	Chickens	Lowered growth rate, low resistance to respiratory diseases (relatively high doses)
Arsenic	Copper smelters, power plants, etc.	Honeybees	Weakening or death of colonies
		Horses, cows, sheep	Nose ulcers, partial paralysis of diaphragm, weak pulse, partial paralysis of hind limbs (air in 100 sq. miles surrounding a copper smelter)
		Red deer, wild hares	Loss of hair, skin injuries, antler malformation, liver cirrhosis, etc. (confirmed by laboratory finding of arsenic)
Beryllium (beryllium metal dust, beryllium fluoride, etc.)	Rocket exhausts	Dogs	Acute: labored breathing, convulsions, death
		Rats	Chronic: weight loss, anemia, lung damage
		Rats	Chronic: inflammatory lung disease, cancer (9 months exposure)
Cadmium (Cadmium oxide, cadmium chloride)	Metal plating for automobile industry	Rats	Permanent lung damage
		Dogs	Salivation, asthmatic breathing, rapid pulse, death

108

Substance	Source	Animals affected	Effects
Carbon monoxide	Automobile exhaust	Rats, mice, rabbits, hamsters, pigeons	Destruction of male gonadal tissue. (Subcutaneous injection, not inhalation)
		Dogs	Chronic: disturbances of reflexes and gait, heart damage (less in dogs acclimated to high altitudes or accustomed to carbon monoxide exposure)
		Canaries, mice, chickens, small dogs, pigeons, English sparrows, guinea pigs, rabbits	Various effects; decreasing order of susceptibility by species (man fits in approximately after pigeon)
Fluorides	Phosphate plants, aluminum and iron forges, brick kilns, volcanoes (in U.S., especially Florida, Tennessee, Utah, Washington, Oregon)	Cattle, sheep, horses, small rabbits, poultry	Lameness, muscle weakness, loss of appetite, thirst, dental changes, lowered reproduction, diarrhea, bone fractures, emphysema, death
		Honeybees	Muscle paralysis, death (slow attrition of colonies)
			"Airborne fluorides have caused more worldwide damage to domestic animals than any other air pollutant"
Lead	Paints, gasoline, orchard sprays, etc.	Cattle, horses, sheep, cats (especially young animals)	Dry coats, loss of appetite, emaciation, muscle spasm and paralysis, excitability, hemorrhage, reduced respiration, abortion followed by sterility, "melancholy," diarrhea alternating with constipation, death
Molybdenum	Steel and metal alloy plants (especially Sweden and other parts of Europe)	Cattle	Diarrhea, emaciation, reduced milk yields, enteritis, change in hide color, stiffness of legs and backs, death
Nitrogen oxides (nitrogen dioxide primarily)	Automobile exhausts, industrial emissions, nitrogen fertilizers, silo gases	Cattle, swine, poultry, rats	Panting, salivation, lacrimation, mucous discharge, reduced feeding, lung damage, lowered resistance to some bacterial infections, skeletal muscle damage, death

Some effects of specific air pollutants on domestic animals* (cont.)

Pollutant	Source	Animals Affected	Nature of Effect
Sulfur oxides (Sulfur dioxide, sulfur trioxide, sulfuric acid mist)	Industrial emissions, automobiles, house heating	Rabbits, swine, rats	Deep-lung damage, lowered vitamin C content of blood, decreased activity of certain enzymes, lowered disease resistance (little field data available; in humans, respiratory effects are most evident among infants and adults over 45)
	Industry in Great Britain and Central Europe	Salmon in southern Norway	Salmon eggs unable to develop in streams made acid by sulfur dioxide fallout windborne far from its source; some salmon runs have been eliminated
Vanadium	Emissions from sulfuric acid plants, fuel oil soot	Cattle, chickens	Weakness, diarrhea, emaciation, lethargy, congestion and hemorrhage of liver and lungs, depressed egg production and hatchability, death
		Rabbits	Cholesterol metabolism altered (inhibited synthesis, accelerated breakdown)
Combinations of pollutants	Many sources	Various animals	Combinations are often more toxic than pollutants alone (synergistic effect); occasionally less toxic. For example, beryllium-fluoride and sulfur oxide-arsenic combinations are highly toxic, while ammonia reduces the toxicity of sulfuric acid mist.

* Results of both field and laboratory studies. Effective pollutant dosages are omitted because they vary widely according to the mode of administration, type of study, and animals studied. (Primary source of data: Robert J. Lillie, *Air Pollutants Affecting the Performance of Domestic Animals: A Literature Review*, Agriculture Handbook No. 380, U. S. Dept. of Agriculture, 1970.)

a five to ten percent increase in the atmospheric carbon dioxide concentration. This carbon dioxide acts as a one-way filter, preventing the re-radiated heat energy from leaving the earth's atmosphere, but continuing to transmit the incoming higher energy radiation from the sun. Theoretically, this ought to produce a warming trend on earth that is similar to the effect of a glass-covered greenhouse.

The actual results of the increase in atmospheric carbon dioxide are difficult to interpret because of other variables (such as atmospheric humidity and the role of the oceans in absorbing carbon dioxide), and it is harder yet to make sound predictions. During the past fifty years the average temperature of the earth has warmed about 1°C. (nearly 2°F.), and some glaciers are melting. There may, however, be indications of a more recent cooling trend, and considering the Ice Age history of glacial fluctuations, it would be foolish to insist on a causal relationship between glacial movements and the activities of industrial man. Moreover, the greenhouse effect of carbon dioxide may be in part counteracted by the great increase in the atmospheric concentration of another by-product of industrialization, particulate matter.

In the future, the atmospheric carbon dioxide balance will depend on the extent of our conversion to the use of nuclear fuels and on the amount of vegetation remaining on earth. Whether there will be further warming, with associated changes in climate, melting of polar ice, and submergence of low-lying coastal areas, remains to be seen, but in the interim it should not be forgotten that pollution, including air pollution, can have global effects of a most serious and unpredictable nature.

Industrial Accidents

Not all industrial accidents affect factory employees only; some cause serious damage to ecosystems. Although in one sense accidents constitute just another source of pollution, they are considered separately because they are an increasing threat to the environment and because different kinds of laws and regulations are needed to deal with them.

Nearly all the accidents that concern us here involve some phase of

Oil from the stranded Getty-owned tanker *Wafra* covers the beach at Cape Agulhas, South Africa, while workers attempt to remove it with straw. Approximately 13,000 tons of medium and light crude oil were spilled when the tanker struck a reef five miles from South Africa's southernmost point of land on February 27, 1971. Hundreds of sea birds and much marine life perished along ten miles of this magnificent coast. The tanker was eventually floated off the reef, towed out to sea, and sunk by the South African Air Force. South African scientists and officials are worried because eight to ten tankers carrying an average total of 500,000 tons of crude oil pass through the dangerous seas off the Cape of Good Hope (Cape of Storms) each day. This one disaster, which was handled promptly and well, cost the South African government more than $1,400,000. (Argus Africa News Service—Photo Trends)

A cormorant killed by oil from the tanker *Wafra*. (Argus Africa News Service—Photo Trends)

the transport and storage of bulk chemicals. Stories of chlorine gas escaping from tank cars, pipeline explosions, and storage tank fires are disturbingly common; as industry expands to keep pace with population, the industrial traffic grows and accidents increase. Nor are accidents confined to industry. The United States has confirmed that debris from shattered but unexploded hydrogen bombs has been scattered around the landscape in at least two separate accidents. Numerous types of accidents, both military and industrial, can contribute to pollution; two examples will suffice here.

On March 18, 1967, the giant tanker *Torrey Canyon*, carrying a cargo of 117,000 tons of crude oil, went aground on Seven Stones Reef off the Cornish Coast of England and began to break apart. During the weeks that followed, most of the oil floated out of the tanks and great masses of tarry sludge began to drift in to the beaches of Cornwall and Brittany. Efforts to burn the oil were unsuccessful, so 12,500 tons of detergent were used by the British in an ill-considered attempt to emulsify and disperse it. According to scientists of the Plymouth Laboratory the immediate harmful biological effect of the oil alone was on marine birds primarily, but the detergents proved extremely toxic to intertidal forms such as limpets, crabs, scallops, and barnacles and to plankton in the open seas. The disaster is estimated to have killed at least 20,000 penguinlike murres and 5000 razorbills. Eight thousand birds were "rescued" by the people of the British coastal areas; however, oil-soaked birds have a high mortality, and the 450 that were cleaned and recovered lacked the natural oils to keep their feathers from becoming waterlogged in the sea. Less than one percent survived to return to their natural habitat. The French, battling the same oil but profiting from the British mistakes, avoided using detergents and instead dropped powdered chalk on the oil. (The chalk-oil complex sinks to the bottom, where it causes serious but less important damage than would occur if it reached the coastal intertidal zone.) Fortunately, an unusual northerly wind kept most of the oil out at sea; otherwise the damage to beaches and productive shallow-water communities might have been much worse.

An oil-covered jackass penguin, having been washed with liquid parafin and dusted with Fuller's earth to absorb the remaining oil, is showered to remove the earth-oil mixture. (Argus Africa News Service—Photo Trends)

Jackass penguins, cleaned of oil and ready for release. Th[
percent. This very successful result can be attributed to th[
National Foundation for the Conservation of Coastal Bir[
Foundation. (Argus Africa News Service—Photo Trends)

…urvival rate for cleaned penguins in the *Wafra* disaster was approximately sixty
…ophisticated cleaning methods developed by E. O. J. Westphal and the South African
…ith the assistance of James Naviaux of California's National Wildlife Health

Godrevy Point, England, May 10, 1967. Barnacles at high-water mark almost completely covered by oil but untouched by cleaning operations, still alive after six weeks' exposure to pollution from the *Torrey Canyon*. (Courtesy A. J. Southward—Marine Biological Association)

Indirect effects of the oil and detergents may continue for many years. The murre population had been declining before the accident, presumably because of many other oil spills during the past half-century (an accident off the Scandinavian coast in the 1950s killed 30,000 birds). Sea gulls, which have evidently learned to avoid oil, were not killed, but the gull populations in the disaster area did not nest in 1967, for unknown reasons. Since oil is degraded very slowly in sea water, tarry "souvenirs" of the *Torrey Canyon* may continue to disrupt the biology and scenery of the British and French coasts for decades.

Scientists at the Woods Hole Oceanographic Institute have recently made studies of an oil spill in Buzzard's Bay, Massachusetts. Their work has shown how the oil, which is both more toxic and more durable than previously believed, can spread and can mobilize the sediments on the bottom of a shallow, productive bay, creating a long-lasting lifeless zone in its wake. Economically valuable species of shellfish

118

Porthleven Reef, England, May 8, 1967. Barnacles at high-water mark almost all killed by detergent cleansing operations. (Courtesy A. J. Southward—Marine Biological Association)

decrease in number or become tainted and unfit for consumption. Oil coats and kills underwater grasses. Short-term damage is particularly high when refined petroleum products, which are very toxic, are spilled, but both crude oil *(Torrey Canyon)* and refined petroleum (Buzzard's Bay) cause a long-term decrease in species diversity. The effects of oil in concentrating DDT and other fat-soluble poisons and moving them into food chains (possibly via oil-eating bacteria) has not been studied.

The wreck of the *Torrey Canyon* was an accident, but a preventable one. A Liberian board of inquiry reported that the tanker ran aground solely because of human error, and recommended, perhaps somewhat belatedly, that the license of its master be revoked. One of the major difficulties in formulating policy to deal with accidents of this sort is the high incidence of deliberate fouling that simulates the accidental release of oil. In 1966, in one of the rare cases in which such an offense was proved, a Japanese tanker was identified as the source of an eight-mile oil slick that appeared off Land's End, the westernmost tip of Cornwall. After the *Torrey Canyon* shipwreck, there were reliable reports of ships sluicing out their tanks in the English Channel, secure in the knowledge that the pollution would be attributed to the accident. Even if this kind of deliberate pollution is not considered, the frequency and magnitude of accidents involving hazardous cargoes is increasing as more and larger ships are built. The *Torrey Canyon*'s cargo weighed a little more than 100,000 tons. The *Idemitsu Maru*, a Japanese tanker, carries 210,000 tons, and 500,000-ton cargo vessels are being planned. The thought of a ship of this size loaded with insecticides or herbicides is an ecologist's nightmare.

Other kinds of industrial accidents may have devastating effects on the environment. To date, nuclear reactor accidents have been providentially few; although lack of publicity prevents a critical review of damage done to surrounding areas, presumably it has not been great. But the number and variety of reactors is increasing rapidly. P. H. Abelson, the editor of *Science*, writes:

> As of 1 April 1968, about 35 percent of scheduled additions to electrical capacity were nuclear. Recent events, however, have caused some observers to fear that optimism was overdone. The utilities have gambled heavily on unproven equipment, some of which will be brought on line far behind schedule. . . . A conspicuous example is the installation at Oyster Creek, New Jersey. . . . During field hydrostatic testing of the water reactor pressure vessel on 29 September 1967, a leak was detected. . . . Detailed examination revealed localized intergranular cracking in 123 of 137 field welds joining the stub tubes and the control rod housings. . . . Even had . . . failure occurred, there would not have been a violent nuclear accident. However, if a leak or a weld failure had occurred after the reactor had operated for some time, the difficulty of repairing the defect would have been great, owing to intense radioactivity.

Both the Soviet Union and the United States have placed their hopes for future nuclear power production in a new kind of atomic plant, the Liquid-Metal-Cooled Fast Breeder Reactor (LMFBR). Not yet in operation, these reactors will generate plutonium (now scarce) from inexpensive uranium-238. Theoretically, malfunction in a LMFBR, unlike existing power reactors, *could* trigger a variety of unique and dangerous conditions. A partial prototype, the Fermi Reactor outside Detroit, was shut down for several years after a frightening and unpublicized accident in 1966. Despite the accident potential, however, LMFBR research and development has received official top priority (and the lion's share of reactor research funds) in the United States. The Soviet Union may be even farther ahead in its LMFBR program, reportedly at the expense of some design safety features.

In the years to come we may find that we have controlled routine industrial pollution only to replace it with episodic and unexpected pollution caused by massive accidents. We can accept Abelson's statement that the defects found in the Oyster Creek reactor would not have caused a nuclear explosion.* But we must not overlook the warning implicit in the data he supplies on welding defects: not only does human error cause defects; it also causes defects to be overlooked. Accidents are usually unpredictable, and the discovery of a multitude of errors that might have caused them, rather than being a reason for rejoicing, is a sign to the dispassionate statistician that other mistakes may yet lie hidden.

Introduction of Exotic Species

In 1884 a visitor returning to Florida from the Cotton States Exposition in New Orleans brought back a live water plant that had been on display. It was a floating plant with large curled green leaves and a handsome lavender flower—a native of Central America—and it looked fine against the black waters of a Florida cypress swamp. Its

---

* Although nuclear explosion is not a danger in conventional reactors, nuclear physicist Ralph Lapp has pointed out that a failure of plumbing (a broken pipe, for example, in the cooling system) could cause a disastrous overheating of the reactor's radioactive core. Quoting from a U.S. Atomic Energy Commission report, Dr. Lapp says that "within fifty to 100 seconds temperatures might soar to 3,360 degrees [fahrenheit]." Melting through its containers and restraints, the radioactive mass "would sink into the earth and continue to grow in size for about two years." It would persist for a decade.

descendants still look fine, and they please the tourists who drive south to Miami. There is no need to go out of the way to find them now; the water hyacinth, at last count, covered 90,000 acres of Florida's fresh-water lakes and streams with an impenetrable mat of curly leaves and purple blossoms. The plants all look healthy, and with good reason; they have no natural enemies in Florida.

But besides their attractiveness, water hyacinths now represent one of the major obstacles to the passage of boats on the inland waterways of the southeastern United States. They have spread as far north as the Potomac River, limited in their advance only by the northern winter. Millions of dollars have been spent to control them and millions more will be needed; they are sprayed with herbicides and devoured by obliging manatees (sea cows), which are even transported to inland waters for that purpose, but still the hyacinths are everywhere. Not only do they interrupt navigation, but they shade the naturally occurring water flora from the sun, and without this normally abundant and varied source of food the animal community of herbivores and carnivores breaks down. In most hyacinth-covered ponds, the number of minnows, turtles, waterfowl, predatory fish, and alligators is greatly reduced. A few adaptable animals take shelter among the hyacinths, including certain insects, fish, and small water snakes, but these are the exceptions; and there is little else that a biologist can say in favor of the water hyacinth in the United States.

Hyacinths are widespread and common throughout Central America. They often block streams or rivers, but only temporarily, and in most waterways are found in sheltered coves and along the banks, alternating with other water plants. After a little observation, some but not all of the reasons for this natural control become clear. Where the hyacinths touch the banks one can sometimes see undulating trails of parasol ants coming out of the underbrush to meet them, and on the hyacinths themselves teams of ants snip out and carry away sections of leaves to nourish their underground fungus gardens. The whole scene looks like a hyacinth assembly line run backward; the plants are chewed up at a great rate. On the other side, where the plants jut out into deep water, the manatees eat them by the bushel (in the larger, coastal rivers). In the upland streams, the frequent torrential rains cause floods that wash the hyacinths downstream, where great islands of them, dozens of feet in diameter, drift past in the muddy water on the way to the sea. And during times of drought, when the blue wedge of ocean water infiltrates the lagoons and scours the intracoastal waterways, the salt-sensitive hyacinths die by the millions. The water hyacinth is not new to Central America; and there it is under control by virtue of its integration in the natural community, where checks and balances exist to prevent one species from aggrandizing itself at the expense of the rest.

Ever since man first began to travel long distances he has wittingly and unwittingly brought other creatures along with him. The dingo, Australia's only placental carnivore, evidently came to the island continent as the companion of prehistoric man during the late Ice Age, so transplantation is not new. As the human population increases and as rapid travel becomes commonplace, nonhuman hitchhikers abound: insects and spiders accompany bananas; rats, mice, and even cats sneak off ships that are loading cargo at remote, oceanic islands; and the American traveler returning from Europe brings back European cold viruses along with new watches, scarves, and ash trays (the European traveler in America does the same). Foreign organisms are spread in other ways. Agricultural animals (such as pigs and goats) and plants (such as coconuts) escape readily from domestication. People also transport and release animals and plants because they like them or because they like to hunt them or fish for them. Flocks of hundreds of Australian budgerigars (parakeets) wheel over St. Petersburg, Florida, and schools of coho (Pacific) salmon thrive in Lakes Michigan and Superior, where they give joy to fishermen and feed on another recent arrival, the alewife.

Generalizations in ecology are always somewhat risky, but one must be offered at this point. The introduction of exotic plants and animals is usually a bad thing if the exotic survives; the damage ranges from the loss of a few native competing species to the total collapse of entire

Walking catfish. This destructive and aggressive Asiatic species was introduced into Florida in the 1960s by pet fanciers. It facilitates its own spread

communities (see table, pp. 126-27). The stock explanation for the explosive success of introduced species is that freedom from predators and parasites gives them an unfair advantage in competition with native species. Although the truth probably exists somewhere in the vicinity of this vague notion, it is far from satisfying. There are times when introduced species do well in the face of many direct challenges. For example, five muskrats were introduced into Bohemia (Czechoslovakia) in 1905; they multiplied and spread exceptionally rapidly, despite heavy predation by foxes, polecats, domestic cats, owls, hunters, and trappers, and despite the deliberate use of the virulent bacterium *Salmonella typhimurium*. Europe now has millions of muskrats. There are also the invariable counter-examples; not all species do well where they might be expected to thrive. The Burmese mongoose, which wreaked havoc among the small mammals and birds of Cuba and Haiti, has fortunately been unable to penetrate the dense jungles of Central America.

When the phenomenon of the rapid spread of exotics is better understood, it seems very likely that the role of the introduced species itself will not be pictured as passively as it is now. A successful exotic is not simply the lucky recipient of a ticket to a foreign Shangri-La where food is abundant and danger nonexistent. The introduced species often changes, too—changes its behavior if it is an animal and adapts its growth patterns if a plant. For example, the North American moth *Hyphantria cunea* (fall webworm) was introduced in Hungary in 1940. In Europe, its caterpillars show marked preference for mulberry leaves,

124

by walking overland for considerable distances. Extension of its range has fortunately been limited by winter weather. (Charles Trainor—*Miami News*)

although in America they specifically avoid them. Many other examples could be cited.

There is no need to rely on the classic example of rabbits in Australia in an account of the damage done by imported species; few parts of the world have escaped harm. One cannot help but recognize the unpredictability of the consequences of introductions; not until we understand all the interactions of an ecosystem (a remote possibility) will we be able to introduce new species with complete safety. In the marshy areas of the Canea Valley, Colombia, eucalyptus trees were planted to dry the land enough for sugar-cane planting. Now the water table is so low that irrigation wells have become useless. Similar phenomena are occurring in the beleaguered Everglades, where an introduced ornamental tree, the meleleuca, is infiltrating and drying cypress swamps and other areas, and in the Rio Grande Valley, where the introduced shrub *Tamarix* is having the same effect.

The heaviest damage has been done to oceanic islands, whose limited and often unique floras and faunas form communities that are particularly susceptible to attack by competition-hardened invaders from the mainland. The most extreme example is Hawaii. The herpetologist Wayne King has described the situation there: "Approximately 60 percent of the 60 endemic land birds of Hawaii are extinct following the intrusion of rats, mongoose, European rabbits, cats, goats, sheep, horses,

125

Some injurious animals and plants imported into the U.S.

Name	Origin	Mode of Transport	Type of Damage
Mammals			
European wild boar (Sus scrofa)	Russia	Intentionally imported (1912); escaped captivity	Destruction of habitat by rooting; crop damage
Nutria or coypu (Myocaster copyus), a giant rodent	Argentina	Intentionally imported; escaped captivity (1940)	Alteration of marsh ecology; damage to levees and earth dams; crop destruction
Birds			
European starling (Sturnus vulgaris)	Europe	Released intentionally (1890)	Noise; competition with native songbirds; crop damage; transmission of swine diseases; airport interference
House sparrow (Passer domesticus)	England	Released intentionally by Brooklyn Institute (1853)	Crop damage; displacement of native songbirds
Reptiles			
Cuban ground anole (Anolis sagrei sagrei), a small lizard	Cuba	Three separate, accidental introductions via ports (1931, 1960, 1964)	Replacing native anole; ecological effects unknown
Amphibians			
Giant toad (Bufo marinus)	Surinam, Colombia	Imported by animal dealers; accidental and intentional releases (1955, 1963, 1964)	Displacement of native toad species; poisoning of dogs (?); ecological effects unknown
Fish			
Carp (Cyprinus carpio)	Germany	Intentionally released (1877)	Displacement of native fish; uprooting of water plants with loss of waterfowl populations
Sea lamprey (Petromyzon marinus)	North Atlantic Ocean	Via Welland Canal (1829 . . .)	Destruction of lake trout, lake whitefish, turbot, and suckers in Great Lakes

Insects			
Argentine ant (*Iridomyrmex humilis*)	Argentina	Via coffee shipments from Brazil? (1891)	Crop damage (?); destruction of native ant faunas
Camphor scale insect (*Pseudaonidia duplex*)	Japan	Accidentally imported on nursery stock (1920?)	Damages nearly 200 species of plants in Louisiana, Texas, and Alabama
Japanese beetle (*Popillia japonica*)	Japan	Accidentally imported on irises or azaleas (1911)	Defoliation of more than 250 species of trees and other plants, including many of commercial importance
Plants			
Alligator weed (*Alternanthera philoxeroides*)	South America	Dumping of ship ballast? (1897)	Clogs waterways
Chestnut blight (*Endothia parasitica*), a fungus	Asia	Accidentally imported on nursery plants (*ca.* 1900)	Destruction of nearly all eastern American chestnuts; disturbance of forest ecology
Dutch elm disease			
(1) *Cerastomella ulmi* (a fungus; the disease agent)	Europe	Accidentally imported in infected elm timber used for veneers (1930)	Destruction of millions of elms; disturbance of forest ecology
(2) Bark beetle (*Scolytus multistriatus*; the disease carrier)	Europe	Accidentally imported in unbarked elm timber (1909)	

cattle, and pigs. The list of exotic animals in Hawaii goes further, however. It also includes over 500 species of insects, more than 50 species of birds, and numerous reptiles, amphibians, and mollusks."

Although biological control is occasionally the best way of curbing the effects of exotic intruders, it can be dangerous and tricky. King describes the outcome of one such attempt in Hawaii:

> The giant African snail (*Achatina fulica*) was introduced into Hawaii in 1936, where it rapidly became established. . . . Not only does it damage crops, but the large calciferous shells of dead snails can change the pH [acidity] of the soil in areas where they are plentiful, making it difficult to grow crops that require acid soil. When bounties, chemical and mechanical methods failed to control the snails, biological control was attempted by introducing predators from other parts of the world. . . . sixteen more animals were introduced [including beetles, flies, and other snails from Africa, India, Japan, Cuba, California, Florida, and New York]. The original pest is still present, and several of the predaceous species are attacking not only the African giant but also the endemic Hawaiian snails. . . . These colorful endemic snails are rapidly diminishing in numbers. . . .

What other effects the sixteen "control" species are having is not known.

One of the few kinds of species introduction that is not always an unmitigated disaster is that involving sport and food fish. Many varieties of trout and salmon have been carried around the world: brown trout have been taken from England to Tasmania to New Zealand and from Germany and Scotland to the United States. Although the trout introductions have not been a complete success everywhere (brown trout destroy rainbow and brook trout in the United States), most fishermen have welcomed the addition of this wily and handsome fish to their native waters. Commercial food fish have also been widely and successfully transplanted. H. Blegvad has described the massive transplantation of plaice (the European flounder, *Pleuronectus*) from the North Sea to the Belt Sea (the waters around the Danish islands of Fünen and Sealand). The North Sea subspecies grows much more rapidly than its local Belt Sea relative, and spawns in its new home. The Danish fishing industry has gained 200,000 to 400,000 kroner ($40,000-$80,000) annually, while the transplantations cost the Danish government only 70,000 to 80,000 kroner ($14,000-$16,000). On the other hand, trout introduced in Lake Tota and other Andean lakes have destroyed a number of endemic species of fish and have upset aquatic communities. And G. Laycock reports that largemouth bass introduced in Guatemala's Lake Atitlan have nearly led to the extinction of the lake's unique flightless bird, the giant pied-billed grebe. The bass eat the young of the grebes as soon as they leave their floating nests. These two examples of misfortunes in relatively simple lake communities should warn us that the success of many sport and food fish introductions performed in marine waters may be an illusion fostered by our ignorance of the complex ecology of the communities that lie hidden beneath the surface of the sea.

Removal of "Key Species"

Some animals and plants hold central positions in the meshwork of interrelationships that forms a community; if these species are selectively removed, the community structure begins to collapse. These kinds of organisms are referred to here for convenience as "key species." It is easy to appreciate the significance of key species in very simple ecosystems like the Antarctic Ocean, where the handful of short food chains converge in a very few kinds of organisms. However, complex communities also have their key species; it just may take a little longer to figure out which ones they are.

One of the best examples of a key species in a complex community is the alligator in the Everglades. This remarkable animal, whose only close relative is nearing extinction in China, is one of the few large and dangerous predators that never attacks man in the wild unless badly imposed upon. Despite its agreeable disposition and its willingness to live in a variety of habitats (wild alligators inhabit a pond on the campus of the University of Florida), the alligator is being exterminated over most of its former range, primarily by poachers who send the illegally taken hides to the New York and other markets. No population of alligators is now safe from these poachers, who even raid zoos, private game farms, and the Everglades National Park. Ironically, it is only as the once-abundant alligator disappears that its ecological importance is being appreciated.

The alligator's vital role in its community has been described by Archie Carr, F. C. Craighead, Sr., and others. Carr writes: "All animals to some degree affect the landscape they live in. The alligator does so to a greater extent than most. Its habit of controlling its environment is part of the special resilience which has allowed the species to live through the ages. To an alligator, home is a nest, a "gator hole" or pool, a cavelike den, and a system of trails. All affect the look of the landscape." This rearrangement of the landscape is one of the alligator's major contributions to its environment.

The holes excavated by the giant reptiles form the deepest pools in the Everglades and are the last places to become dry during a drought. In all but the worst dry spells, these gator holes serve as collecting points and biological reservoirs for the dwindling life of the glades. Nourished by the droppings of the alligator and by the remains of its meals, the water of the gator holes supports a rich growth of algae, ferns, and higher plants, and these in turn maintain a variety of animal life. Fish, amphibians, reptiles, and aquatic invertebrates all find shelter here, ready to begin an explosive breeding cycle that will re-populate the glades when the drought ends. Birds and mammals also rely on the gator holes for food and water.

In addition to enlarging their home ponds, female alligators make large nest mounds out of sticks and mud, and hollow them out to receive their thirty to seventy eggs. When built in the same place for long periods, these mounds, together with the mud dredged from the den and pool, often form islands high enough to support trees in the midst of the glades. The trees that grow on alligator islands are popu-lar nesting sites for herons, egrets, and other birds; there is some indication that the presence of the alligator guarding her nest is sufficient to frighten away raccoons and wildcats that could climb the trees to destroy the bird rookery. In return for this favor, the alligator will eat baby birds that fall from the nest and fish dropped by the adult birds. The alligator's nest mound is itself frequently used by

American alligators. Once the range of these giant reptiles extended as far north as Virginia's Dismal Swamp; but with heavy pressure from the leather industry, they survive primarily in a few remote and protected areas in the Deep South. (Courtesy Florida News Bureau)

other animals, such as turtles and snakes, as a shelter for their own eggs, which receive the benefit of her maternal care—exceptional for a reptile. Also, in moving to and from its nest to the pond, and in moving along its trails through the aquatic vegetation, the alligator helps keep the pond area open and clear, and delays the inevitable succession to a marsh community.

The alligator's feeding habits exert another powerful influence on the community. There is no doubt that its fondness for crunching turtles and ability to eat and be bitten by poisonous snakes with impunity are important in Everglades ecology. But far more significant is the

131

A "gator hole" in the Everglades, surrounded by low vegetation. The entrance to the alligator's den can be seen to the left of the pond. Florida wildlife officers are tagging the alligator. (Charles Trainor—*Miami News*)

large number of gar consumed by alligators. The spotted gar, which grows to a length of two and a half feet, is the principal predatory fish of the Everglades, feeding on bass, bream, and other game fish. Where there are many alligators, the gar population is low, and smaller fish can thrive. In areas where the alligators have been exterminated, gar are numerous, the composition of the aquatic community changes, and the quality of fishing declines.

Hopefully, future research will uncover more of the ecological ties of the alligator with its community, and hopefully something will be done in time to prevent the extinction of both the species and the community that depends on it, for this loss of a beneficial species can never be compensated by the market value of the hides it supplies. Such a loss would be a grim indictment of the health and spirit of the kind of society that values alligator shoes and handbags more than living alligators.

132

Epilogue

Prior to the twentieth century there were few who noticed or were concerned with man's impact on the natural environment. Yet during the eighteenth and nineteenth centuries we were even more heedless of the fate of our surroundings than we are now. What saved our ancestors from experiencing the consequences of their folly was the vast expanse of the natural world, the comparatively small human population, and the undeveloped state of technology. Now the picture has changed. Human population strains the habitable confines of a limited earth, and the side effects of technology threaten the remaining biotic communities.

All life on earth is linked together by an infinity of connections, and this vast structure is influenced by and influences inanimate properties of the planet, such as climate, atmosphere, and landform. Small alterations in the environment, like the addition of some grains of sand to a gear box, may have effects far out of proportion to their own physical significance. Biologists fear that the simple act of dredging shallow portions of the Suez Canal will cause catastrophic changes in the fauna of the Mediterranean Sea by allowing foreign predators from the Red Sea to enter. Similarly, no one knows what will happen if a new sea-level canal across Central America permits large volumes of Pacific Ocean water to flow into the Caribbean Sea.* We have not yet learned to live with the idea that the results of our actions may be amplified many times and that the unforeseen consequences can come full circle to haunt us. Never has the question of the dredger, "Which is more important, fish or people?" sounded so foolish; we are all involved together in the same system.

* One possibility was recently reported by marine biologist J. B. Graham and two colleagues, in the *Proceedings of the National Academy of Sciences* (U.S.; 1971). It concerns the deadly poisonous yellow-bellied sea snake, *Pelamis platurus*, currently a resident of the tropical Indian and Pacific Oceans. After a study of the temperature tolerance and feeding habits of the snake, they concluded: "In the event of its transit through the proposed Central American Sea-Level Canal, *P. platurus* would colonize the Atlantic Ocean and, during the summer months, would be able to extend its north Atlantic distribution to as far as Cape Cod and the English Channel."

4

Two Endangered
Natural Communities

The Oklawaha River Valley and the
Cross-Florida Barge Canal

The predominant impression that can be gleaned from the writings of
the early travelers in Florida is of great natural abundance, the kind of
primeval lushness and bounty that was occasionally portrayed by
Coleridge and Wordsworth, and which in distorted detail forms part
of everyone's image of America. The following passage, published in
1791 by the great naturalist William Bartram, is a good illustration:

> We had a large and fat one [soft-shelled turtle] served up for our
> supper, which I at first apprehended we had made a very extrava-
> gant waste of, not being able to consume one half of its flesh,
> though excellently well cooked. My companions, however, seemed
> regardless, being in the midst of plenty and variety, at any time
> within our reach, and to be obtained with little or no trouble or
> fatigue on our part; when herds of deer were feeding in the green
> meadows before us: flocks of turkeys walking in the groves
> around us, and myriads of fish, of the greatest variety and
> delicacy, sporting in the crystalline floods before our eyes.

When Bartram observed this scene he was passing through northeast
Florida, not far from a stream the Indians called the Ockli-Waha, or
Great River.

The River Styx, a black-water cypress swamp near the Oklawaha River. Dense mats of floating water hyacinths can be seen in the center. (Courtesy David W. Ehrenfeld)

Today the landmarks described by Bartram are mostly gone, replaced by shoddy development communities, by endless miles of monotonous, slash-pine tree farms, and by the sprawling Duval County urban complex, whose acrid paper mill fumes penetrate the cabins of arriving jet liners even before they touch the runway at Jacksonville's International Airport. Yet, surprisingly, in the midst of this disorderly change, one extensive and self-contained wilderness area, the Oklawaha Valley, was preserved intact in northeast Florida, through accident or oversight, until the latter part of the 1960s.

The Oklawaha River could hardly have been considered "great" by the Indians, who had the mighty St. Johns for comparison; perhaps "magnificent" is a better translation. The Oklawaha arose in several large lakes of central Florida and flowed northward for sixty miles, joining the St. Johns River eight miles north of Lake George. Along its course it received additional waters from Silver Springs and from Orange Lake. It was a sand-bottomed river with transparent, tea-colored waters stained by the humic acids leached from the surrounding hardwood forest. The river's course was tortuous, with many turns and oxbows, and it flowed through a mile-wide valley that it had cut during its long geological history. The valley itself was often flooded by the river during wet years; and the edaphic climax vegetation included water-resistant trees such as the tupelo, swamp red bay, sweet gum, red maple, loblolly bay, water hickory, water oak, cabbage palm, and the spectacular bald cypress. At the sides of the valley, where the land sloped upward and was free of flooding, and on the islands of higher ground scattered through the valley, one could find the typical trees of the Florida climatic climax: laurel oak, blue beech, hop hornbeam, and magnolia.

As could be predicted from the plant community, the fauna of the Oklawaha River and its valley was exceptionally diverse. Several species that require extensive wilderness habitat did well there: the wild turkey, one of the largest of North American birds, is a good example; the Oklawaha Valley was one of the last strongholds of this traditional game bird in Florida. Other birds included limpkins, bitterns, rails, herons, snake birds (*Anhinga*), and until recent years roseate spoonbills and ivory-billed woodpeckers. A variety of reptiles —snakes, turtles, and alligators—could be seen sunning themselves at the water's edge. Among the more notable mammals were black bears, wildcats, otters, and raccoons. An occasional panther still found refuge in the forest, enticed by the same deer herds that attracted hunters from all over the state to the surrounding scrub land. In the river itself and in its feeder springs there was a luxurious growth of multicolored aquatic plants and an abundance of fish, including chain pickerel, redbreast sunfish, shell-cracker, speckled perch, huge largemouth bass, and perhaps the tastiest of all freshwater fish in the southeast, the channel catfish.

Within or adjacent to the Oklawaha region were five major Florida springs of considerable recreational value and of great interest to ecologists, geologists, paleontologists, and other scientists. Fifteen miles to the west of the Oklawaha River, two large and relatively unspoiled lakes, Lochloosa and Orange, added to the wildlife-carrying capacity of the region. To complete the picture, it should be mentioned that the Oklawaha region was sparsely populated, containing no large towns or major highways. Viewing the region from an airplane, David Anthony described it as follows: "Flying north from the Silver Springs area the Oklawaha Valley appears as a broad, densely-forested belt that curves for more than forty miles around the northern third of the Ocala National Forest. To the west lie open pine lands, and the dry low forest of the Big Scrub spreads out to the east. Clearly, the valley forest serves as a safe highway and sanctuary for wildlife over an enormous area."

In 1942, Congress approved the plans of the Army Corps of Engineers for the proposed route of a Cross-Florida Barge Canal, to be constructed, in part, by damming and flooding the Oklawaha Valley. Financial support was not forthcoming, however, and interest in the project waned during the next two decades as it became clear that the canal would be of questionable economic and aesthetic value. During these post–World War II years, the Corps was busy in southern Florida, rearranging (and, as we have seen, damaging) the landscape to suit the immediate needs of a mismatched assortment of special interests: real estate, industry, and occasionally agriculture. Meanwhile, a few hundred miles to the north, analogous interests—in particular, the powerful phosphate and pulpwood producers and the heavy construction industry—had not lost sight of the barge canal plans, which had the conspicuous advantage of prior congressional sanction. The presidential campaigns of 1960 and 1964 afforded these interests the opportunity to make public their demands for federal support for the canal, and they were promptly joined by individuals whose land holdings on and near the canal right-of-way were likely to increase in value, as well as by several communities (for example, Palatka) that expected to benefit economically from the anticipated barge traffic. By 1966 the Corps of Engineers had awarded contracts for construction of the Rodman and Eureka dams in the Oklawaha Valley.

As might have been expected, virtually all private conservation organizations in the state, with a combined membership exceeding 100,000 Floridians, opposed the destruction of the river valley; but the private citizens who actively led them constituted a much smaller group, largely inexperienced in lobbying, and able to muster only limited funds. Rather than register total opposition to the canal project, they proposed an alternate route (see map, opposite page), which would have preserved the lower forty-five miles of the Oklawaha Valley.

On the basis of topographic and economic data, which the Corps first referred to as part of a "careful study" but which later was described as rough estimates, the alternate route was rejected by the Corps at the annual Water Resources Meeting in Tallahassee on January 25, 1966. They concluded that the effect of relocation would be to dry up the Oklawaha River and to increase construction and maintenance costs of the canal. "Recreational" and "flood control" benefits were also deemed to be jeopardized by the conservationists' alternate route. Unprepared for this objection to their compromise solution, the conservationists could not reply at the meeting. Several weeks later, their careful evaluation of the district engineer's grossly misleading report was too late. Among the many points that they raised were the following:

The water level in the Oklawaha, downstream from the alternate route cut-off, could be maintained by a single pumping station.

The Corps' map of the land profile over the alternate route showed several miles of ground with an elevation greater than ninety feet above sea level, where the canal excavation costs would supposedly be high. However, the U.S. Geological Survey map of the same area (1964) shows an elevation of less than seventy-five feet.

The uniform dwarfed scrub pine forest along the alternate route would be much easier to clear for excavation than the mixed hardwood forest of the Oklawaha Valley.

The Corps failed to explain how the two locks, built side by side,

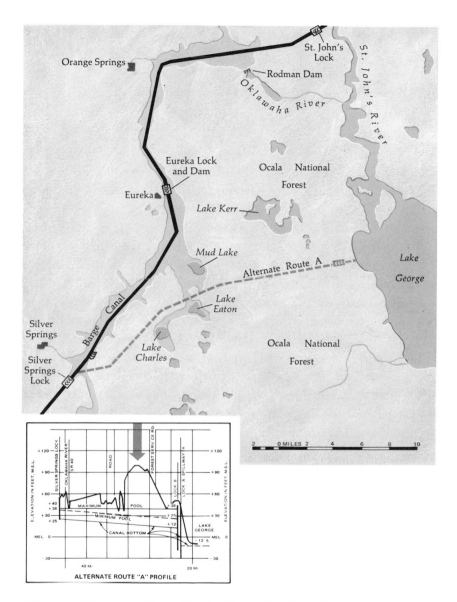

Oklawaha River and Cross-Florida Barge Canal, with proposed alternate route. Inset shows Corps of Engineers' land profile for the alternate route; arrow indicates questionably high value for land elevation (see text for further details).

and the twenty-three miles of canal that comprised the alternate route would cost more to maintain than would their original route of thirty-nine miles of canal, a 27,000-acre reservoir, and two locks and two dams located in three different places.

Calculations by the Corps of direct and collateral benefits that would result from construction of the original canal route were based on invalid and discredited methods of benefit analysis.

At this point a brief explanation is indicated for those who wonder what place should be given to economic matters in a book on biological conservation. We live in a capitalist economy and therefore are accustomed to valuing material things according to a price determined by a semi-free market rather than through the decisions of state planners. Traditionally, natural or "undeveloped" land has commanded a low market value, which was perhaps permissible and was certainly understandable when such land was in abundant supply. Unfortunately, now that natural communities of self-perpetuating size are scarce, we find ourselves still tied to the traditional monetary valuations.* Since natural communities are evaluated only in terms of their fancied or real potential for development, conservation battles are frequently fought entirely on conventional economic grounds, and conservationists no longer can consider themselves above the mundane considerations of budgets and accounting.

In 1963 the departments of Agriculture and Interior issued a joint "River Area Inventory" statement about the Oklawaha, which they concluded as follows: "This river is of sufficient size and unique character and should be included in any system of wild rivers. It is felt that this use outweighs any other possible functions that have been proposed for the general area." Obviously these findings were subsequently ignored by the federal government when it decided to build the canal. Ordinarily, one would suspect that the government's decision was based on the usual failure of conservationists to translate aesthetic

---

* Curiously, in communist countries, where most land is in the public domain and not subject to sale, centralized state planning can occasionally lead to a distressingly similar scale of priorities and values with respect to land use. The Soviet government's belated and perhaps inadequate response to the impending destruction of the magnificent Lake Baikal by effluvia from pulp mills is one example.

and long-term speculative considerations into dollars and cents. But for once this was not so. The conservationists had provided a sound and detailed economic argument to support the value judgment contained in the area inventory. After a summary of this argument, we can consider briefly what nevertheless went wrong.

In 1946, in a project study and report on the proposed canal, the Army Corps of Engineers found a benefit/cost ratio of 1.05:1.00, which was considered economically unsound. A 1958 review reconfirmed the Corps' decision not to recommend construction. In 1962, however, in a second review, the Corps announced that the benefit/cost ratio was approximately 1.20:1.00, and that the project could proceed. This sudden change in the estimated economic worth of the canal surprised a great many people, including Raymond W. Stuck, who was chief of the Civil Works Division of the Corps prior to the final project study. In a letter reprinted in the U.S. Senate Congressional Record, August 23, 1965, Stuck wrote:

> In the 1962 Addendum Report the same quantities were used as in the 1946 Report but five additional highway bridges were found to be necessary. Yet, surprisingly, the estimated cost was 13½% less than the 1946 estimate and the benefit-cost ratio was now 1.20 to 1.00.
>
> Conservative evaluations show that all construction costs have increased since the war years at about 2% per year but we have the very unusual situation on this project where construction costs [were] presumed to decrease even for an expanded project."

Moreover, as was pointed out by the conservationist and economist Col. F. W. Hodge, the Corps neglected in 1962 to include interest charges in its cost figures, which would have added an extra $13 million to the construction figure of $157,900,000. Furthermore, in computing the discount rate (a way of accounting for loss of income due to postponement of the return on an investment) the Corps unaccountably used the value of 2.875 percent, little more than half the commonly accepted figure of 4.2 percent. Finally, federal construction estimates, even if computed in a realistic way, have generally tended to be grossly undervalued. It is clear, therefore, that if the Corps had performed a valid appraisal of the costs alone, the Cross-Florida Barge

Canal would have been found to be even more unsound a venture in 1962 than previously.

Between 1958 and 1962 there was also a curious manipulation of the benefit side of the ratio. In addition to direct benefits such as transportation savings, a new category of yearly benefits amounting to $907,000 was listed for the first time. These "collateral benefits" included "land enhancement" and "flood control." In the past, "land enhancement" claims have been rejected as vague during congressional hearings and have been described by the noted economist Otto Eckstein as an unfair way of counting again an item that has already been included as a direct benefit. Also, in the case of the barge canal, the "enhanced" land would largely border on a flooded area about two feet deep and filled with standing dead trees. Even if these considerations did not apply, it is doubtful whether the private profits of a few real estate speculators are a public "benefit," since no price reduction in goods or services will ever be passed on to the consumer. The "flood control" benefit is, if anything, more dubious than the claimed land enhancement value. As Colonel Hodge has pointed out, flood control is "effected by the permanent flooding of the Oklawaha River valley," and agricultural development in other areas that will be protected from flooding will depend on extra investment of private capital and will not automatically result from the canal project.

Of the several direct benefits, "transportation savings" was by far the largest item, amounting to $7,016,000 per year. This is probably the most heavily exaggerated figure of the entire Corps of Engineers report. According to Senator William Proxmire (D.-Wis.), who challenged the report in Congress, "The savings claimed are almost four times greater than those claimed for any other inland waterway." Among the various ingenious methods used by the Corps to inflate the figure was the assumption that as much pulpwood would pass through the canal as is carried by the entire Mississippi-Ohio traffic system. Using standard accounting practices of the Corps of Engineers, Colonel Hodge calculated the transportation savings to be $2,776,008; and Charles A. Welsh, director of the Graduate Program of Business Administration at Rollins College, computed a figure of $3,163,031, both less than half of the 1962 estimate made by the Corps.

Besides underestimating construction costs and exaggerating bene-fits, the Corps neglected to account for such indirect costs as damage to many kinds of fish and game habitats in the vicinity of the canal. One example, according to the U.S. Fish and Wildlife Service, is the destruction of "a sizeable amount of littoral zone" in the Gulf of Mexico, caused by dredging and spoil disposal activities extending to a point six miles offshore. Another indirect (and incalculable) cost of the canal would be the attraction to Florida of the kind of heavy in-dustry that is least desirable in an area whose healthy economy is based on the tourist trade, the citrus industry, cattle ranches, and stock farms. Already there have been widespread complaints in the southern part of the state that fumes from phosphate and other factories are harmful to citrus and cattle.

In summary, the Corps of Engineers' precariously favorable benefit-cost ratio of approximately 1.20 seems little more than an economic subterfuge. Senator Proxmire has stated, "The actual benefit-cost ratio should be, at the very most, 0.79." If correct, this would hardly justify constructing a bicycle path, let alone a $157,900,000 barge canal.

Evidently the pressures to "develop" the remaining natural land-scapes—if the Cross-Florida Barge Canal is a representative example —can be generated by the economic demands of particular individuals and corporations rather than by the needs of the public. The Florida canal is likely to be in both the short and long run an economic dis-aster for the taxpayers; however, in spite of ample evidence to prove this, construction plans were neither cancelled nor substantially modi-fied, nor even postponed. One reason for this insensitivity of govern-mental agencies like the Army Corps of Engineers to the very realistic requests of large numbers of citizens is the lack of any firmly insti-tutionalized mechanism whereby the public can delay the federal (or state) land condemnation process. Public hearings involving the Corps and related agencies are too often a sham, used only to invest pre-arranged policies with a semblance of procedural regularity.

Land development is irreversible—waiting is not. Any battle in which the setbacks on one side are always temporary and the losses on the other are always permanent can have only one outcome. With one small qualification, the fate of the Oklawaha Valley can serve as a warning that conservationists in all countries must find a way to help the concerned public restore the odds against a bureaucracy unresponsive to their needs.

The "small qualification" is that at this writing the Cross-Florida Barge Canal had not been completed, and it probably never will be. It is the barge canal that is dead, not the Oklawaha Valley. The Oklawaha has been described in the past tense in the preceding pages not to fool or irritate the reader, but to make a point. The point is simple: in nearly all similar cases the canal would have been built. Indeed, from 1964 to 1971 all knowledgeable conservationists but one were certain that the Oklawaha was a lost cause. That one person was Marjorie Carr of Micanopy, Florida, a biologist and the wife of Archie Carr, a noted ecologist and conservationist at the University of Florida. Outraged by the canal project, she somehow managed to balance an enormous anger with a cheerfulness and optimism that her friends found difficult to understand. Her task seemed more than preposterous: she had to stop congressionally funded and presidentially sanctioned construction that was likely to be worth approximately a quarter of a billion dollars to private contractors and special interest groups. She was, of course, not alone in this work, but it was her vitality that kept the struggle from dying out at many points.

The first four or five years of effort were marked by continuous failure. Contracts were let out and construction began. Rodman Dam was completed and the water began to accumulate behind it. But at this point the Corps' luck started to change.

As the water backed up behind the dam, there was evidence of severe and unforeseen difficulties resulting from the canal construction. In the Rodman water-storage area, the trees of part of the original Oklawaha forest, having been felled and pressed into the earth by a giant forest-crushing machine developed for the Corps, began to pop up to the surface of the water at irregular intervals—hardly an auspicious beginning for the boating paradise that had been promised. Embarrassed, the Corps retired its Rube Goldberg monster from the canal project, and in a heavy-handed attempt to cover its tracks, bestowed a beautification award on the hideous, log-choked mudhole now known as Lake Rodman. Elsewhere along the canal construction route, the Oklawaha water, deprived of the natural organic acids once supplied by the surrounding forest, began to turn more alkaline. This, in turn, favored the growth of water weeds, including dense mats of enormous water hyacinths capable of stopping any barge. In its original construction and maintenance budget, the Corps had not provided any funds for weed control, but even if money were available there would still have been no acceptable hyacinth-removal method on which to spend it.

With these new indications of serious trouble in the canal project, and with the canal's impact on the water system of central Florida yet to come, Mrs. Carr and her associates abruptly changed their tactics and went to court. Forming a group known as Florida Defenders of the Environment, composed of conservationists, professional scientists, lawyers, politicians, economists, businessmen, and philanthropists, they called in New York's Environmental Defense Fund for legal aid. By late 1970 the case had reached Federal District Court in Washington, and parallel efforts were being made to reach the President through his Council on Environmental Quality. In January 1971, the federal judge issued temporary injunctions halting construction of the Cross-Florida Barge Canal; a few days later, in an independent action, President Nixon used his authority as Commander-in-Chief of the Army (including the Corps of Engineers) to order an end to the Canal project.

Even so, the work was not done. Smoking more and sleeping less, Mrs. Carr was still proving considerably tougher than the various generals and colonels who had been so amused and condescending towards her early efforts. The next task was to achieve the "drawdown" of Lake Rodman, so that the remaining trees of the forest would have a chance of survival, and to facilitate the speedy recovery of the Oklawaha ecosystem. This entailed additional hearings in several district courts. Meanwhile, the Florida Canal Authority, in a desperate attempt to keep the barge canal alive, sought in another court action to have the President's order ruled unconstitutional. At this writing, neither case had been settled, but the conservationists obviously had the upper hand. If the legal obstacles can be cleared away, Congress may eventually act on a recent U.S. Forest Service recommendation that the Oklawaha be declared a Wild and Scenic River, a designation conferring permanent protection, insofar as that is possible. There is no doubt in the minds of Mrs. Carr and her allies that permanent protection will be necessary: there is always another election on the horizon, and no Corps project is ever entirely forgotten.

The Pacific Coast Redwood Communities

The example of the Oklawaha River Valley shows how complex economic and bureaucratic issues can lie at the core of a conservation problem. The Oklawaha is a large and self-contained wilderness unit and needs little more than minimal management by state conservation and game officers. Now that it has escaped "development" for the moment, its preservation should be a relatively simple matter. The Pacific Coast redwood communities of California and southwestern Oregon present a very different kind of challenge to the conservationist.

Although many of the oldest and most magnificent of the redwood groves are under heavy pressure from lumber companies, this aspect of the redwood controversy will not be discussed here. Suffice it to say that the lumber companies have exploited what should have been a public trust, and their tree farms filled with redwood saplings are hardly an adequate substitute for the one- to two-thousand-year-old giants that have been cut down. There is, however, more to the story. During the 1960s, foresters and other ecologists began to realize that the redwoods are but a part of a complex ecosystem, an ecosystem that might still be in trouble even if the lumber companies were to vanish overnight.

One of the few studies in depth of the redwood ecosystems was made by an Australian forester, R. G. Florence, at the School of Forestry of the University of California. Florence saw no reason to assume that redwood forests were a classical climax community, and

Redwoods in Del Norte County, California. The undergrowth is a dense mixture of ferns and evergreen huckleberry. Note the relative size of the man standing at the lower left. (Dan Todd—Courtesy U.S. Forest Service)

set out to study the growth rate of redwood seedlings in a variety of soils, including soil from established redwood forests. He examined in the laboratory soils from upland, old-growth, redwood–Douglas fir forests, floodplain redwood forests, and earlier seral stages consisting largely of tan-oak brush or madrone, and tested their ability to support growth of redwood seedlings under several conditions. His results clearly showed a "development in the redwood forest soil of a condition in which microbiological populations are depleted, respiratory activity low, mineralization of nitrogen adversely affected, and in which root rot fungi can attack the redwood seedlings."

As Florence points out, these results are not entirely surprising— many species of trees in old-growth forests seem to create soil conditions unfavorable for the growth of their own seedlings. A subtle and rhythmic alternation of species may therefore occur, even in a "climax" forest. In the case of the upland redwood–Douglas fir forests, there is some evidence that this alternation does happen under undisturbed conditions, with various hardwood species like tan oak emerging and becoming dominant in the older redwood stands, only to give way to new redwood and Douglas fir growth when the soil has been rejuvenated after fifty years or more. This postulated alternation is probably not total, for all species coexist during all phases; only the relative proportions change. Obviously then, management of such upland redwood groves in park land is not simply a matter of preserving the redwoods. Similarly, lumber companies have found that after logging in old redwood stands, regrowth of redwoods is slow until a hardwood phase has been completed.

Although soil depletion is almost certainly a feature of alluvial flat (floodplain) redwood groves, the upland type of species alternation does not seem to occur here, and nearly pure stands of redwood maintain and replenish themselves for immense periods of time in regions that have been periodically flooded in the past. Arguments about the causes of the success and vigor of these alluvial flat redwoods have produced sharp differences between foresters and professional conservationists as to how the old-growth alluvial forests should be managed in order to keep them in good condition.

In an article published in *Science*, Edward C. Stone and Richard B.

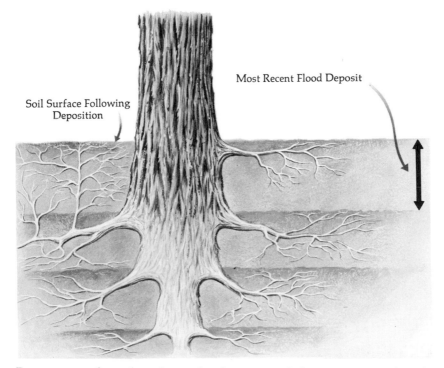

Most Recent Flood Deposit

Soil Surface Following
Deposition

Root system of a redwood tree that has survived three major root burials. After each burial, there is first a vertical invasion of new soil by roots from below, then, several years later, the development of a horizontal root system from the buried trunk. Once established, the horizontal root system replaces the vertical one, which dies. (Modified after Edward C. Stone and Richard B. Vasey, "Preservation of Coast Redwood on Alluvial Flats," from *Science*, *159*, p. 157 (1968). © American Association for the Advancement of Science, 1968)

Vasey of the School of Forestry, University of California, Berkeley, claimed that the reason the redwood is predominant on the alluvial flats is that it has a number of special features that render it resistant to both fire and flood. The bark is thick and fire-resistant; and the crown of the tree can regenerate from adventitious (unusually placed) buds along the branches and stems. In the case of floods, it can compensate for the tendency to lean in the unstable alluvial soil by adding enormous supporting buttresses to the trunk in the direction of tilt and by strengthening those roots under most tension. Also, after heavy silt deposition during floods, redwoods can rapidly readjust their root systems to take advantage of the newly deposited soil layer (see diagram above). This is not only beneficial but necessary: during the past

149

thousand years—well within the life-span of many large redwoods—
fifteen major floods have raised the level of the alluvial flats in the
region under study by more than thirty feet. According to Stone and
Vasey, none of the major competitors of alluvial redwoods (tan oak,
Douglas fir, bay, and grand fir) can withstand both fire and flood.

Many foresters claim that, in addition to reducing competition,
periodic flooding in the past has, by virtue of new soil deposition, circumvented the problem of soil exhaustion in old stands of redwood.
It is one thing, however, to allow fire and flood to maintain redwood
forests over a broad undisturbed area prior to the twentieth century—
it is another to rely on these same natural agents to preserve the few
old groves of alluvial flat redwoods that remain in comparatively small
parks. Severe fires and floods can be locally destructive even to redwoods; besides, fire and flood control is now an accepted fact of life.
What, then, should be done with floodplain redwoods?

Up to now the professional conservationists' viewpoint has not been
represented. Bestor Robinson, a director of the Sierra Club, has chal-
lenged the conclusions reached by Stone and Vasey. In a letter also
published in *Science*, he claims that "although fire and siltation may
help, neither of these agents is necessary. The redwood, given proper
growing conditions . . . has weapons and competitive advantages (including long lifespan, rapid growth rate, vigorous root competition,
disease resistance, and great height) that enable it to become a climax
species as against its competitors in this region. . . ." Furthermore,
flooding has the major disadvantages, according to Robinson, of providing new soil free, for several years, of redwood roots and therefore
accessible to invasion by competing seedlings; undermining and top-
pling thousands of large redwoods; and raising the water table, which
kills redwoods through a disease known as "sour root."

Responding to Robinson's criticism, Stone and Vasey wrote: ". . .
they [the conservationists] have failed to appreciate the dynamic character of the ecosystem involved. They have focused their attention on
preserving the trees now standing, ignoring the rest of the ecosystem
which was responsible for these redwoods being present and upon
which their replacements depend."

Clearly, there is an honest and fundamental difference in viewpoint concerning the nature of the alluvial-flat redwood ecosystem (the difference is perhaps less pronounced in the case of the uplands redwoods). Believing in the importance of fire and flood, Stone and Vasey have written: ". . . time is running out for the alluvial-flat redwoods and . . . flood control could be the final blow unless man actively intervenes with herbicides, the ax, or the chainsaw [to control redwood competitors]." Many conservationists feel, to the contrary, that the ecological effects of flood and fire control alone do not justify additional and potentially dangerous interference with a delicate ecosystem.

In the background of this controversy looms the larger conservation problem of whether succession (or other kinds of ecological change) can or should be arrested in an area originally set aside and protected because of the special qualities of one seral stage. It would take a clairvoyant to ascertain where the truth lies, but one thing is certain: if the various interests that are trying to save the redwoods cannot find a practical forest management compromise, they will never be able to work together to resist the kind of politico-economic pressures that nearly destroyed the Oklawaha Valley.

5
How Species Are Threatened

A biological species can be defined as a group of sexually reproducing organisms, all of whose members can share in a common gene pool (i.e., they can potentially exchange genes through interbreeding); however, most of the several million types of organisms in the world that have been called "species" by biologists have never been put to the official test of the definition. Although we assume that members of the same species can interbreed and produce fertile offspring and that they cannot do this under natural conditions with members of closely related but different species; it has not been possible to check many species in this regard. This problem—that the functional definition is usually nontestable—is one that we would gladly leave to the evolutionists and taxonomists; but occasionally the meaning of species worries the conservationist as well. For example, the coyote, *Canis latrans*, and the red wolf, *Canis niger*, are named and treated as separate species by mammalogists, who thereby commit themselves to the implicit idea that there is no gene exchange between the two populations. Yet it is now claimed that the coyote, which has increased its range by tens of thousands of square miles during the twentieth century, is threatening to wipe out the last remnants of the Texas red wolf population through hybridization.

152

Coyote (*Canis latrans*), above (Conway-Scala); red wolf (*Canis niger*), below. (Edward F. D'Arms, Jr.) Cross-breeding with far more numerous coyotes has nearly obliterated red wolves as distinct animals.

If, indeed, it turns out to be true that the constellation of genes that we now know as *Canis niger* is being swallowed up and lost in the constellation of genes that we know as *Canis latrans*, should we be concerned? If, when the 150 extant red wolves die, they have left behind offspring that are part coyote, will there be any difference in the zoological status of the world? The answer is clearly "yes." The red wolf is a recognizably different animal from the coyote, regardless of whether it is called a separate species. Uniqueness, for the conservationist, is often a function of populations, not necessarily of species. This does not mean that species are unreal or uninteresting to conservationists. The species is the fundamental unit of any natural system of classification of sexual organisms; without it, neither higher nor lower levels of classification could be fully defined or understood. Not only is it important to know the species identity of animals and plants in order to make conservation policy decisions (as in the example just described), but the valid identification of a creature rests on its species designation and not on any other taxonomic or popular nomenclature. Therefore the concept of "species" is used (though at times rather loosely) throughout this chapter; but it is never meant to imply that local populations are of little importance.

The Value of Species

On the Cumbrian and Scottish shores the mussel beds yielded pale irregular pearls. The oysters of Colchester and Whitstable were famous; so were Selsey cockles and the shrimps of the sandy Lancashire shores. The Thames estuary had its teeming population of sprats and eels; eels, larger and richer, were the boast of northern Ireland, and lampreys were the specialty of the Severn estuary. Pilchards from Plymouth and Penzance were famous in far countries; mussels were the pride of Minehead. Plump sea-gulls were in demand, and the tiny, naked new-hatched gannet were carried away by the basket load from the Bass Rock to be swallowed, at one succulent, greasy mouthful, by revellers in Edinburgh. Berwick had long been famous for salmon and shellfish but had recently fallen upon evil times; the fisher folk, tempted by the possibility of a record haul, had broken the Sab-

bath and gone out in their boats. Since that time the salmon had deserted Berwick whose present distress was held up as a warning to all who despised the commandments.

From the North Sea the Yarmouth herring boats brought home by the barrel-load the silvery, living harvest of the deep, and fisher folk came in their cobbles from as far north as the coast of Durham and as far west as Lyme to sell their herring on the Yarmouth quays to be split and smoked and marketed. From the ports of East Anglia—Lynn, Southwold, Dunwich, Aldeburgh— the Iceland ships went out for codling. On fish quays up and down the kingdom, housewives bargained for plaice and sole, cod and mackerel, turbot, skate, whiting and "poor John," as they familiarly called the vulgar hake, the Friday fare of the people. Sturgeon and whale, cast up on the coast, were for the King's use.

c. v. WEDGWOOD, *The King's Peace: 1637-1641*

The ecological importance of biological diversity has already been discussed. This diversity is naturally based in large measure upon *the number of different species* in a given community (and in part upon the number of individuals in each species). Sudden reduction of species diversity is not only an indication of outside, disruptive interference— such as pollution—but a warning of possibly severe ecological problems to follow. In some cases it is obvious that a community will not be able to function properly if a particular species is deleted. On the other hand, in no case can we be certain that a species is dispensable. It becomes, then, a matter of retaining the maximum number of options for the future; lost gene pools represent lost and irreplaceable biological "information." What kind of person would give a jigsaw puzzle to his child, having first thrown away, at random, twenty percent of the pieces? Yet we do exactly that sort of thing when we allow species to become extinct because of the actions of our fellow man. This, in outline, is the ecological rationale for the conservation of particular species; but there are other valid and important reasons.

Although the ecological justifications for conserving species carry more weight with the "tough-minded," those who treasure their sentiments and subjectivity as a mark and condition of human existence can be persuaded that there are other good reasons for preventing extinctions. In *The Savage Mind* Claude Lévi-Strauss pointed out that there is a basic human need for the intellectual activity of naming and classifying amidst the complexity of the natural world. "Classifying, as opposed to not classifying, has a value of its own," he writes; and he cites many examples of so-called savage peoples whose classification and knowledge extend to things that play *no practical role* in their lives. Conklin, whom he quotes, asserts that the Hanunoo tribe of the southern Philippines distinguishes 1625 plant types (corresponding to 1100 species in scientific botany), usually in a binomial nomenclature similar to our own system of botanical classification. Of these, only five to six hundred are edible, and 406 are medicinal. The rest are not lumped together as useless; they are named as carefully as the plants of obvious practical value.

One can extend this idea of Lévi-Strauss in another important direction. Not only is it a vital human function to classify, order, and arrange, but the richness of the natural world stimulates and encourages this propensity in a way that man-made environments fail to do. In the history of our own culture, European cities may once have provided an entirely acceptable partial substitute for this natural diversity—indeed, integrated as they were with their semi-natural surroundings, they offered a vast improvement over a wild existence. But cities have changed. Now, even if one accepts the substitute for natural diversity it does not seem wise to destroy the original, especially when the model-makers seem so clumsy, disorganized, and devoid of a sense of history. Those of us who have experienced a perfect late spring day in a mountain meadow, who can recall the color and movement of the flowers and grass stems, the sensation of a warm breeze and the touch of growing plants on the skin, the commingled sounds of insects and birds, the smell of moist earth mixed with nectar, and perhaps the taste of wild strawberries, will be loath to give all this up for a coarse and suspect promise of something better. Even those who know the flower colors only from Monet and the sounds of spring from Vivaldi may agree. If the mechanomorphs succeed entirely in removing the residual taint that still clings to the word "artificial," the degradation of humanity will have become complete—our descendants will all dwell in a fabricated world and probably, as far as their atrophied capacity for uniquely human response permits, they will like it.

Once, even for city dwellers, a myriad of birds, insects, small mammals, fish, reptiles, trees, flowers, lichens, ferns, and mosses, an infinite and harmonious variety of movements, responses, hues, shades, patterns, rhythms, tones, and textures were part of the world of men and blended with their activities. Today, the patterns are all likely to be composed of right angles, the movement is mechanical and dull, the textures have the monotonous, insubstantial quality of most plastic, the colors are few and garish, and everything seems to clash with everything else while man moves in the midst of his creations and plans an arrogant future. Not long ago I had an eighteen-year-old biology laboratory assistant who confessed, to my disbelief, that she had never before seen a live turtle. I thought that that was sad; but at least she liked the animal.

Finally, in considering the value of species, we must pause briefly to dispel a misconception. Anti-conservationists have come up with a new, fatalistic argument for complacency in the face of a wave of extinction. It goes something like this: "Why are we so concerned if a few unfit relics of the Pleistocene* fauna, animals such as the rhinoceros, are finally following the predestined path of the mammoth and other extinct creatures? Ninety-nine percent of the species that have ever lived on earth are extinct; extinction is a natural process, and we can't hold it back." It is difficult to take such monstrous nonsense seriously, but there are enough people who believe it to warrant a brief reply.

The rhinoceros (as well as other "examples" of this sort) was doing fine until one hundred years ago. If it was on the road to extinction (an unanswerable question) it was probably moving at the customary, dignified pace—measured in tens or hundreds of thousands of years. Besides, the world needs the rhinoceros, having nothing remotely like

---

* The Pleistocene epoch lasted from 1,000,000 to 10,000 years ago, and included the recent ice ages.

it to take its place. Having experienced the rhinoceros, if only in zoos, most people would save it if they could, and rightly so. If an intrepid explorer were to discover a small colony of living mammoths in central Greenland, would we hesitate a moment to feed and protect them, too? The economic value of the rhinoceros is irrelevant to this argument, but it does have one, and that fact can also be noted.

Furthermore, it is true that most animals that have ever lived are extinct, but this is an ongoing process that so far has taken several billion years. In this span of time, the history of man on earth is like a few seconds in a day. It does not take an expert to see that we are causing unprecedented wholesale exterminations of plant and animal species. Nevertheless, in a fit of exasperation I once made some calculations for some skeptics who had difficulty telling a glacier from an icicle. By these admittedly rough estimates, the current rate of extinction among most groups of mammals is approximately *a thousand times greater* than in the late Pleistocene, a geologic epoch distinguished by a "high" extinction rate. We are masters of extermination, yet creation is beyond our powers. Complacency in the face of this terrible dilemma is inexcusable.

Ecosystem Alteration

The principal cause of the loss of species is the alteration of the ecosystems in which they live. The *Red Data Books* of the International Union for the Conservation of Nature list hundreds of cases where man's alteration of the environment is causing the extinction of particular species—but two examples must suffice here. Both were chosen because they have had little attention to date, and deserve more.

Game and sport fish are among the most carefully tended and conserved of all natural resources, but the rest of our native fishes receive virtually no attention and a number have become extinct in recent years or are in danger of extinction. This is especially true of the freshwater fishes of the southwestern United States, where there is hardly a river or stream that has not been affected by the activities of man. Because aquatic habitats in the desert are isolated for long periods

"Graveyard" of extinct species, Bronx Zoo, "Earth Day," May 22, 1970. (Horst Schäfer—Photo Trends)

of time, punctuated infrequently by floods, the distribution pattern of the fishes of the Southwest once provided an exceptional opportunity for the study of evolution and the distribution of animals. Now the pattern has been thoroughly disrupted, often unnecessarily, and if anything like it still exists in the world, it is not in North America.

Biologists W. L. Minckley and James E. Deacon, who have made one of the most comprehensive studies of the current status of southwestern fishes, divide organisms into four general categories with respect to habitat needs:

1. Species having habitats produced by or changed by man, which have responded to man's influence by extending their range and abundance.

159

2. Organisms that have not responded to man's influence and which inhabit large geographic areas and are at present common.

3. Animals that require large special habitats.

4. Species living in small, unique habitats as relics or isolated endemics.

The first two categories are discussed elsewhere. The third and fourth approximate most closely the situation in the rivers, streams, and springs of the Southwest.

The alteration of natural aquatic communities in the Southwest has been so extensive that the widespread distribution of many of the fishes in category 3 offers them no protection. Were it not for historical records, a number of species that forty years ago occupied entire river systems would now be classified as peculiar local forms. For example, the Gila topminnow (*Poeciliopsis occidentalis*) formerly was found throughout the Gila River basin, and as late as 1941 was described as one of the most common fishes in the southern part of the Colorado River drainage. According to Minckley and Deacon, the Gila topminnow now "persists only in one spring area in Santa Cruz County, Arizona." Under the conditions that prevail today, categories 3 and 4 tend to merge, and it is no longer possible without prior information to distinguish between species whose range has been restricted naturally by geographic and ecologic barriers, and species whose range has been restricted recently by man. Because of the spotty distribution of many of the remaining species, the pattern of extinction is now as haphazard and unpredictable as man's activities in the region. Here and there, in a comparatively undisturbed creek or spring, a unique species or subspecies survives for the present, while others less fortunately situated disappear without fanfare.

The causes of the extinction of the southwestern desert fishes are as varied as the causes of the alteration of their habitat. Human population growth and agricultural and industrial development are rapidly outpacing the development of water resources, which is limited in the long run by the arid climate. After a certain point, which probably already has been reached in the Colorado River system, the construction of more dams in a river basin does nothing but juggle the existing supply of water about, giving it to some regions at the expense of others. Dams do not create water, and reservoirs waste it through evaporation and seepage into the porous rock. Because of the overconstruction of dams, many streams and rivers have become dry or have been reduced to a small trickle. Nearly all the surface run-off waters in the Southwest are now being used by man; this leaves long stretches of river bed below the dams where the remaining thin streams of water, often saline and polluted, must be supplied entirely by seepage of waste and irrigation discharge. The lakes above dams are similarly unsuitable for a number of local species that are adapted for life in turbulent clean-bottomed streams. In addition to surface waters, underground water supplies have been tapped extensively, resulting in a lowering of the water table. When the water table drops far enough, springs in the vicinity dry up; this has happened in many places. In some watersheds, twice as much water is being used each year as is being returned (through rainfall and waste outflow) to the underground reservoirs.

Clearly, this means that unless water is brought in from elsewhere, or unless population increase, industrial expansion, and agricultural growth are curtailed, the price of the current exploitation of southwestern water reserves will be paid in full by the next generation. Unfortunately, the native fauna has paid in advance, as so often happens in exploited environments.

Environmental alteration by man can be less obvious than the construction of dams. The Moapa dace (*Moapa coriacea*) was common in the Moapa River, Nevada, when Hubbs and Miller collected it in 1933, but it declined abruptly in the early 1950s. In this case, stream flow was unchanged and the physical environment had not visibly altered. Minckley and Deacon correlate the decline of the Moapa dace with the introduction of another fish, the shortfin molly (*Poecilia mexicana*): "The introduction of *P. mexicana* resulted in a decrease in the population density of *Moapa*, apparently through an increase in parasitism . . . and possibly through direct competitive interaction. A primary danger to *Moapa* is the possibility that additional introductions will cause another population decline from which it might not recover; such circumstances are not predictable." Another native fish being displaced by an exotic species is illustrated on the page opposite; the invader (the red shiner, *Notropis lutrensis*) is an aggressive fish that escapes from fishermen's bait buckets and subsequently spreads rapidly. Although the present manner of surface and subsurface water use is a debatable subject, the introduction of non-native species is not. It is a biologically hazardous undertaking whose effects—often deleterious—can be only partially known after extensive ecological study; pending such studies, introductions should be curtailed through public education and, if necessary, by law.

The plight of the indigenous fishes of the Southwest is especially serious because often the affected populations represent the entire gene pool of a species, not just a fragment of it. If these curious little desert fishes had been salmon or bass, there would undoubtedly be large organized groups of sportsmen clamoring for their protection. But they are not salmon or bass, and their loss impoverishes the environment only in subtle ways; by obscuring relationships of scientific significance, by further unbalancing delicate ecosystems, and by promoting the kind of biological uniformity that has an architectural counterpart in the deadly housing developments of the 1950s and 1960s. Unfortunately, the majority of the public has not been made aware of these considerations; if any of the threatened species are preserved in their natural environments, it will probably not be through direct action, but will be an indirect consequence of action taken to correct the seventy-five-year-old pattern of abuse of water resources.

Among the measures that might be taken are limitation of the rights of property owners pertaining to water resources and water use, regional coordination and regulation of irrigation throughout entire

(A) Present distribution of the introduced red shiner in the Gila River basin. (B) Present and past distribution of the native Gila spinedace. Gray circles are localities of former occurrence where the recent absence of the fish has been confirmed; open circles are localities that have not been reexamined; black circles are localities where the spinedace persists. (Modified after W. L. Minckley and J. Deacon, *Science 159* [1968], © American Association for the Advancement of Science, 1968)

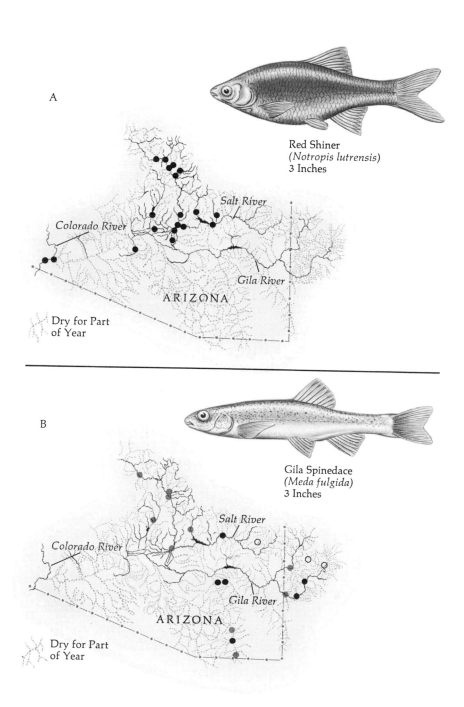

A

Red Shiner
(*Notropis lutrensis*)
3 Inches

Salt River

Colorado River

Gila River

ARIZONA

Dry for Part
of Year

B

Gila Spinedace
(*Meda fulgida*)
3 Inches

Salt River

Colorado River

Gila River

ARIZONA

Dry for Part
of Year

watersheds so as not to deplete the surface reserves or lower the water table, strict "zoning" of the other kinds of water use (also on a regional watershed basis), and the rapid implementation of a high-priority program to bring additional water from the north. Above all, the inhabitants of the Southwest will have to recognize that the population size and industrialization of their communities will soon be limited by the supply of water and that they will be more comfortable if they deal realistically with the situation in advance.

Like the fishes of the southwestern United States, the wild animals of India have suffered primarily from the destruction of their native ecosystems. Here a significant part of the fauna of an entire subcontinent has disappeared almost unnoticed. The decline has been particularly striking because India, like Africa, used to have extensive forests and savannas containing some of the most spectacular species in the world. Unlike Africa, however, India has done little to preserve its native fauna; were it not for the American field biologist and ethologist George B. Schaller, few would even be aware of the problem. Schaller, who first attracted wide attention with his book on the mountain gorilla, one of the earliest studies of the habits of a great ape in its natural environment, went to India to study the behavior and ecology of the native deer and the tiger but found himself increasingly involved in the gigantic problem of preserving Indian wildlife and wildlife habitats.

Although poaching and unrestricted hunting are now the immediate threat to many of the mammals and birds of India, these creatures would not be in such a precarious position were it not for the devastation of the Indian landscape. As an example, we can consider the present status of the Gir Forest, a "wildlife sanctuary" on the Kathiawar peninsula in western India near the Gulf of Cambay. The area of the Gir Forest is 483 square miles, but it is utilized by more than 7000 people and at least 57,000 domestic cattle, many of which are diseased and transmit their parasites to the wild ungulates, in addition to competing with them for food in the overgrazed forest. Tragically, the cattle of the Gir Forest and throughout India are of limited use to most of the inhabitants, who cannot kill them because of Hindu religious beliefs. In India domestic cattle are often the economic equivalent of giant rats, multiplying uncontrollably (like the human population) and devouring every blade of grass in their paths.

The Indian lion, a subspecies distinct from the more common African lion, once ranged widely from Asia Minor, Palestine, and Arabia to Persia and India; it is now largely confined to the Gir Forest. In 1960 it was estimated that there were 350 lions in the forest; in 1968, 162 were counted. The decline is occurring in spite of the lion's high reproductive potential (its gestation period is only 100 days), which might even be able to overcome the loss of 100 animals per year by poisoning were it not for the destruction of the forest itself. Because of the proliferation of cattle, both the vegetative cover and the deer that constitute the natural food of the lion are fast disappearing. Lee M. Talbot estimated in 1960 that "at the present rate of attrition the Gir should only last another 20 years. . . ." When the forest is gone, the world population of Indian lions will consist of approximately fifty animals distributed among a little more than a dozen zoos.

Sound wildlife management and habitat conservation are virtually unknown in India. According to Schaller: "The rare Indian wild dog is persecuted wherever it is found. In one park all these dogs were shot on sight because they destroyed deer. At the same time the deer were shot because they destroyed tree seedlings!" The most vivid example of wanton and unnecessary habitat destruction cited by Schaller is that of the Keoladeo Othana Sanctuary, which, like the great Nairobi National Park six miles from the capital of Kenya, is close enough to a large city, Agra, to be a potential major tourist attraction. Yet, this tiny eleven-square-mile patch of woods now contains more than 5600 head of cattle and buffalo and is rapidly becoming a wasteland. Ironically, India was probably the first nation on earth to practice land conservation and wildlife management: the late E. P. Gee, one of India's few noted conservationists, found that in the year 300 B.C. government decrees set aside certain areas where "the extraction of timber, burning of charcoal, collection of grass, fuel and leaves, the cutting of cane and bamboo, trapping for fur skins and tooth and bone were all totally prohibited." Since that time the sense of these regulations has been forgotten, and large parts of India have been lost to both man and

Status of some characteristic Indian species

Species	Description	Status	Cause of Decline
Bengal Tiger (*Panthera tigris tigris*)	The most numerous subspecies of a group nearing extinction everywhere else (Siberia, China, Java, etc.); the largest and handsomest of the big cats; habits poorly understood	Population in 1920 approximately 40,000; in 1969, less than 2500	Destruction of habitat and food supply; grossly excessive hunting; poisoning with agricultural pesticides
Snow Leopard (*Panthera uncia*)	A cat of the high Himalayas (12,000 ft. in summer); exceptionally beautiful gray-white fur much sought after. Habits poorly understood	Population in 1968, 200-600 (total for entire Himalayan range); totally protected in USSR; classified as "vermin" in Kashmir	Excessive hunting for fur (one of the few Indian animals not threatened by habitat destruction)
Asiatic Cheetah (*Acinonyx jubatus venaticus*)	A medium-sized, spotted cat, resident of open savannas; fastest-running mammal; valuable fur. Tames readily but has not been bred in captivity	Extinct in India; perhaps a few hundred remain in other parts of Asia	Destruction of habitat and food supply (blackbuck); excessive hunting
Blackbuck (*Antilope cervicapra*)	A graceful and striking medium-sized antelope; males with long spirally twisted horns; celebrated in Indian mythology; principal prey of the cheetah	Nearly extinct in most Indian states; very abundant 50 years ago	Habitat destruction and competition with cattle; grossly excessive hunting (were used as targets to sight-in rifles)
Gaur (*Bos gaurus*)	The Indian bison; largest of the world's wild cattle; prefers high, grassy tablelands; travels in herds of 5-20; secretive	Once fairly common; now much reduced in numbers	Seriously afflicted by rinderpest and foot-and-mouth disease transmitted by native cattle

Species	Description	Status	Causes
Manipur Brow-Antlered Deer (*Cervus eldi eldi*)	A medium-sized deer with unusual, stately antlers; tends to wander great distances; lives in the floating swamp of Logtak Lake in Manipur State	Declared extinct in 1951; re-discovered in 1952. Approximately 100 in 1968. May be increasing, thanks to impenetrability of habitat and vegetarian customs of nearby villagers. Manipur government taking steps to protect it	Habitat destruction; poaching and wild dogs, especially during unsettled conditions after World War II
Great Indian Rhinoceros (*Rhinoceros unicornis*)	Largest Asiatic rhinoceros; primarily confined to reserves in India and Nepal; subject of an unusually successful Indian conservation effort	About 700 in India and Nepal; stable population, but still threatened by competition with cattle for food, and by cattle diseases	Originally, habitat destruction; later, hunting. Much of its former habitat in west and northwest India now desert, because of bad agricultural practices
Pigmy Hog (*Sus salvanius*)	A tiny wild pig; full-grown boars were less than 12 in. high; a nocturnal forest animal of the Himalayan foothills	Rare and declining. Last seen in 1969 in the Tezpur area	Habitat destruction; possibly introduced diseases
Sloth Bear (*Melursus ursinus*)	A comical-looking, unaggressive bear; eats termites, grubs, and fruits, and snores loudly in sleep.	Greatly reduced in numbers; has retreated into the remaining forests	Habitat destruction
Pink-Headed Duck (*Rhodonessa caryophyllacea*)	A unique and beautiful bird, perhaps related to American canvasback; confined to swampy jungle	*Extinct.* A wild bird was last shot in 1935; last captive specimen died in Britain in 1944. The Indian government passed a law protecting it in 1956(!) Was never common	Drainage of swamp habitat; market hunting

167

nature through indiscriminate lumbering and overgrazing, leading in turn to desiccation of the remaining vegetation, fire, and massive soil erosion. Crowded into patchy and ever-contracting fragments of the original landscape, the last representatives of India's fauna fall easy prey to poachers from all social classes, whose activities are totally unregulated (see table, pp. 166-67). This, then, is perhaps the bleakest chapter of the whole conservation story. Remedies could be suggested, but that would be to introduce what seems a fatuous note of optimism. India's problems are too immense and intertwined to be attacked piecemeal, and even if a concerted effort were possible, it is hard to see how it could accrue enough force in time to oppose the gathering momentum of the landslide.

The fates of the southwestern U.S. fishes and the wildlife of India provide one lesson in common: the widespread and often preventable destruction of natural communities and subsequent general loss of species foreshadows and often is accompanied by severe environmental problems for the human inhabitants of the region, regardless of their technology. If the other motives and objectives for maintaining the diversity of the environment fall on deaf ears, this ominous correlation at least should provoke concern.

The Pet Trade, Zoos, and Medical Institutions

Habitat destruction is the most significant cause of species extinctions, but by no means the only one. The destruction of habitat usually effects an overall reduction in the number of species present; but particular species can be endangered in a variety of ways, even within relatively intact communities.

One of the most unrelenting and insidious drains on remaining stocks of wild animals (and occasionally plants) is the collecting of live specimens for the pet trade. A surprising variety of species are threatened, including such unlikely and unsuitable "pets" as sea turtles (which require facilities beyond the reach of nearly all reptile fanciers), ocelots (which after being declawed, castrated, and confined become pitiful caricatures of a superb animal), and monkeys (which are too destructive to be allowed to roam free around a house, too intelligent to be closely confined, and too fragile to survive the dietary and climatic abuse that is usually their lot in captivity).

The sale of wild animals as pets has become big business, especially in the United States. In June 1968, the pet trade was described by William G. Conway, general director of the New York Zoological Society (which includes the Bronx Zoo and the New York Aquarium):

> Although the exotic pet trade has tangible and intangible values it must be regulated. Many wild animal populations can withstand well-managed collecting but many rare forms cannot. Moreover, exceptionally delicate or highly specialized animals must not be sold as personal pets whether they are rare or common. The problem is one of cruelty as much as conservation. A few days ago, as I wandered through the pet department of a local five-and-ten-cent store, I happened upon a terrarium filled with "common" horned lizards.
>
> The trade in horned lizards has been going on for decades. . . . The unforgivably immoral nature of this piece of commercialization is that horned lizards almost invariably starve to death after a few weeks in captivity. This tells us something about the character of the exotic pet trade for it is well known that horned lizards have highly specialized and poorly understood food and temperature requirements, which few pet buyers could hope to meet.

Among the rare and delicate species sold in New York pet stores Conway has seen golden-headed quetzals, South American cocks-of-the-rock, equatorial barbets, Indonesian fairy bluebirds, South American hummingbirds, Saki monkeys, Malayan flying lizards, tamanduas (arboreal anteaters), three-toed sloths, uncommon species of parrots, and Texas tortoises. If such importations were unusual, it would be a matter for concern only in the case of those species whose total population size is of the order of a few hundred or thousand individuals. But the magnitude of the traffic in wild animals is staggering. In 1967 the U.S. Fish and Wildlife Service reported that among imports into the United States were 74,304 mammals, 203,189 birds (not including parrot-family birds and canaries), 405,134 reptiles, 137,697 amphibians, and 27,759,332 fish. When one adds to this the annual totals for other pet-loving countries such as Great Britain and Germany, it is easy to see why species are threatened by the pet trade.

The wild animal import figures (for those countries that keep them) show only a fraction of the impact of this self-destructive industry because many, often most, and sometimes all wild animals being shipped from one country to another die during capture or en route. For example, incomplete figures for nine months of 1962 show that Ethiopia exported 40,000 birds. How many died during and immediately after capture but before export is not known; we can guess that the number is of the same order of magnitude as the 40,000 that survived to be counted. How many of the birds reached pet stores alive is also not known, but 20,000 is probably an overestimate.

The Amazon basin, usually thought of as an immense reservoir of wild country and wild species, has already been mentioned as an example of an area in which the pet trade has seriously eroded the native fauna. Endangered species and populations include jungle cats, many kinds of rare monkeys and marmosets, alligatorlike caimen (sold as baby "alligators" in the United States), birds of many descriptions, a variety of small mammals, and tropical fish. According to Charles W. Quaintance, of Eastern Oregon College: "The native Indians who hunt the animals were reported to be penetrating deeper and deeper into the forest to secure their specimens which they sold daily to the honorary U.S. Consul at Leticia, Colombia, and he, in turn, shipped out great quantities of animals without any regard for their increasing scarcity." Other major ports of exit for Amazon animal shipments are Manaos, Brazil, and Iquitos, Peru.

It has been argued that maintenance of the pet trade is essential to the Indian economy of the Amazon region; however, it is doubtful whether any economy has, in the long run, benefited from an industry that operates by permanently destroying local resources. Whether one is referring to diamonds and gold in the Matto Grosso, to farmland in South Dakota, or to wildlife in the Amazon basin, the North and South American Indians have never profited from external exploitation, and it is the grossest hypocrisy to promote an unregulated exploitative trade on the grounds that it is in their behalf.

Zoos are an ancient institution in the civilized world, and their quality is judged by the strangeness of the animals they exhibit. Until 1967 many zoos competed openly for rare and endangered species. Although this undoubtedly resulted in saving a few species that could be bred in captivity, the high prices paid for rare animals also had the undesirable effect of subsidizing the legitimate or clandestine activities of wild animal collectors and dealers. The result was a vicious circle of diminishing populations, rising prices, and increasing pressure to collect more specimens. The circle was finally interrupted, largely because of the conservation activities of Barbara Harrisson of Malaysia, who publicized the rapidly deteriorating status of the orangutan (Pongo pygmaeus), one of the four major types of great ape still existing in the world and among the closest relatives of man.

The great nineteenth-century naturalist and zoogeographer Alfred Russel Wallace supplied unknowingly all the reasons why the orangutan would be nearing extinction a century after the publication in 1869 of his book, The Malay Archipelago: The Land of the Orang-Utan and the Bird of Paradise. Wallace wrote: "It is very remarkable that an animal so large, so peculiar, and of such a high type of form as the Orang-Utan, should be confined to so limited a district—to two islands [Sumatra and Borneo]. . . . Now it seems to be probable, that a wide extent of unbroken and equally lofty virgin forest is necessary to the comfortable existence of these animals." In pointing out the orangutan's restricted range and highly specific ecological requirements, Wallace provided the key to its vulnerability. He also stated: "I have myself examined the bodies of seventeen freshly-killed orangs . . . ," foreshadowing the more extensive and less justifiable slaughter that was to follow. By 1966 the extensive destruction of habitat and the activities of animal collectors (including many members of the Indonesian Army) had reduced the total orangutan population to approximately 5000. The demand for baby orangs by pet dealers, medical institutions, and zoos increased steadily during the 1960s. Since the common method of collecting baby orangs involves shooting the mother, and since one in six infants survives this experience, it is easy to see why the continued existence of the species is in doubt.

Although it is now questionable whether orangutans will be able to survive in the wild, the publicity attending the plight of these shy, vegetarian animals has had two beneficial results. First, it was discovered by Mrs. Harrisson that Section 43, Title 18 of the United States Code states that "transportation of wildlife taken in violation of State, National, *or foreign laws* [my italics]" is a crime, and that a person convicted of this crime "shall be fined not more than $500 or imprisoned not more than six months, or both; and the wild animals or birds, or the dead bodies or parts thereof, or the eggs of such birds, shall be forfeited." With this law in the statute books of the major purchaser of orangutans, it remained only for Mrs. Harrisson to locate or secure passage of protective laws in each of the countries that exported the animals. With such "foreign laws" in effect, entry into the United States was automatically prohibited, and the major market was closed. Indonesia, Sarawak, and Sabah now have the necessary laws. They may be too late to preserve the orang, but this important legal precedent provides the means for protecting other domestic and foreign wildlife. Another U.S. law, the Wildlife Preservation Act of 1969, enables the Secretary of the Interior to publish a list of endangered species and prevent importation of these animals or their products. The law is technically imperfect, however, and has proved a poor deterrent to the trade in endangered species or populations of animals.

Second, partly because of the efforts of Mrs. Harrisson and other conservationists, the American Association of Zoological Parks and Aquariums, meeting in Mexico City on March 14, 1967, took self-regulatory action to control the international traffic in endangered species. The voting member zoos agreed unanimously not to purchase, accept as a gift, sell, or trade any orangutans, monkey-eating eagles, Javan and Sumatran rhinoceroses, Galapagos and Aldabran giant tortoises, or any other rare species that may be added to the list by a two-thirds vote of the membership unless the AAZPA Subcommittee on Endangered Species approves the specific case. Although clandestine violations still occur, the agreement has been moderately effective.

Medical institutions and medical researchers have never been particularly concerned about the sources of their experimental animals; the

Young wild orangutan, Sarawak. Among our closest relatives, but little studied in the wild, orangutans live in a virgin forest habitat that is fast disappearing. (Courtesy Barbara Harrisson—© Sarawak Museum)

flourishing trade in stolen dogs and cats testifies to this in the United States. The demands of medical research are placing an increasingly heavy burden on wild stocks of certain animals—particularly primates. According to Conway: "In 1967, 65,526 wild primates, mostly for laboratory research, were imported into the United States." The yearly total has, on occasion, risen above 200,000. The consumption of wild primates for medical research now threatens many kinds of monkeys and most species of great apes, including the chimpanzee, the most numerous, whose total population is less than 250,000. Medical researchers are often thoughtlessly wasteful when working with wild animals, a habit that may be due partly to prior experiences with the inexhaustible supplies of laboratory rats and mice and partly to ignorance. Quaintance reports that biologists at a wildlife conference in Colombia cited the case of a medical research team from the United States that killed more than 400 monkeys, mostly howlers, in order to examine their aortas, but made no other use of the bodies. Nearly all species of monkeys and apes used in medical research will breed in captivity; however, few laboratories have assumed the responsibility of renewing the resource that they are so rapidly destroying. The purchase by laboratories of wild-caught primates should be prohibited unless they are to be used as breeding stock.

Not all the abuse of wild-caught research animals has occurred in strictly medical laboratories. At the Marine Biological Laboratories at Woods Hole, Massachusetts, sea urchin (*Arbacia*) eggs have been used for many years in a wide variety of biological experiments. The dead sea urchins are discarded after their eggs have been physically or chemically removed. This kind of careless waste of animals probably played a major role in the severe depletion of sea urchins and other marine invertebrates in the waters around Woods Hole (although there has been a recent recovery of sea urchin populations as investigators turn to other organisms). In contrast, the marine laboratory at Friday Harbor, Washington, usually obtains its sea urchin (*Strongylocentrotus*) eggs by allowing the captured animals to release them spontaneously into the water of the holding tanks. The sea urchins are then returned to the underwater area where they originated, and that area is left undisturbed for a year or more. There has never been a shortage of sea urchins at Friday Harbor.

Neither biomedical researchers nor anyone else will benefit from the extinction of the animals they need and use. Moreover, the exigencies of research do not justify an inadequate conservation policy, because conservation and research are perfectly compatible if a little foresight and planning are exercised.

Museum Collecting

The hunting, by trapping or shooting, of specimens for museum collections sometimes constitutes an important drain on populations of endangered species. According to Conway: "A 1962 estimate of the number of mammal skins in some 307 public and private collections was 1,586,000. The American Museum of Natural History alone has nearly a million bird skins in its permanent collection." Fortunately, most (but not all) contemporary vertebrates are already well represented in museum collections, and the analysis of existing material now occupies more time than collecting expeditions. When collections are made, it is generally with more care than in the past, although occasional excesses do still occur.

By and large, the collection of museum specimens is more than justified by the scientific value of the collection. It is important, however, that museum scientists be aware of the population status of the species in which they are interested. Hopefully, if a responsible collecting policy is adopted by both individuals and institutions, we may never again witness depredations like the California Academy of Science's 1906 Galapagos expedition, in which, for example, eighty-six giant tortoises, constituting at least forty percent of the living members of one species, were removed from the three-mile-wide Duncan Island.

Personal Collecting

Zoo and museum collecting can cause occasional damage to wild populations, but at least these institutions serve essential functions and their curators are generally aware of the waste involved in overcollecting. A much greater threat to species conservation is posed by the individual collector, ever bent on increasing his raggedy stock of live, half-dead, or preserved specimens.

The personal collector is a complex and curious creature. One feels compelled to write about him as if he were suffering from a disease; in extreme cases this may indeed be true. It is tempting to try to define the personality type of the collector (modifiers such as "insecure," "fussy," and "anal" come to mind), but I am not really qualified to undertake such a technical job. Perhaps some day a psychiatrist with nothing better to do will write up a series of cases for a medical journal and speculate professionally on the role of mother and father in the etiology of the condition; indeed perhaps one already has. All I can do here is describe the collector's syndrome and hope that any reader who feels personally affronted will be mollified by the confession that I write from firsthand experience.

First of all, the collector collects. He does so at every opportunity. If he is not collecting, but could be, he feels guilty and anxious; this feeling is temporarily relieved by collecting, much as milk relieves ulcer pain. If others are collecting, the anxiety is increased; at this level it is alleviated only by a "great find" or by the failure of everyone else. Characteristically, "great finds" confer only the most temporary and fleeting satisfaction.

Most collectors collect a variety of items, including such unlikely forms of solid waste as bottle caps, matchbooks, discarded fragments of disintegrated machinery, and bits of brightly colored glass. Here we are concerned only with animal (and plant) collecting; other types are usually much less objectionable.

Among wild animals nearly everything is fair game. The list of types of creatures collected is so long that only the most common categories are indicated here, as follows: (1) dangerous or reputedly dangerous animals, including poisonous snakes of all kinds and temperaments, tarantula spiders, Gila monsters, and scorpions; (2) animals that most persons would consider loathsome, repulsive, or just disgustingly ugly, including cockroaches, slugs, and mata matas; (3) extreme animals, those with an exaggerated feature or characteristic that makes them unusual, including legless lizards and amphibians, leaf-nosed bats, pythons, giant anteaters, and pygmy owls; (4) cute, beautiful, attractive, or intriguing animals, including marmosets, box turtles, butterflies, indigo snakes, and land snails; (5) defined biological categories or groups of animals, such as all monitor lizards, all African finches, and all dung beetles; and (6) rare or hard-to-find animals, including bog turtles, peregrine falcons, bush babies, and island-dwelling lorikeets.

Naturally if an animal falls into several categories at once it is apt to be collected widely. Among vertebrates, the reptiles seem especially prized, although animals so different as snakes, lizards, crocodilians, and turtles will each attract a particular subtype of collector.

The fate of collected animals in the hands of their discoverers is one of the most curious features of the syndrome. Considering the triumph experienced after a successful collection, one might think that the specimen would be valued above rubies. It is not. After an initial bout of gloating it is likely to be ignored. In the case of a dead specimen, it may never be looked at again. If it is, it is usually not studied with profit or described in the scientific literature. Live animals may either languish or receive sumptuous care (at least until the next prize is collected), but collected animals hardly ever reproduce themselves in captivity. Thus the net result, even after the typical collector's "breeding program," is a loss to the population from which the animals were taken. The true collector has too many animals to care for them properly; if he trades animals they may not be in one place long enough to become inured to captivity.

The rule of numbers prevails in collecting. Two is more and therefore better than one. Ten is much better than two. "Good" collecting is not constrained by practical considerations; one rarely meets a collector who is satisfied with less than all. Thus every now and then the Sunday feature page carries a story about Miss Jukes or Mr. Kallikak who has thirty-four turtles in a three-bedroom house in Palo Alto, California, and is anxiously seeking new specimens. Restraint, especially while actively collecting, is unheard of.

By most societal norms animal collecting is considered a somewhat

strange activity, and many collectors have evolved justifications for
it. Perhaps the most realistic of these is the profit motive, although
frequently the proceeds of an animal sale are used just to support
more collecting. Education is another claimed benefit; no doubt this
is also true, but the kind of education gained is too often relevant
primarily to collecting. The amateur naturalist can learn as much from
keeping a single snake at a time as the harried collector can glean
from twenty. Finally, there is the indignant response encountered
among biologists who also happen to be personal collectors that their
activity has scientific value. Occasionally this is quite true; often it is
not. It seems apparent to everyone but these collectors that mere
mindless, compulsive acquisition, regardless of the neatness of the
specimen labels, may be of no use whatever to anyone. Even more
objectionable is the implication, thinly veiled in these arguments, that
the advance of scientific knowledge justifies any activity of scientists,
regardless of consequences. As a corollary to all justifications, every
collector insists that his own collecting does not jeopardize local populations or species of animals.

The results of personal collecting can be disastrous, particularly to
populations and communities that have already been severely stressed.
A good example is provided by Payne's Prairie in northern Florida near
Gainesville, a fifty-square mile sunken savanna-grassland with watery
sloughs and marshy places. It was once filled with a huge and bewilder-
ing array of snakes (mostly non-poisonous). In 1941, after a hurricane
had flooded the lowlands, Archie Carr counted 723 live and freshly
killed snakes on a two-mile stretch of road through Payne's Prairie.
Today two superhighways cross the Prairie. Except for a relative
paucity of snakes, there are few conspicuous changes. But one can
now drive across on a summer day without seeing one snake, nearly
an impossibility in the past. What has changed? The highways are a
likely culprit, but they hardly account for the whole decline in so
vast an area. But there is another factor: virtually every night for
thirty-five years the Prairie was crisscrossed by the beams of powerful
flashlights, as collectors from neighboring towns, from the University
of Florida, and from all over the United States prowled about, lured by

the fabulous and once-deserved reputation of Payne's Prairie as a haven for snakes.

Personal collecting may seem to occupy a disproportionate amount of space in these pages; but this is not because of a vendetta against collectors. Personal collecting is worth attention, not only because of the actual threat to wild populations, but because of the implications of the collecting syndrome. In a way, the world of personal collecting is a microcosm in which some of the larger questions of man and conservation can be studied to advantage.

The most surprising and distressing aspect of overcollecting is that the collector is frequently highly educated; often he is a biologist, fully aware of the meaning of the concept of an endangered population. Intellectually he knows that there is good reason not to pick up that handsome Agassiz's tortoise. It looks better in the desert than it will in a terrarium, its kind are growing scarce in most places, and it will probably fare poorly in captivity anyway. Yet into the bag it goes. Alternatively, our collector-biologist is also aware that he does not really need the thirty-first bat that flies into his mist net that evening. His tropical ecology students will learn enough from the thirty bats they have already sacrificed for stomach content analysis. Yet as long as there are bats around, the mist net stays up.

There are usually at least two ways to explain this odd departure from common sense: first, it is difficult to believe that the removal of one tortoise from a desert or the thirty-first bat from a jungle will make any difference. Naturally this is true, but since every collector thinks in the same fashion the numbers have a curious way of adding up. This is Garrett Hardin's concept of the "tragedy of the commons," which will come up again later, in a different context.

Second, there is the problem of ego. Collecting is gratifying to the collector. By assigning himself goals that can occasionally and unexpectedly be fulfilled, he achieves a satisfaction he may not find in the routine competitions and affairs of life. His "great finds" are infrequent, which means he has achieved something memorable and difficult; moreover the discoveries are unexpected, which means he has good luck, magical powers, that fortunately do not demand close analysis. Few people with such personal motivations can release an animal they have collected, especially with so many good rationalizations close at hand. (The same argument can apply to purchases in a pet store or to excessive hunting.)

Here, then, is representation in miniature of one of the central problems of conservation. The same ego that can make a collector collect against his better judgment can make an engineer fight for and build a dam he knows is unnecessary and ecologically unsound, or compel an agricultural scientist to accept an insecticide manufacturer's generous research grant when he knows that only one kind of experimental result will make his benefactor happy. Indeed, the individual egos of men are ultimately conservation's worst problem.

With such an array of powerful motives driving them on, it is not surprising that personal collectors are so resistant to self-restraint or external persuasion. Short of well-enforced legislation to protect specific populations (and enforcement is often impossible to carry out), about the only corrective methods that seem to be left to the conservationist are the ancient practices of exposure and ridicule of irrational behavior.

Hunting

The per capita demand for many animal products has decreased in the twentieth century as a result of the development of industrial technology and subsequent manufacture of synthetic materials derived from wood, coal, and oil. In some cases, however, the favorable impact on animal populations of this decrease has been more than offset by the increase in human population and the increased market for luxury items in some countries. Thus, although whale oil is no longer needed for lamps, whale meat is now used in some of the noncereal pet foods available in Europe and the United States. Two species—the blue whale and the green turtle—currently near extinction because of exploitation by animal products industries will be discussed later.

Among the various causes of species destruction, many of the animal products industries deserve special notice because they take advantage of scarcity of a species to increase demand and raise prices. Even in the early part of this century, when animal populations were much greater and human populations were smaller and poorer, short-lived fads for animal products brought several species to the verge of extinction. The craze for egret and ostrich feathers during the late 1800s and early 1900s nearly succeeded in wiping out a number of species of these once abundant birds. As Vinzenz Ziswiler has written in his excellent book, *Extinct and Vanishing Animals,* "When we consider that in the single year of 1912 more than 160 tons of ostrich feathers were sold in France alone, it becomes distressingly clear how close the African ostrich (*Struthio camelus*) came to falling a victim to women's whimsey. Fortunately, shortly before this fate was realized it became possible to meet the demand through ostrich farms, and in due time, much to the sorrow of the African ostrich-breeders the fashions changed." Similarly, the American egret (*Casmerodius albus*) was saved just in time by the same change of fashion and by the actions of groups like the Audubon Society and individuals like E. A. McIlhenny, who turned part of his vast Louisiana land holdings into a bird sanctuary where the egrets could effectively be protected and their habits studied.

Also saved in time by the death of a fad was the diamondback terrapin (*Malaclemys terrapin*), an inhabitant of Atlantic coastal salt marshes. The diamondback's northern and southern subspecies were relished by gourmets after the turn of the century. Archie Carr writes: "Originally so abundant that eighteenth-century tidewater slaves once struck for relief from a diet too heavy in terrapin, the diamondback gradually found a place on the tables of the privileged, and during the roseate period that extended from the heyday of Diamond Jim Brady to the close of the First World War it came to be surrounded by an aura of superlative elegance as synthetic as a latest Paris fashion." In 1891 the total catch in the Chesapeake Bay area was estimated at 89,150 pounds valued at $20,559; by 1920 the total catch had fallen to 823 pounds worth $1000. In 1921 the attractive six-inch turtles were selling for as much as $90 a dozen in Savannah. As with the ostrich, commercial breeding "farms" were established, but the real relief for

Diamondback terrapin in a salt marsh. This attractive little turtle was nearly exterminated by the demands of the luxury soup market. (Jack Dermid— Courtesy National Audubon Society)

the diamondbacks came when the fad expired during the Great Depression. Terrapin populations have now recovered slightly in some localities such as Connecticut and Maryland but these animals came very close to extinction.

At present, there are few species that can resist the fur and hide industries the way the egret resisted the feather hunters and the diamondback terrapin resisted the restaurant demand. Snow leopard furs are still being advertised and sold by some furriers, despite the fact that there are scarcely enough snow leopards left in all the Himalayas to provide a hundred coats. New tiger coats are still on sale in the United States even though there are now less than 2500 Bengal tigers in India and scarcely 500 tigers in all of Southeast Asia, China, Siberia, and the Transcaspian region. Many other cats are endangered by the fur trade; virtually none of the large or showy varieties is safe at the time of this writing. For example, when the price paid to the hunter for an ocelot hide rose to $100 on the Costa Rican coast in 1967-68, many able-bodied men stopped what they were doing, bought rolls of piano wire, and turned to setting choke snares in the bush. In 1967 the U.S. Customs Department passed 115,458 ocelot skins alone. But cats are not the only animals used by these industries; the vicuña, a camel-like inhabitant of the Central Andean plateau, has fallen in numbers from 400,000 in 1957 to less than 10,000 in 1968. Its especially fine wool now commands $25 a pound; one vicuña has one-third to one-half a pound of wool. According to the conservationist Peter Scott, a single British firm is importing two tons of vicuña wool

Snow leopard in the Hindu Kush, Pakistan, 7500 feet. Perhaps the only photograph of this rare cat in the wild. Still coveted for their fur, only a few hundred remain. (G. Schaller—Bruce Coleman, Inc.)

a year. There is good evidence to indicate that the vicuña would respond well to wildlife management or semi-domestication for commercial purposes, yet the Peruvian and Bolivian governments are only now beginning to explore this possibility. As is common practice in the fur and hide industries, commercially profitable conservation measures are rarely initiated before the wild resource has been exhausted.

Unlike the vogue for feathers or the fleeting popularity of certain furs, the public's desire for reptile leathers has been sustained, with minor ups and downs, for many years. The greater part of the hunting pressure has fallen on the Nile crocodile, the South American caiman, and the American alligator. The situation of the Nile crocodile is illustrative of the problems with all crocodilians. Hugh B. Cott of Cambridge University's Museum of Zoology has studied the ecology of these animals and describes the difficulty of protecting them:

> The main immediate threat to the crocodile's survival comes from the techniques now employed by professional hunters. Working at night in fast motor boats, these men easily locate their quarry in the beam of a powerful spot-light, approach at speed, shoot at point-blank range and gaff the dying animal before it can sink. Against this form of attack the crocodile has virtually no defense . . . as the supply fails elsewhere, the crocodiles that remain hitherto preserved in reserves and national parks offer an irresistible attraction.

Cott has recently found that poachers in Uganda's Murchison Falls Park have reduced the once prodigious number of crocodiles to about 250 nesting females; overpopulation of storks, baboons, monitor lizards, hyenas, and mongooses, the result of ecological imbalance, threatens the few eggs and young that are still produced. Unfortunately, the crocodiles killed by poachers are drawn almost entirely from the breeding population. In areas of heavy crocodile hunting, the remaining animals are almost all too young to breed. This is a classical sign of overhunting.

The Nile crocodile is an important member of a major African ecosystem; like the alligator it benefits fishing as well as the tourist industry. But as Cott points out, the future of the species is in doubt if the

Nile crocodile, Africa. Not yet in danger of extinction, but declining rapidly, these crocodiles share the fate of all reptiles that are hunted for their hides. (Norman Myers—Bruce Coleman, Inc.)

hide industry continues to mine this resource like an exhaustible metal deposit rather than crop the surplus in a regulated way so that the crocodile population can be maintained for future use. Although it is hardly necessary to repeat the justification for the conservation of species each time a new species is mentioned, Cott's statement on this subject deserves quotation:

> Crocodiles essentially like the modern species existed in Jurassic times [150 million years ago] and were contemporaries of the dinosaurs. As the only remaining members of the archosaurian stock which have survived the age of reptiles, they are of quite exceptional scientific importance, not least from the indirect light

185

Piles of ridley sea turtle shells near a beach in Oaxaca State, Mexico. Only the skin of the foreflippers has been taken for the shoe and handbag industry; tons of meat and thousands of eggs are left to rot in the sun. (Courtesy Herbert M. Eder)

which studies of anatomy, physiology, ecology and behaviour can throw upon the biology of ancestors long extinct. It would be a grave loss to science and research, and to posterity, if these saurians—which have survived for over a hundred million years —were now to be sacrificed to the demands of uninformed public opinion, and subordinated to a passing fashion in leather goods.

In the mid-1960s the leather trade began to process and sell (at very high prices) women's handbags and shoes made of sea turtle skin. Since a new market was created by advertising, this introduction of another source of reptile leather did nothing to relieve the hunting pressure on the crocodilian and lizard populations. Furthermore, the world populations of sea turtles of all species were already dangerously low, too low to support the demands of the reptile leather market. Evidently the industry saw this merely as an opportunity to make a quick profit in a previously unexploited area—nothing more.' The piles of hundreds of female Pacific ridley turtles (*Lepidochelys olivacea*) illegally killed on Mexican and Central American beaches still attest to this unscrupulous policy; in many cases, only the skin of the fore-flippers is taken, while the carcasses, amounting to tons of edible meat and thousands of fertile eggs—the future of the species—are left to rot in the sun.

Game hunting is an ancient human activity, probably as old as our species. There are still races and tribes of man who must hunt to live, but the vast majority of us do not depend on a gun, a spear, or a bow to bring home dinner. Nevertheless, hunting survives and flourishes as a sport in all technologically advanced countries, particularly in the United States, which, more than any other nation, has glorified its recent frontier history.

If properly regulated, game hunting is primarily a conservation activity. It serves to control the population sizes of animals such as deer, squirrels, and rabbits that would tend to multiply excessively in the absence of their original predators. Hunting provides revenue—through the purchase of duck stamps and hunting licenses and sales taxes on sports equipment—to run many governmental conservation activities. Most important, good hunters are familiar with natural environments, recognize both their unique value and precarious balance, and are often eager to work as a group to prevent them from being ruined. In an increasingly urban world, game hunters form an essential link between the natural earth and the constructed earth—two realms that can be separated only at the peril of both.

However, there remain abuses of hunting which threaten to cloud the image of the sport and to damage species. With a few exceptions, the hunting of "big game" is no longer a reasonable activity in the modern world; yet a handful of wealthy men are willing to risk causing the extinction of entire species for the sake of a few trophies. A notorious example of this befouling of an ancient sport is the hunting of polar bears in Alaska. The bears are spotted by plane, and the "sportsman" is then landed at a convenient (and safe) spot to await the arrival of the bear, which may be driven into his gunsights by another plane. One result is a bearskin—to which a real hunter would be ashamed to lay claim; another is that the state of Alaska becomes richer by a few thousand dollars left behind by the free-spending tourist. The polar bear population in Alaska is rapidly dwindling to extinction (female polar bears breed only once every three years; hence the recuperative abilities of the population are low). Fortunately, both Canada and the Soviet Union have taken steps to protect the polar bear in their territories, but it is a national scandal that the people of the United States should permit the loss of one of their most exciting and magnificent native animals for lack of federal legislation to control the irresponsible actions of a single state.

Similar abuses of good hunting practice still occur in Africa, where big game is occasionally chased down and shot by hunters in planes, but an increasing number of persons on safari have discovered that after the thrill and danger of stalking a rhino in the traditional manner, the most rewarding shot may be with a camera. For those who insist on a trophy, several African national parks and conservation departments issue restricted hunting licenses as a way of reducing local surpluses of potentially destructive animals such as elephants.

Other difficulties crop up besides the hunting of inappropriate prey and the use of unsporting "overkill" aids like airplanes. In North America, Canadian and U.S. conservation officials have often been weak and derelict in their duties in the face of direct demands and indirect political pressures applied by vocal minority groups of hunters. Thus, according to Glen Sherwood in a carefully documented article in *Audubon*, it is now legal to hunt the smaller race of the noble sandhill crane in New Mexico, Texas, Colorado, Oklahoma, North and South Dakota, Alaska, and the Canadian provinces of Saskatchewan and Manitoba. The magnificent whistling swan is legally shot in Utah, Nevada, and Montana. Crippling rates (birds shot but

Leopard head trophies in Nairobi, Kenya. (Loomis Dean—*Life* Magazine, © Time Inc.)

not downed and recovered) average approximately a third of the known kill, and illegal hunting boosts the total much higher. Government wildlife officials claim that hunting permits will be halted if bird populations decline; but since the population dynamics of these precarious species have not adequately been studied, their bland assurances are as worthless as they are dishonest. Preliminary evaluation by ecologists already indicates that the whistling swan may not be able to survive the challenge of legal hunting in North America.

In some countries where the army has considerable leisure time to spend in wilderness areas, or where soldiers can contrive to keep their weapons after they leave the service, a new danger has arisen. No hunted species or natural community can withstand a heavy influx of armed men, especially if ammunition is free. It was pointed out earlier that the Indonesian Army in Sumatra constitutes a severe threat to the survival of the orangutan; similarly, in many Central and South American countries soldiers and ex-soldiers hunt with submachine

Some animals hunted for superstitious reasons

Species	Range	Estimated population	Superstition
Somali Wild Ass (*Equus asinus somalicus*)	Ethiopia, Somali Republic	200 in Ethiopia; 10-12 in Somalia	Fat cures tuberculosis
Javan Rhinoceros (*Rhinoceros sondaicus*)	Java	50	Every part of the body is used for medicinal purposes in south and east Asia
Snub-Nosed Monkey (*Rhinopithecus roxellanae*)	Northwest China	Unknown, but very small	Fur used (formerly?) to prevent rheumatism
Chinese Tiger (*Panthera tigris amoyensis*)	China	Unknown, but very small	Bones impart vitality and strength
Barbary Hyaena (*Hyaena hyaena barbara*)	Morocco	400-500	Mane hairs used in black magic; brain has medicinal qualities
Giant Armadillo (*Periodontes giganteus*)	Eastern South America	Unknown	Claws possess magical powers
Shansi Sika (a deer, *Cervus nippon grassianus*)	Shansi region (China)	Unknown; probably extinct	Antler velvet has aphrodisiac properties
West Indian Manatee (sea cow, *Trichechus manatus manatus*)	Coasts and coastal rivers of Gulf of Mexico and Caribbean	Several thousand	Bones used as charms
Imperial Woodpecker (*Campephilus imperialis*)	Sierra Madre (Mexico)	Unknown; probably almost extinct	Has medicinal value
Hawaiian Crow (*Corvus tropicus*)	Mt. Hualalai (Hawaii)	250	Feathers once used for dressing idols
Green Turtle (*Chelonia mydas*)	Pan-tropical	Unknown, but decreasing rapidly	Eggs thought to have aphrodisiac properties throughout Latin America

guns or semiautomatic weapons, and the damage is compounded by the fact that they generally shoot at anything that moves—even the smaller songbirds. Finally, according to the *New York Times* (September 13, 1968), "One of the biggest losers of the Vietnam war has been the elephant of the Central Highlands and northern provinces, which is frequently shot down by patrols and by machine-gun fire from helicopter. . . . Many South Vietnamese officials are concerned about what [they] call the indiscriminate shooting of elephants from the air." Other Vietnamese, Cambodian, and Laotian animals that have been killed or driven into less suitable habitats include deer, tigers, rhinoceroses, monkeys, wild boar, and many species of birds.

A wide variety of animals are hunted for superstitious reasons, in the belief that their fur, skin, bones, or other parts will have medicinal or magical powers (see table, opposite page). Although such beliefs occur among most of the human populations of the world, the demands of Chinese medicine have placed the greatest strain on threatened species. The Asiatic rhinoceroses have been particularly hard hit. According to Ziswiler, "Chinese merchants gain huge profits by marketing the powdered rhinoceros horn as an aphrodisiac. Furthermore, goblets carved from rhino horn are supposedly able to detect poisoned drinks." There are now approximately 50 Javanese, 100-170 Sumatran, and 740 Indian rhinos surviving in the world. In the United States there are still Chinese families that treat their ailments with powdered tiger bone and rhinoceros horn, imported at considerable expense from the Chinese mainland via Hong Kong.

Predator Control

Predators are a component of virtually all ecosystems; they include the direct ancestors of man back to the time of the Australopithecine man-apes, and perhaps before. S. Eimerl and I. DeVore have written: "It would be hard to exaggerate the importance of predation—or hunting—in the development of man. Together with bipedalism and the use of tools, hunting was the principal element which set him on the evolutionary path that was to lead, ultimately, to his position of dominance over all other animals." Despite his background, however, man has shown little fondness for other predators, regarding them, understandably, as competitors, and less understandably in the twentieth century as dangerous, undesirable, and somehow unnatural. Although nearly all biologists, supported by a mass of good data, now advance the thesis that predators serve a necessary function in natural and semi-natural communities, misguided attempts to exterminate these creatures are still going forward in many countries.

Predator control programs are generally based on two popular myths. The first is that medium-sized and large predators are dangerous to man. Nearly all reports of wild animals attacking man without considerable provocation prove to be false (an exception is the grizzly bear; see p. 289). According to John Hillaby, ". . . dispassionate travellers have stated that the big Labrador wolf has never been known to attack a man. In Sault Ste. Marie, the center of a region renowned for its blood-curdling wolf stories, the editor of the local paper offered $100 for authenticated accounts of wolf attacks. The cash is said to be still in the till." Similarly, the alligator is not nearly so fearsome as its reputation. Although reports of attacks by wild alligators date back to the time of the early explorers, it is curious that the "victims," if identified, always managed to escape unharmed. Alligators, like other predators, have a well-developed sense of the appropriate size and shape of their prey; they are not averse to nibbling on pet dachshunds, when available, but they do not attack people (captive, restrained, or semitame alligators used to being offered food are an exception). E. A. McIlhenny, the pioneer in the study of alligator behavior, recalled that when he was a boy in Louisiana the local swimming area was peacefully shared with a great many alligators of enormous size.

There are, of course, a number of marine predators, including some sharks, barracudas, and some groupers, whose reputation is partially deserved; and most large terrestrial predators such as bears and tigers have been known to attack man. But man does not live in a marine environment, and the terrestrial attacks are so rare that they never justify the extirpation of a species.

The second myth is that predators are a serious threat to domestic livestock and wild game. As with other animals, as well as man himself, the most dramatic, striking, and easily observable aggressive actions of predators are the ones that receive the most attention. Thus we hear about foxes and coyotes in South Dakota killing pheasants and snatching chickens from farms; we hear about snapping turtles in northeastern lakes striking at migratory ducks and smallmouth bass; and we hear about wolves in Canada eating moose and caribou. All of these accounts are true, but it is essential not to pass judgment before some additional questions are answered in each case: first, does the predator keep the population of its prey at an undesirably low level? Second, do the activities of the predator have any directly or indirectly beneficial effects?

Nearly all studies to date of predator-prey relationships support the idea that wild vertebrate predators do not usually cause drastic reductions in the population density of prey species; in fact they seem to have little effect at all other than to check gross overpopulation (the converse is not always true; predator population size is closely controlled by the availability of prey, especially in simple ecosystems). This viewpoint was expressed by Paul Errington, who made extensive investigations of the effects of predation on bobwhite quail and muskrat populations: ". . . the more a prey population is basically limited by some non-predatory feature of its environment, or by its own intolerance of crowding, the less it can be basically limited by predation. I do not say, and never have said, that predation cannot be a limiting factor with some populations; but with the living forms with which I am most familiar, I believe that the population effect of predation is often greatly overrated. . . ."

In South Dakota in 1966, when 409,757 acres of prime pheasant land were withdrawn from the soil bank program and mowed at the height of the nesting season, the resulting sharp drop in the pheasant population was naturally blamed on foxes and coyotes. Despite a vigorous program of predator control, the pheasant population did not fully recover. The governor of South Dakota commissioned a group of scientists to study the situation, and they reported that "reduction of foxes in large areas has resulted in no significant change in the pheasant

populations but has resulted in a sharp rise in rabbit and rodent populations." Evidently the populations of rabbits and rodents, high to begin
with, were kept from an overpopulation crisis only by the predators,
while the inroads of the foxes on the depleted pheasant population
were small in comparison with the effects of habitat destruction. Similarly, no one but professional bounty hunters believes that the decline
of the caribou can be attributed to the wolf. Before the days of uncontrolled hunting and poaching with modern weapons, both caribou and
wolf populations were much greater. In the case of exclusively domestic
animals, some farmers and ranchers are accustomed to attribute almost
any stock losses on the range to the activities of predators. In listening
to these accounts one gets the impression that the average mountain
lion kills one or two cows a day, and that each ranch is infested with
mountain lions the way a barn is infested with mice. Similarly, every
coyote seen feeding at the carcass of a lamb or sheep that has died of
disease or starvation is labelled a "sheep-killer."

Even the common American snapping turtle *(Chelydra serpentina)*,
which claims few friends other than customers of some Philadelphia
restaurants, does not deserve the abuse it receives from fishermen and
duck hunters. Karl Lagler, who examined the stomach and colon con-
tents of several hundred snapping turtles, stated: "It seems a conservative estimate that on the average not more than one game or pan fish
is eaten per day by the individual snapping turtle." Nor was there any
evidence that the snapping turtle was competing with game fish for
the smaller "forage" fish that constitute the latter's food. Since a normal snapping turtle population approximates only two adult turtles per
acre of water, Lagler came to the one sensible conclusion that: "there
need be little concern as to the adverse relations of snapping turtles to
game fish populations in wild waters." The same statement might be
made about ducks, which are caught by snapping turtles relatively
infrequently, and are a minor item of the reptile's diet.

A number of beneficial effects of predators have been demonstrated
or claimed. The most significant of these is certainly the widespread
tendency of predators to prevent overpopulation of prey species. Numerous examples could be cited, including many in which animals have

Mountain lion cornered by bounty hunters in Colorado. (Carl Iwasaki—*Life* Magazine, © Time Inc.)

been introduced into new areas where they have no natural predators—the most notorious instance being importation of rabbits into Australia; they soon achieved huge population sizes and ate everything in sight (they were later controlled by the deliberate introduction of a rabbit disease virus). Thus a desirable effect of predators is pest control. Most predators regularly eat at least some animals that humans consider pests, such as rodents; it is surprising to see how much of the diet of even large animals such as wolves is composed of field mice and other small rodents. The discovery that foxes and coyotes provided much of the natural rodent control in South Dakota is in accord with the results of many other studies of the effects of predators. For example, in the West Yellowstone area an uncontrolled increase in destructive rodent populations followed the use of cyanide bombs to eliminate coyotes. In at least one area, Colorado's Yampa Valley, enlightened ranchers halted a coyote extermination program in order to avoid these same consequences.

An indirect beneficial effect attributed to predators is the maintenance of their prey species in a healthy condition. A number of biologists claim that, in addition to preventing overpopulation, predators improve the genetic fitness of their prey and increase the food and shelter resources available to the healthier animals by culling the weak and handicapped individuals from the prey population; wolf-caribou and wolf-moose interactions are usually cited as examples. Other indirect benefits have been observed. For example, on several islands off the west coast of Florida, a variety of herons and ibises nest in low trees in surprisingly unprotected locations. Here, their eggs and young are, in effect, guarded by unusually large numbers of poisonous water moccasins (*Ancistrodon piscivorous*), which cluster at the base of the trees and by their presence prevent the establishment on the island of other more arboreal predators such as raccoons. The moccasins eat the occasional baby birds that fall out of the nest and any fish that may be dropped by the adult birds.

Although it is likely that many predators do exert some favorable effects on their prey, it is neither necessary nor desirable to rest the case against predator control on this argument. The idea that predators are "bad" and therefore should be controlled is a value judgment based on questionable philosophical grounds and contrary to scientific evidence. Predators do not harm the ecosystems in which they evolved, and are necessary, in one way or another, for the proper functioning of those ecosystems. It is not the predators but the massive predator control programs that should be eliminated.

Some of the motivation behind predator control programs is emotional, although it is hard to see how the occasional chicken-killing fox justifies the extermination of all foxes; and, more important, much of the motivation is economic. The old Predator and Rodent Control Branch (now euphemistically called the Division of Wildlife Services) of the U.S. government had hundreds of employees and has spent tens of millions of dollars on the killing of coyotes, beavers, badgers, bobcats, eagles, cocker spaniels, and anything else that happens upon their poisoned baits. Although there are slight indications of recent enlightenment among federal agencies that deal with predators, many state and local governments are still in the ecological dark ages. South Dakota, for example, spent $70,000 in one year (1967) on bounty payments, a large price to pay for nothing more than an increase in the populations of rats and mice.

Endangered Plant Species

Plant species are threatened by many of the same factors that menace animal species: the introduction of exotic competitors, herbivores, and parasites; the practice of selective "hunting" as carried out by lumber and pharmaceutical companies and ornamental plant collectors; pollution; and agricultural land improvement. These and many other influences can lead to the diminution of particular plant populations. There are, of course, differences. Rarely are specific plants deliberately exterminated, and if they are their lack of movement and usually high reproductive capacity makes it likely that some patches will be overlooked. Nevertheless, plant species can face extinction. There is little doubt that some have become extinct during recent times; but unless a plant is showy and its geographic distribution is sharply delineated, its passing may not be noticed.

Only a few perceptive naturalists have written about the disappearance of plants, and as the number of experienced naturalists dwindles, the writings are less frequent. Aldo Leopold, who died in 1948, described with special brilliance the vanishing plants and plant communities of the midwest. "No living man will see again the long-grass prairie, where a sea of prairie flowers lapped at the stirrups of the pioneer. We shall do well to find a forty here and there on which the prairie plants can be kept alive as species. There were a hundred such plants, many of exceptional beauty. Most of them are quite unknown to those who have inherited their domain."

Although as a group the plants of the world's grasslands may have suffered the heaviest casualties, other environments are losing plant species. In the eastern United States several of the most beautiful native flowering plants have become extremely scarce. The fringed gentian *(Gentiana crinita)*, an annual with tubular violet flowers composed of petals fringed at the ends, is an inhabitant of bogs and marshes. As the reckless and excessive drainage of wetlands continues, this plant is becoming nearly impossible to find. The situation is worsened by its being an annual; when an entire clump of its now unusual flowers is picked, it will not reappear in that place the next year. The trailing arbutus or mayflower *(Epigaea repens)* is a low, short-stemmed plant with fragrant pink or white flowers. It grows in light shade and is a late successional or climax species. The trailing arbutus is very intolerant of soil disturbance and disappears rapidly in any area where man's activities are not strictly curtailed. In addition, because of its shape, it is difficult to pick the attractive flowers without damaging the plant or uprooting it entirely. A third endangered species, the pinxter-flower or purple honeysuckle *(Rhododendron nudiflorum)*, is a branched, two- to 8-foot-high shrub with pink-white flowers. It blooms in early spring before it and the surrounding deciduous trees have put out their leaves, and is thus easily spotted from a great distance by ornamental shrub hunters. Once extremely common, like the fringed gentian and the trailing arbutus, it is now encountered much less frequently in its natural setting. (Some states have passed laws to protect endangered plant species, and others have instituted propagation programs for their rare native plants.)

Selective lumbering can threaten tree species, especially in the tropical rain forests where artificial reseeding is difficult or impossible and the high species diversity and thin soils mitigate against the establishment of tree farms (fortunately for the other species). In the North Patagonian Andes, for example, J. C. Lerman found that conifers like *Fitzroya cupressoides* and *Araucaria araucana* (the monkey-puzzle tree), which frequently attain ages greater than a thousand years, have been endangered even in the absence of bulldozers and chain saws by "a few men working every summer with very simple tools and selecting the species and the specimens most suitable for their interests." In the rain forest, major damage to particular, valuable species can go unnoticed; Lerman reported that

Blue fringed gentian, a beautiful native American plant that has grown extremely scarce. (Jeanne White—Courtesy National Audubon Society)

not only is it difficult to detect by aerial inspection selective exploitation within thick rain forests, but it is impossible to evaluate the state of the remaining trees of the species and the damage done to its seedlings if they exist at all. In the air this *Fitzroya* probably appears as a "green virgin forest," as it does to the machete explorer until he begins to find stump after stump hidden by other replacing species.

As is true of animals, plants with extremely restricted ranges are vulnerable to a variety of disturbing factors. On several of the Galapagos Islands, some floral species or subspecies and some floral communities of great interest to biologists may be lost because of excessive grazing by introduced goats. Unfortunately, in the Galapagos and elsewhere, the immense difficulty of preparing floral lists that are both up-to-date and taxonomically sound may prevent us from ever knowing what plants have become extinct because of our activities. In 1970, the International Union for the Conservation of Nature issued a world list (*Red Data Book,* Volume 5) of endangered flowering plants; the volume is similar to those published for mammals, birds, reptiles and amphibians, and fish. Although the omissions from this list are probably far more numerous than the entries, it is a promising beginning in this important area of conservation.

Characteristics of Endangered Species

Not all species are endangered at present; for example, fewer than ten percent of all mammals are clearly faced with the threat of extinction. The percentages vary, however, from one taxonomic group to the next, and even at the level of orders we can see major survival differences (see table, p. 203). Throughout this chapter we have been concerned with external environmental factors that endanger species. But because all species are not endangered equally, the differences must be determined by a set of species characteristics relevant to survival conditions in the modern world. Taken together, these factors determine the extinction potential of a species.

It is possible to analyze qualitatively those characteristics of animal species that can lower their survival potential. There are, of course, exceptions in every category, and interactions between categories may alter the results, but the properties in the table on the next page usually play a role in extinction.

If one could assign a relative "point value" to each of the categories in the table, it would be possible to sum the points for a given species and predict its chances of survival. Complex ecological situations do not lend themselves to such a simple quantiative approach, however; the best we can do is check our categories qualitatively against reality. In so doing, a picture of the hypothetical "most endangered animal" can be constructed. It turns out to be a large predator with a narrow habitat tolerance, long gestation period, and few young per litter. It is hunted for a natural product and for sport, but is not subject to efficient game management. It has a relatively restricted distribution, but travels across international boundaries. It is intolerant of man, reproduces in aggregates, and has nonadaptive behavioral idiosyncracies. Although there probably is no such animal, this model, with one or two exceptions, comes close to being a description of a polar bear. Conversely, if one "constructs" a species by taking the opposite extreme from each category (small, herbivorous, and so forth), one is left with a composite picture of the "typical" wild animal of the twenty-first century—some of the most familiar existing approximations would be the house sparrow, the gray squirrel, the Virginia opposum, and the Norway rat.

Species can be characterized in other ways. Such parameters as size of home range, nocturnality versus diurnality, color, life-span, or population size can play a role in determining the extinction potential of a species. But the effects of these and most other characteristics are so variable that generalization seems unwarranted. One partial exception can be noted. Ziswiler and others have suggested that there is a critical population size that varies from species to species. When the population of a given species falls below this point, the species is likely to become extinct even if accorded full protection. Classic examples of this phenomenon are the passenger pigeon and the heath hen.

The fate of the passenger pigeon is the most dramatic recorded

Characteristics of species affecting survival

Endangered	Safe
Large size (cougar)	Small size (wildcat)
Predator (hawk)	Grazer, scavenger, insectivore (vulture)
Narrow habitat tolerance* (orangutan)	Wide habitat tolerance (chimpanzee)
Valuable fur, hide, oil, etc. (chinchilla)	Not a source of natural products and not exploited for research or pet purposes (gray squirrel)
Hunted for the market or for sport where no effective game management exists (passenger pigeon)	Commonly hunted for sport in game management areas (mourning dove)
Restricted distribution: island, desert watercourse, bog, etc. (Puerto Rico parrot)	Broad distribution (yellow-headed parrot)
Lives largely in international waters or migrates across international boundaries (green sea turtle)	Remains largely within the territory(ies) of a specific country(ies) (loggerhead sea turtle)
Intolerant of the presence of man† (grizzly bear)	Tolerant of man (black bear)
Reproduction in one or two vast aggregates (West Indian flamingo)	Reproduction by solitary pairs or in many small or medium-sized aggregates (bitterns)
Long gestation period; one or two young per litter, and/or maternal care§ (giant panda)	Short gestation period; more than two young per litter, and/or young become independent early and mature quickly (raccoon)
Behavioral idiosyncracies that are non-adaptive today (redheaded woodpecker: flies in front of cars)	Behavior patterns that are particularly adaptive today (burrowing owl: highly tolerant of noise and low-flying aircraft; lives between the runways of airports)

* Especially for vanishing habitats such as grasslands, virgin forests, swamps, etc.
† There is no way to predict what mixture of boldness versus shyness and aggression versus fear will place a species in one of these two categories.
§ George C. Williams has pointed out that "the maximization of individual reproductive success will seldom be achieved by unbridled fecundity." The litter sizes of pandas (1-2) and raccoons (1-7) have presumably been optimized according to the restraints imposed by their internal and external environments; under natural conditions it would be absurd to declare that the reproductive fitness of the raccoon was greater than that of the panda. However, it seems likely (but would be difficult to prove) that the reproductive pattern of high fecundity and high mortality is better suited than the opposite pattern to resist the unnatural threat of civilized man. This would be especially true for those species faced with the direct and selective threat of hunting (as opposed to habitat destruction), where the removal of individuals from the population would, by decreasing intraspecies competition for food and shelter, decrease the usual mortality in the surviving large litters.

Endangered species in selected mammalian orders

Order and Typical Species	No. of Endangered Species	Total No. of Species	Percent Endangered
Carnivora (cats, bears, weasels)	45	232	19
Perissodactyla (horses, rhinos)	11	15	73
Artiodactyla (deer, antelope, cattle, pigs)	59	215	27
Primates (lemurs, monkeys)	35	180	19
Marsupialia (kangaroos, opossums)	33	245	13
Cetacea (whales, porpoises)	7	90	8
baleen whales only	7	11	67
Insectivora* (shrews, moles, hedgehogs)	4	311	1
Pinnipedia (seals, walruses)	11	31	35
Sirenia (sea cows, dugongs)	4	4	100
Edentata (sloths, armadillos, anteaters)	6	30	20

Sources: *Red Data Book, Vol. 1,* compiled by Noel Simon (International Union for the Conservation of Nature), and *Mammals of the World, Vols. 1* and *2,* by Ernest P. Walker (Johns Hopkins, 1964). All endangered races in a given species (e.g., Chinese tiger, Bengal tiger, Javan tiger, Siberian tiger, etc.) are grouped as one. Several orders, including the two largest—rodents and bats—were omitted because of insufficient data.

* Since most insectivores are small and inconspicuous, the status of some endangered species may have gone unnoticed.

example of extinction. Its population declined from several billion in the late 1870s to zero in 1914, when the last survivor died in the Cincinnati Zoo. Evidently the critical population size for this species was very high, because the population continued to fall even though market hunting ceased when there were still many thousands of presumably healthy birds left. Ziswiler suggests a variety of factors that may have played a role in determining the critical population size for this and other species, of which three (paraphrased) are:

Population density too low for males to find females.

Local population density too low to stimulate courtship behavior.

Population density too low to cope with the large numbers of surviving predators or competitors.

We might add a fourth possibility: absolute population size too low to compensate normal losses due to disease, climatic changes, and natural disasters. This fourth factor is analogous to the Monte Carlo "gambler's ruin" rule, which states that even if the odds in a game of chance are exactly equal, a player with a low amount of initial capital is likely to lose when, sooner or later, one of the customary fluctuations of fortune reduces his small assets to zero, thus ending the game. The American heath hen (*Tympanuchus cupido cupido*) is probably an example of a species that succumbed to "gambler's ruin."

In contrast to the passenger pigeon, there are a number of species, characterized in part by highly flexible behavior patterns and great mobility, that seem to have such a low critical population size that the concept has little importance. Perhaps the best example among mammals is the panther of eastern Canada (also known as mountain lion, puma, cougar), *Felis concolor couguar*. Although once believed to be extinct in northeastern North America, the eastern panther has recovered from a breeding nucleus of a very few individuals presumably overlooked in the forests of eastern New Brunswick and western Ontario, and has increased to the point where panthers have been sighted in all but two of the eastern Canadian provinces in recent years. (This comeback, facilitated by the conversion of moose habitat into deer habitat by extensive pulpwood operations, is one of the rare examples of species survival aided by industrial expansion.) If the eastern panther had had a critical population size comparable to that of the heath hen (a few hundred individuals), it would almost certainly have become extinct.

6

The Fate of the Blue Whale

*Wherefore, for all these things, we account the whale immortal
in his species, however perishable in his individuality. He swam
the seas before the continents broke water; he once swam over
the site of the Tuileries, and Windsor Castle, and the Kremlin.
In Noah's flood he despised Noah's Ark; and if ever the world is
to be again flooded, like the Netherlands, to kill off its rats, then
the eternal whale will still survive, and rearing upon the topmost
crest of the equatorial flood, spout his frothed defiance to the skies.*
HERMAN MELVILLE, Moby Dick

Blue whales, *Balaenoptera musculus*, are the largest animals that have
ever lived on earth; they are 25 feet long at birth, are weaned at an
average length of 53 feet when they are seven months old, reach sexual
maturity (females) at an approximate length of 78 feet when they are
five years old, and have been known to attain lengths as great as 106
feet. One 83-foot male weighed 242,397 pounds. Their lifespan probably does not exceed forty years. Blue whales live almost entirely on
two-inch euphausiid shrimp filtered from the water by the baleen
(whalebone) plates that give them their name. They are migratory,
usually spending eight months of the year in the Antarctic Ocean eating
the abundant krill, and staying for the rest of the year in warmer
waters nearly devoid of food, where the calves are born. The least

205

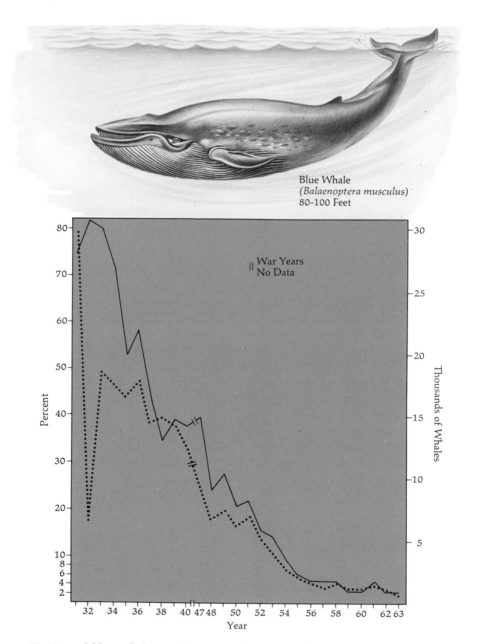

Blue Whale
(*Balaenoptera musculus*)
80-100 Feet

‖ War Years
No Data

Decline of blue whale populations in Antarctic whaling areas, expressed as
numbers of blue whales caught per year (dotted line), and as captured blue
whales as a percentage of blue whales killed in the total Antarctic whale
catch (solid line). (From George Small, doctoral dissertation, Columbia University, 1968)

A ninety-foot blue whale at the station of the Cia. Argentina de Pesca, Grytviken, South Georgia (in the South Atlantic Ocean), October 1925. An unusual photograph of a whale in its natural position, back uppermost. (Courtesy National Institute of Oceanography, Great Britain)

gregarious of all whales in the family Balaenopteridae (baleen whales), blue whales travel singly, or in groups of two or three. Nearly all their lives are spent in international waters, although they occasionally pass near the shores of Chile or South Africa during migrations.

Our knowledge of the size of the blue whale populations in past years is based on commercial whaling figures. Since the efficiency of catching methods, the number of whaling ships, the areas fished, the length of the fishing season, the minimum size requirement, and the reliability of the records have varied from year to year, the size of the annual blue whale catch is only an approximate indication of the true population size. Nevertheless, the trend is depressingly obvious, regardless of how the data are expressed (see graph, opposite page). At this writing, only a few thousand blue whales are left alive in all the waters of the southern hemisphere, and most authorities, fearing that the species is nearing the critical level in most of its remaining populations, predict that this greatest of animals in the history of the planet will be extinct before the end of the century if present trends continue.

There are three major reasons for the destruction of the blue whale by man: the whales' tendency to concentrate in the Antarctic feeding grounds during the summer, allowing them to be caught in large numbers; their exceptionally low reproductive potential; and the existence of a ruthless and suicidal industry that has been able to thwart all meaningful attempts at regulation and has exploited the inability of all countries to give territorial protection to a creature of the high seas.

As can be seen from the graph, virtually all whaling activities ceased during World War II. Yet the recovery of the blue whale population during this hiatus was negligible. Evidently the blue whale reproduces itself very slowly; but this low biotic potential was not documented until 1950, when J. T. Ruud and his colleagues in Norway discovered a method of determining the ages of blue whales by examining growth ridges on their baleen plates. When age was correlated with sexual maturity it was found that female blue whales do not mature sexually until four to seven years of age.

Moreover, a gestation period of approximately one year, plus a seven-month nursing period for the single calf (during which the female does not become pregnant again), when correlated with the annual migration and feeding pattern, mean that a female cannot bear more than one calf every two years—occasionally less often. In other words, as George Small has pointed out, a female blue whale can have borne a maximum of two offspring by age 10. This exceptionally low reproductive rate has made the population very vulnerable to intensive, indiscriminate hunting; for the past twenty years blue whales captured in the Antarctic have averaged less than eighty feet (approximately six years old), at which size the great majority of females are immature, recently matured, or pregnant with their first calf. Clearly, no population of like biotic potential could survive under these conditions.

Most of the information concerning the biotic potential and population structure of the blue whale was obtained after the species had become, for all practical purposes, commercially extinct. Small has calculated that by the time the Japanese had confirmed the age-maturity estimates of Ruud, in 1952, "95.2 per cent of all the blue whales to be taken in the history of Antarctic whaling had already been taken." (Blue whales are still being killed by "Chilean" whaling companies using leased Japanese vessels, but the small numbers taken, although catastrophic in terms of the survival of the species, are negligible when compared with past commercial catches.) In short, sustained-yield management of blue whale stocks based on accurate biological information was hardly possible until most of the whales were gone. This point is academic, however, for the whaling companies and the International Whaling Commission (which they effectively controlled) were uninterested in sustained-yield management. Whaling practices did not change after 1952; if anything, whaling intensified during the 1950s.

Because of their status as an exclusively international resource, blue whales could have been protected only by all whaling nations acting in concert. Yet with the exception of Norway, which instituted strong unilateral conservation measures pertaining to its own industry, the record of the member nations of the International Whaling Commission is a sickening testimonial to corporate and national greed, shortsightedness, and inertia. The Whaling Commission itself had neither inspection nor enforcement powers, and any of its majority decisions could, in effect, be vetoed by a single member nation.

Japan, whose commissioner to the Whaling Commission from 1951 to 1965 was a representative of the Japanese whaling industry, was responsible for defeating nearly every attempt to limit the catch of blue whales in the Antarctic. The attitude of the Japanese whalers was summarized by N. R. Lillie in a letter reprinted in Small's excellent book, *The Blue Whale:*

> The president of the largest Japanese whaling company, Mr. K. Nakabe of Taiyo Fishery Co., Ltd., was indeed difficult to deal with, insisting on breaking off all further discussions if I could not agree with him that there were plenty of whales left and

that the killing could go on without restriction. The president of the third company, Kyokuyo Hogei, while not as extreme, was just as determined to go on with the killing until such time as the industry collapsed from the wiping out of the whales.

During the critical period of the early 1960s, the Japanese even went so far as to insist on the existence of a separate species of "pygmy blue whale" in order to justify their continued catches of undersized animals in one of the Antarctic whaling zones.

The anticonservation attitude of most of the whaling nations cannot be explained in terms of the value of the blue whale catch after 1950. In 1960, according to Small, blue whales were responsible for only 2.52 percent of the total corporate income of Norwegian whaling companies. This had fallen to 0.06 percent by 1963. Although the Japanese whaling industry is more secretive than the Norwegian, the available income figures indicate that the blue whale was of no more commercial importance to the highly diversified Japanese corporations than to the Norwegians, who terminated all official whaling operations in 1969.

If the value of the blue whale catch has been negligible at least since 1958, and if the stocks of other species of great whales are also nearing exhaustion, why have the whaling companies and nations been so reluctant to submit to sane regulation? After all, Japan, the Soviet Union, and the United States have managed, by international agreement, to regulate their equally exploitative fur industries with respect to the Pribilof Island fur seals. These fur seals are now probably more numerous than ever, despite a reasonable sustained annual yield of hides. The difference in whaling seems to depend on the high initial and maintenance costs of factory ships and their accompanying fast catcher boats. Small has pointed out that: "The most important result of the large size and cost of such an operating unit is that fine adjustments in whaling capacity to changes in the stock of whales cannot be made, since a floating factory without its full fleet of catcher boats would be useless." Moreover, factory ships are not readily converted to other purposes, and must therefore be kept in whaling operations for at least twenty years in order to repay the original investment. Small concludes: "Thus an extreme rigidity, manifested by a determination to continue operations despite declining profits, characterizes the industry." As late as 1963 the Soviet Union purchased two factory ships from West Germany at a cost of $16 million each, a decision that bodes ill for whales, and, hopefully, for the state economic planner who made it.

The blue whale population has almost certainly been declining drastically since the 1930s, but whaling interests managed to interpret the data to mean that the species was in good condition right up to the time when it became commercially extinct in the 1960s. Recently Kenneth E. F. Watt, a mathematical ecologist, has formulated a set of warning signs or "symptoms" for use in determining when a population is being dangerously overhunted, some of which are as follows (all signs need not be present in any given case):

1. A decreasing proportion of females pregnant.
2. A decreasing catch per unit effort.
3. A decreasing catch relative to the catch of related species.
4. A failure to increase in numbers rapidly after a respite from harvesting.
5. [paraphrased] A sharply increasing percentage of immature and young adult individuals in the population, such that we can calculate, using our knowledge of the minimum reproductive age, gestation period, etc., that the population can no longer reproduce enough young to replace combined losses from harvesting and natural causes.

The blue whale is thus a classical example of the results of excessive exploitation of an animal species by man. All the warning signs listed by Watt were clearly present in data available to the International Whaling Commission in the 1950s, and the theory and practice of game management were sufficiently well developed at that time for the correct inferences to be drawn. By ignoring these signs, the whalers added new information to our knowledge of the extinction process, but few biologists think the contribution was worth the price.

Recent verification of the existence in the southern hemisphere of a few isolated pockets where small populations of blue whales still survive intact has revived pressure within the Whaling Commission to reopen an official open-sea catching season for the blue whale. Of course land-based coastal operations continue, while the supposedly authorized factory ship whaling activities of nations party to the Commission, especially those of the Soviets, remain virtually unsupervised.

In the meantime, most whalers have shifted their sights to smaller and smaller species of whales as stocks of the larger species become progressively exhausted. The Japanese are even catching porpoises for their insatiable industry. Far from ending, whaling is entering a new phase of expansion based on new techniques that eliminate the need for expensive, single-purpose factory ships. Clandestine private ventures are flourishing, putting still more pressure on the Whaling Commission members to ignore even their own lax caricatures of rules and regulations.

In one notorious case, a group of unscrupulous Norwegian profiteers has purchased a variety of old ships (four by the time of this writing) and fitted them out as modern whaling vessels. They include one factory ship, two catcher boats, and—a new and ominous innovation— a combination catcher-factory ship. At least three of the ships are registered under flags of convenience: Panama, the Bahamas, Liberia, countries not supposed to be involved in whaling. A variety of corporate names is used. The factory ship is equipped with a side hoist, which allows whales to be processed without making expensive modifications of the deck and hull. Whale carcasses are jettisoned, which is both wasteful and against international regulations. The boats operate under radio silence as much as possible; their "home" port is Capetown, South Africa.

The success of this venture is indicated by the fact that the Norwegian owners have increased their assets from one to four ships in two years. Dockside stories have it that in just two weeks of sperm whaling one boat earned enough money to pay for itself. Most of the illicit catch now consists of sei whales (or a closely related species) and sperm whales. It is known that the combined catcher-factory ship killed 69 sei and 31 sperm whales in December 1969 and January 1970 alone. At this rate, three to six hundred whales per year is a fair estimate of the catch of this one boat. No commercial whale species can tolerate the impact of this kind of open-sea piracy for long. Moreover, the new whale processing innovations ensure that these boats can be kept as whalers as long as there are whales, and can then be converted to other uses at little cost to their owners.

A list of the known customers of one of the boats provides a final glimpse of both the hidden intricacies and inherent ugliness of contemporary whaling. The bulk of the whale meat is sent, via a commercial British shipping line, to its British purchaser, a large concern that manufactures pet foods.* Another portion is shipped to Japan; its subsequent fate is unknown. A third consignment of meat is reserved for the Portugese Army fighting in Angola. The oil probably goes first to Rotterdam; afterwards it could have many purchasers, including the United States Department of Defense.

The more quick profits made in pirate whaling, the blacker the future for all great whales. The market demand for whale products is global and multifarious; it cannot easily be exposed to the kind of concerted conservation pressure that has been applied to the market for spotted cat or alligator skins. The only real pressure that can be brought to bear on illicit whaling is by the governments that are now sheltering the owners or their vessels—yet there is no indication to date that either Norway or the Republic of South Africa is particularly concerned about this world problem.†

---

* It is not known whether any whale meat from this particular source reaches the United States, but several American dog food manufacturers have used large quantities of whale meat. Recently, Kal Kan Foods, Inc., one such company, received an Interior Department permit to import 11.5 million pounds of whale meat. (The Environmental Defense Fund urged a boycott of Kal Kan products.) Now that the blue whale is nearly gone, it is sickening to think of the remaining great whales being turned into dog food. This is especially contemptible because it would not be happening if a few unscrupulous advertising agencies had not foisted the idea upon the American public that their dogs will love them more and be healthier if fed "meatier" dog foods rather than the perfectly satisfactory and highly nutritious mixtures of beef by-products, soy grits, cereal grains, dry yeast, and vitamins that have long been in common use.
† I would like to thank Dr. Roger Payne for supplying most of the information on illicit whaling. His sources in South Africa have gathered these facts with care and dedication, and at great personal risk.

7
Preservation of Natural Communities

Population Control

The need for human "population control" is no longer a seriously debated question among scientists concerned with environmental quality; there is scarcely a single conservation problem described so far that is not made worse—or insoluble—by a rapidly increasing human population. Indeed, the population control issue can fairly be said to be emerging (with some exceptions) from its crusading phase and entering a period of sophisticated analysis and self-criticism. As so frequently happens in such transitions, some of the cliches and slogans that helped make scientists and laymen aware of the population crisis are now being re-evaluated by the advocates of population control.

Three concepts prevalent during the first phase of the population control movement now seem to stand in the way of further progress:

The Malthusian doctrine, which implies that the only important danger inherent in population increase is the potential exhaustion of world food supplies.

The idea that population control can be effected primarily by dissemination of birth control information and birth control devices.

The idea that the groups most in need of population control are the lower classes of industrialized countries and the inhabitants of underdeveloped nations.

First of all, it has by no means been proven that the human population is outgrowing its food supply, as Malthus predicted. There is no conclusive evidence that food production is currently lagging behind the increase in population. It is true that social, economic, and political problems that interfere with food production and distribution still plague us (and threaten to worsen), and that because of high population densities, greater numbers of people may die from famine than previously; but there is perhaps as much reason to believe that overall world nutrition will improve during the next fifty years as to believe that it will deteriorate. Jean Mayer, professor of nutrition at Harvard University, has pointed out that "nothing is more dangerous for the cause of formulating sound policy of population control than to approach the problem in nineteenth century terms. . . ." In other words, by continuing to emphasize what may turn out to be a nonexistent inverse correlation between population and food, we run the risk, like the boy who cried "wolf," of losing the confidence and co-operation of the public when the other dangers of overpopulation are pointed out. Considering the damage that excessive numbers of people are *already* doing to their environment and to each other, it would seem both worthwhile and easy to develop a broad-based justification for the practice of population control, emphasizing those dangers of population increase that are clear and present, or inevitable.

The second idea, that the public will control its own population numbers if birth control information and devices are made available to everyone, has insufficient data to back it up. Judith Blake of the University of California, Berkeley, has gathered and analyzed opinion poll data from several sources and concluded that "for most Americans the 'family planning' approach, concentrating as it does on the distribution of contraceptive material and [information] services, is irrelevant, because they already know about efficient contraception and are already 'planning' their families." The real problem, according to Blake, is that Americans "want families of more than three children and thereby generate a growth rate far in excess of that required for population stability." (Arguments against this controversial point of view have been summarized by Harkavy and co-workers, whose disagreement

with Blake appears to concern the current methodology rather than the goals of population control.)

The solution, according to Blake, is twofold: establish in the public consciousness the acceptability of the idea of having few or no children; and, more important, take steps to abolish *existing* social and economic penalties for those who desire to deviate from the current reproductive norm. In particular, women, who constitute more than half our population, must be allowed to have a normal, healthy, and rewarding life in areas other than those relating to child care, and they must not be accused of avoiding "maternal responsibilities" if they choose another life style. The tax laws of the United States seem similarly unresponsive to current needs. There is no reason why married couples should be allowed tax loopholes denied to single persons, nor is there any remaining justification for a federal child subsidy in the form of unlimited child-support exemptions from income tax.

I do not advocate that existing birth control and family-planning programs be halted; they are vital short-term measures, and almost certainly account for part of the current decline of the birth rate in the United States. This decline, however, is only in the rate of increase; the population is still expanding rapidly, and, if the population planners

216

are to be successful in their goal of complete population stabilization, the existence of the pill, the intrauterine device, and rapid male sterilization techniques cannot be used as excuses to avoid confrontation with the long-range motivational problems of population control. Needless to say, this motivational difficulty exists in many countries.

The third idea, that the "excess" in "population excess" is contributed primarily by the poor and underprivileged members of society, is the most palpably and demonstrably untrue of the population cliches, particularly for the United States, West Germany, Japan, Canada, and other countries with large technology-dependent middle classes; yet it is the most stubbornly rooted idea in both conservative and liberal political philosophies (for different reasons). It is the privileged who are consuming living space at a frightening rate while the poor crowd more to a room; it is the privileged who discard a six-pound Sunday newspaper after one casual reading; it is the privileged who will not eat fish flour and who buy prime beef; it is the privileged who purchase the vast quantity of automobiles that spend their last days rusting in piles at the edges of highways or in once-productive salt marshes; it is the privileged who can attempt to shield themselves from the effects (rather than deal with the causes) of pollution and deforestation by

217

means of zoning restrictions, resort vacations, and air conditioning; and it is, ironically, the privileged who will ultimately have the most difficult time adjusting to the limited carrying capacity of a finite planet. Although assigning blame is not particularly productive, the question of who is damaging the earth more—the rich or the poor—will no doubt be raised by some. Of the various possibilities, the conclusion that seems to make the most sense is that in poor countries the poor are at fault; in rich countries, the rich. The difference is that the poor degrade their environment directly while the rich use technology and can thus indirectly achieve the same effect with far fewer numbers.

The percentage of "privileged" varies greatly from country to country. In the United States it includes a considerable majority of the population. But in Haiti, where people occasionally venture seventy-five miles through the open sea in small boats to scavenge broken crockery, odd bits of scrap metal, and empty bottles on a neighboring island, an enterprising person could learn the names of most of the country's privileged families. But regardless of the amount and distribution of national wealth, it is not the point of this discussion to prove that population control should proceed at the expense of any one economic or social class. Rather, if we desire the ratio of privileged to underprivileged to increase, and if the life-style implication of "privileged" is to remain unchanged, then the current rate of destruction of nonrenewable resources makes necessary a significant reduction in total world population, a reduction shared proportionately by all segments of that population. The only reasonable alternative that might not necessitate a reduction in population would have to involve a re-evaluation and modification of the privileged variety of life-style in order to bring it more into accord with the real needs of man and nature. I will return to this point in the last chapter.

Pollution Control

Pollution, like usury and discrimination, is a good thing to be against in the last third of the twentieth century. One journal published by the American Chemical Society (*Environmental Science and Technology*) now features a "Pollution Control Directory," which lists, among other things, more than eight hundred corporations supplying pollution control equipment or services. A national pollution control exposition, trying to enlist new industrial exhibitors, advertised in the same journal: ". . . your pollution control products will be exposed to 4,000 bona fide buyers—all under one roof."

Unfortunately, along with this popular burst of enthusiasm has come the fairly widespread belief—even among biologists—that pollution control is entirely a question of economics: is manufacturer A willing to pay the price of a water purification apparatus? Is manufacturer B willing to invest in the research and equipment necessary to retool his assembly line to produce a less polluting product? If modern technology were simple, this simplistic assumption might be correct, but it is not. Certainly, economic factors are implicated in most pollution problems; compared, however, with the ecological and sociological difficulties, and with the contradictions and obstacles inherent in technology itself, the economic problems seem refreshingly straight-forward and approachable.

There are two ways of controlling pollution: amelioration and prevention. Their use is often dictated by circumstances rather than by choice; amelioration, being least disruptive of the status quo, is generally chosen.

Much of the effort now expended on pollution control is used to treat existing pollutants in such a way that they become less injurious to the environment, rather than to alter the source of the pollution. Although this involves a continuing or long-term expense for treatment facilities, it offers the short-term economic advantage of allowing production to continue; moreover, it does not require total revamping of industrial equipment and processes.

Some of the recent treatment methods are extremely efficient. One example is a curious new way of dealing with suspended solids in fast-flowing streams. In watersheds where extensive land-clearing and building are under way, great quantities of raw, exposed earth are washed into streams during storms. One result is that silt rapidly accumulates in lakes and ponds, smothering the bottom-dwelling plants and animals, driving away game fish, and making the water shallower. This problem is particularly severe in the Rock Creek–Mill Creek watershed near Washington, D.C., where five or six feet of loosely packed silt can accumulate in a lake or pond in a few years.

Ideally, we would outlaw all building practices that lead to erosion; or failing that, have some way of preventing exposed dirt from washing away. But since neither alternative seems practical at the moment, the next best approach, an ameliorative one, is to cause the suspended solids in streams to settle out in predetermined settling ponds before they reach recreational lakes. For this purpose the Dow Chemical Company has developed a flocculant compound (Purifloc C-31) that, when added in low concentrations to streams, causes the suspended particles of dirt to clump together in large aggregates. The resulting flocs settle quickly to the bottom as soon as they reach nonturbulent water. If settling ponds are strategically located upstream from lakes, very little silt reaches the lakes, even during storms, provided the proper amount of flocculant has been added upstream.

In a pilot study of the system, a stream flow-monitoring station was installed at Mill Creek above Lake Needwood. When the flow rate increased significantly, flocculant was automatically added in the appropriate amount. During one major storm, fifty gallons of chemical were added to the creek and an estimated 145 tons of solids were deposited, mostly in the stream itself and in the settling pond. During a similar storm, a control study (without flocculant) indicated that nearly ten times as much solid material was reaching the settling pond still in suspension; much of this was subsequently carried on into Lake Needwood.

If the flocculation system works, it could be of great use in protecting suburban lakes from silt "pollution"; and the settling ponds could provide an abundance of high-grade landfill (an estimated 15,000 cubic yards per year at Mill Creek-Needwood). Against these prospective benefits must be weighed the potential hazards, none of which has been experimentally evaluated.

Flocculant addition facility at Rock Creek, Maryland. Pipe releases chemical automatically according to stream flow (see text). (Courtesy Dow Chemical Co.)

First, it will be necessary to determine whether there is any biological damage to the stream flora and fauna because of flocculated material that settles before reaching the settling ponds. This is particularly important because the bottom-dwelling organisms of fast streams generally need a clean sandy or gravelly substrate. Second, although the flocculant is described as "nontoxic" and "biodegradable," this will have to be proved during continuous field trials over several years. Work will also be needed to determine the eutrophication effects of the degraded flocculant. Third, the fate of the flocculated silt after degradation of the flocculant will have to be ascertained. This pertains especially to silt originally deposited in running water upstream from the settling ponds. Finally, the local authority managing the project must have a realistic plan for preventing the settling ponds, with their occasional power scoops and dirt-handling equipment, from becoming regional eyesores.

Forms of ameliorative pollution control are numerous. Among the more promising stop-gap measures are the use of abandoned strip mines for the disposal of trash, the use of compaction techniques to turn garbage and other solid wastes into construction materials, and the use of deep wells for disposal of heavily polluted waste water. Again, most methods have their risks and side effects. Strip mines can be used for trash disposal only after engineers have studied their drainage patterns and only if an experienced bulldozer operator is available. Even then, a hastily prepared public may react unfavorably to such projects, unaware that the mine, when filled, will be available as parkland. Deep-well injection is associated with still more serious hazards: if the underground geologic formations are of the wrong kind, if the well is improperly made, or if the waste is disposed of at incorrect pressures, polluted water may escape from the deep formations and contaminate usable subsurface water supplies; or in some areas the water may open fissures, allowing slippage along rock faults and increasing the danger of earthquake. For example, an increase in the number of earthquakes around Denver has been attributed to deep-well waste disposal carried out by the Army.

No ameliorative pollution control method should be put into practice until the ultimate fate of the pollutant or pollutant by-product has been analyzed. There are, in the last analysis, only three places pollutants can go: the soil, air, or water. Until a pollutant has been traced—in whatever form it may be—to one of these final resting places, and the consequences of all steps along the route examined, a "pollution control system" has not been thoroughly evaluated.

Preventing pollution is usually preferable to treating it later; in fact, some pollutants (such as cyanide, heavy metals, arsenic, and selenium in municipal sewage systems) are virtually impossible to deal with once they have left the source and become diluted in air or water or absorbed by the soil. As with ameliorative control, a variety of problems are associated with prevention. These seem to fall into two categories.

There are, first of all, internal technological problems, including "pollution exchange." There is no theoretical scientific reason why technology should be able, using only its own resources, to solve every pollution problem. Only those who believe in technology the way others believe in a religion would think so. The fact that technological societies have so few alternatives ready when technology fails (as it often does) indicates that the belief is widespread. Hope may spring eternal, but ecosystems, unfortunately, don't. Not all factories can maintain or even approximate a closed-circle efficiency in recycling. Even some that do still produce products whose use or eventual disposal causes severe pollution. Furthermore, the factory that claims effective pollution control through efficient recycling of wastes is almost certainly leaving the pollution costs of its raw materials and power consumption off the balance sheet.

One brief example will suffice. The recycling of paper is a popular and much publicized way of preventing pollution. Indeed it should be practiced, and what follows should not discourage readers from helping to recycle paper; by 1970, recycling was saving an estimated 200 million trees annually. Nevertheless, recycling is not a process that magically turns old paper into new without attendant difficulties. According to an article by Carol E. Knapp, printed in the chemical journal *Environmental Science and Technology* (October 1970), "Most waste paper is so contaminated that it is impractical for reuse." Even after paper sorting at the collection center (assuming reliable volunteer labor), ten percent of the paper stock is contaminant, including grit, sand, glass, wire, paper clips, tin scraps, aluminum foil, staples, plastics, wood, "hot melt" coatings, rubber bands, and pressure-sensitive adhesives. Plastic coatings—many of the dangerous PVC (polyvinyl chloride) variety—are the hardest to deal with. One current method involves the use of an organic solvent, trichloroethylene, to dissolve them. Disposal of this chemical presents a new pollution problem. The other metal and non-metal scraps have no economic value and become solid wastes. Massive quantities of ink must also be removed by trichloroethylene or by other solvents, and this mixture must be discarded or possibly recycled.

Finally, there is apparently one absolute limitation to the value of paper recycling. According to Knapp, "As the recycling rate is increased, difficulties concerning quality may appear. Paper can be recycled repeatedly, but with each reuse the fibers become shorter and less desirable. Under the present recycling rate, enough 'new' fibers are introduced to compensate for the presence of any low-quality fiber. However, with the increase of a recycled paper portion of total paper output, more 'quality problems' may be encountered. . . ." In other words, it is not theoretically possible to recycle all or even most paper for anything remotely resembling its original use.* Other examples of the intrinsic limitations of pollution control systems are common enough.

Part of the dilemma inherent in the technological approach to pollu-

---

* These problems pertain to paper that is recycled for use as stationery, high-quality book paper, and the like, but are not encountered if paper is recycled to a lower grade of usage category: paperboard, tar paper, tablet backs, filler material, and even livestock fodder (mixed with blackstrap molasses). According to *Environmental Quality* (March 1972), the Bergstrom Paper Company of Neenah, Wisconsin, has been using recycled fibers for more than seventy years; one of its products, made from 100 percent recycled waste paper without de-inking, is sufficiently attractive to be used for greeting cards.

The point of the above discussion is to show that the number of re-use cycles is limited if the trend is always towards products of lower value. As Bergstrom has shown, recycling is highly desirable whenever possible. Nevertheless, no technological solutions are perfect; when we employ them, we must be aware of their limitations.

tion control is the problem of "pollution exchange," in which prevention of one kind of pollution is achieved by increasing another kind. This has already been alluded to in the case of paper recycling; there are, however, better examples. The most important concerns the generation of electric power.

The drawbacks associated with the burning of conventional fuel have already been mentioned: they include the release of carbon dioxide and the possible dangers of the greenhouse effect; the release of carbon monoxide, soot, sulfur dioxide, and other components of smog; the destruction of ecosystems because of strip mining, offshore oil well fires, and oil spills; and, possibly, the consumption of oxygen and lowering of world oxygen reserves. (On the basis of current information, this does not appear to be a global problem. Although Tokyo has experienced transient oxygen crises, they seem to be related not to the burning of fossil fuel but to the exposure of the air to oxygen-consuming soils during certain kinds of heavy construction.)

The introduction of nuclear power reactors can eliminate all these problems, but in return there are new or increased dangers: the release of radioactive pollutants from mines, uranium processing plants, ordinary reactor operations and accidents, and reactor waste disposal; serious thermal accidents, especially in liquid-metal fast breeder reactors; thermal pollution; and the secondary effects of massive amounts of cheap power on the world's ecosystems.

Technology has tackled all of these pollution exchange problems, except the last, with varying degrees of success. Only in the case of thermal pollution is there any chance to evaluate the results. Most power plants scheduled to start operations during the 1970s are at least ten times as large in terms of megawatt output as pre–World War II units. Since nuclear plants require forty percent more cooling water than fossil-fuel plants, the cooling burden placed on freshwater streams and lakes in the United States will be excessive. In order to prevent thermal pollution, a number of power companies have turned to cooling towers, which are either air-cooled by forced draft or depend on the evaporation of water for cooling. Because air has a far lower heat capacity than water, the forced draft towers must be enormous, and huge volumes of air must circulate rapidly through them. This, in turn, creates both an aesthetic problem (particularly in flat country) and an economic one. The evaporative coolers, on the other hand, release air laden with moisture, which in certain climates will condense to form giant fog banks. From the biological viewpoint, the cooling towers, despite their drawbacks, seem in most cases clearly preferable to the use of rivers or lakes for cooling. This might, therefore, be scored as a qualified technological success, although because of their cost few nuclear power facilities are now using towers. For most of the major pollution problems, however, even such little victories are rare indeed.

The second category consists of problems external to technology that have to do with public attitudes. Faced with the problem of industries which pollute either because there is no technological or economic alternative compatible with their survival or because it is convenient and profitable, the public seems incapable of coping with the situation via a meaningful change in life style. The recycling of paper is a necessary, albeit limited, way of coping with the pollution that goes along with the production and use of paper. But how much easier to use less paper in the first place! Consumption of everything from wrapping to note paper could be drastically reduced with little effort; but few make that effort. Computers, for example, spit out frightening quantities of paper each second, most of it absolutely blank. Each user may take home twenty or thirty feet of his computer "run," with possibly no more than one or two short words or numbers per double-spaced line. Big computers have the capacity to be programmed to save their own paper; the inconveniences would be trivial, yet it is rarely, if ever, done.

Another example is "throwaway" beverage containers. According to A. J. Darnay, Jr., of the Midwest Research Institute, production of nonreturnable bottles and cans (for beer and soft drinks) increased from 10 billion units in 1958 to 25.6 billion units in 1966, and, if the trend is allowed to continue, will reach 58 billion units in 1976. These containers contribute substantially to air and water pollution during their manufacture; and they are nondegradable and thus disfigure the landscape if they are discarded carelessly, or consume needed trash-disposal space when they find their way into refuse collection systems. Deposit-return bottles do not present this problem, and they are only a small inconvenience to the consumer, who may not even want to pay the extra cost of the throwaways. Yet throwaway containers have rapidly displaced returnable containers from the market. The average returnable bottle is sold and refilled twenty times before it breaks, so that for each deposit-return bottle twenty throwaways must be manufactured and ultimately discarded. According to the European Information Centre for Nature Conservation (Council of Europe), the use of glass throwaway and plastic substitutes for returnable bottles has also increased in Europe; but Finland and Norway have outlawed disposable bottles, and similar legislation is pending in Denmark and the Netherlands. In the United States, the state of Oregon banned throwaway cans and bottles after October 1, 1972. Although people seem quite willing to be coerced into conservation by such laws (indeed, they support the laws) they rarely take a *personal*, non-passive initiative to buy returnable bottles if the throwaways are also available.

In the case of some necessary consumer products, such as auto-mobiles and electric fixtures, the consumer has no choice but to pollute. Automobiles are offered for sale only with internal combustion engines. The external combustion steam engine is thought to be potentially safe, quiet, inexpensive to produce, and economical to drive and maintain; it allegedly can perform well and will not pollute the atmosphere with lead, carbon monoxide, and hydrocarbons. Yet the automobile industry, unwilling to pay for a complete retooling, is resisting even discussion of a possible change. Still more are the American auto, airline, and highway construction industries resisting the resuscitation of the cleanest and cheapest form of transportation, the railroads. Pollution is equally unavoidable in the case of electric fixtures and other items molded in plastic; these products must be discarded when they break because they are manufactured so that they cannot be repaired.

When the public *must* conform to the non-cyclical pattern of extraction and processing of raw materials, manufacture and consumption of finished products, and finally waste of finished products, then the economic factor may be the most important. Nevertheless, to repeat a statement made earlier, basic economics is not everything in pollution control. As the examples of waste paper and disposable containers demonstrate, something else is at work. Perhaps it is just inertia; perhaps it is misinformation; perhaps it is the same ego problem we saw operating in personal collecting; and perhaps, as the following paragraphs will attempt to show, it is something a bit more complicated.

Part of the problem has been characterized by the biologist Garrett Hardin as "the tragedy of the commons," where the "commons" refers to elements of our environment, such as air, which we think of as belonging to no one, and those of our activities, such as reproduction, which we think of as subject to no one's control. As Hardin points out, in the absence of coercion the rational individual (or industry) places himself at an intolerable competitive disadvantage if he heeds his conscience and stops exploiting the commons. "The rational man finds that his share of the cost of the wastes he discharges into the commons is less than the cost of purifying his wastes before releasing them." (These are not necessarily economic costs; frequently they amount to little more than a minor expenditure of time or effort.) In other words, the tragedy of the commons is that our system pits short-term self-interest (private interest) against long-term self-interest (public interest) in an impossible struggle.

The tragedy of the commons is not simply a matter of competitive disadvantage in trade. It is also a question of numbers and of feeling foolish. A public-spirited subway rider in New York, having finished the last piece of chewing gum in his pack, looks around for a trash barrel where he can leave the wrapper. The nearest one is a hundred feet away, but a quick glance in front of him shows the train tracks awash with old newspapers, bits of plastic, empty cigarette packs, fragments of glass bottles, brown paper bags—a living shrine and museum of garbage. One gum wrapper more or less really makes no difference; only a fool or a holy man would walk the hundred feet to the trash barrel. There are finally enough people in the world so that the sum total of thousands of individually insignificant assaults on the once limitless public resources of space, scenery, fauna, flora, air, water, and earth is very damaging, yet the individual act, *whether it be pollution or public-spirited restraint,* remains insignificant.

This dilemma goes far toward explaining why the public and business have been so resistant to the idea of voluntary control of pollution, even in the face of advertising campaigns, individual and group protest, and moral condemnation. All but the saints among us are polluters and nothing short of completely removing threatened areas from the realm of the commons—that is, instituting coercive control over everyone's access to air, land, and water—is likely to prevent us from destroying our environment and each other. Whether, in the long run, this represents a net loss or a gain in personal freedom is not yet clear, but the need to survive has made the question academic, for certain freedoms now endanger survival. That is why the last decades of the twentieth century will probably be characterized by increasing government control over individual activities that were once considered beyond the scope of mass regulation, freedoms that many of us will be loath to give up.

After a brief survey of the pitfalls and irregularities of the real world of pollution control, we return to the naive simplicity of the concept of the "technological fix." This is an ugly little phrase for such a grandiose idea: "Technology has disrupted our ecosystems and created many of our environmental problems; now let's use technology to fix the damage and set everything in order again." A fine and noble thought—provided one has never heard of Humpty Dumpty—but, sadly, a hopelessly impractical one, for several reasons.

First, the disintegration of some ecosystems is, on the time scale of human history, irreversible. Impatient engineers can no more restore them than they can repeal the laws of planetary motion. Even when secondary succession is restorative it is generally slow. Only in the case of river pollution are technological abatement procedures likely to bring the kind of quick results that impress those persons who think nature ought to function like a giant machine.

Second, there is the serious problem of pollution exchange. A large fraction of the technological triumphs of pollution control of which I am aware have on close examination seemed to stir up as many new environmental problems as they have solved. In some cases, at least, there may be nothing to be done about this within the context of the technology itself.

Third, there is the overwhelming obstacle of the limitation of the technological vision. The example of electric power generation is instructive. We have seen how the power industry has thrashed from one clumsy "solution" to another: from high sulfur oil to low sulfur oil, from oil to conventional nuclear reactors, from conventional reactors to fast breeder reactors, and so forth. Only in a few isolated and long-delayed instances has it occurred to the industry to ask the public to use less power. Clearly there is no technological solution for the environmental sequelae of power generation; for even if we were to find new ways of generating power without environmental hazard; this only accounts for the power *until the point at which it leaves the generating plant.* But power in any form has an impact on ecosystems and their communities; enormous uses of power cannot fail to pollute enormously. The answer here lies outside the technological vision and beyond the technological solution. We have come to the point in our development where we must ask, "Is technology, *per se,* a destructive force?" The response is "yes," insofar as we rely on it to cope with its own monsters. The "developed" world is suffering from a disease of misplaced context. Nearly all pollution control efforts are confounded in some degree by human population growth, by an economic system based on perpetual expansion, by the tragedy of the commons, by the monolithic and massive responses of modern government (in which all mistakes are big mistakes), and by the persnickety and obscure behavior of the biological world. Small wonder that we cannot fix everything by tightening gaskets and installing filters.

Industrial Accident Control

The complexity of the problem of industrial accident control is reflected in the measures necessary to prevent or reduce the danger of oil spills at sea. Ameliorative proposals center on the need for contingency plans, more research on oil-clearance methods, and an unscrambling of the international legal confusion concerning inquiry and liability in the event of accident. In the United States, contingency plans were prepared following a presidential memorandum in 1968; however, the apparent confusion surrounding clean-up efforts after the oil-well leak in California's Santa Barbara Channel in 1969 testifies to the need for further action. Detergents were used despite the Plymouth Laboratory's findings published after the *Torrey Canyon* disaster: "The more efficacious the detergent, the more toxic it is." Adequate contingency planning should provide for depots near all major waterways where oil booms, straw, powdered chalk, steam-cleaning equipment, and other comparatively safe oil removal aids can be stored for emergency use. Transportation and storage facilities for the recovered oil are also necessary. Local officials responsible for navigation, harbors, and beaches must be trained to cope with oil spills. Research on oil removal and disposal techniques should be intensified and should be concerned with finding substitutes for the toxic components of existing detergents. More work is also needed on methods of sinking oil at sea (only when this is deemed to be biologically the least offensive alternative) and of removing oil-sand crusts from beaches without causing erosion. Oil-eating bacteria offer some promise in a variety of applications. Finally, the Intergovernmental Maritime Consultative Organization (IMCO), an agency of the United Nations, has set up a committee to help define the legal rights of coastal states, assignment of liability, participants in investigations, insurance requirements for tankers, and regulations concerning the movement of salvage equipment when oil spills occur at sea.

Oil spills in marine or fresh waters could be greatly reduced by improvement in navigation aids and vessel design and by passage of tough enforceable laws requiring ship companies and offshore oil-well owners to observe safety precautions. The IMCO subcommittee on safety of navigation is concerned with sea lanes, navigational equipment, shore guidance, speed restrictions, periodic equipment checks, officer and crew training, use of automatic pilots, identification and charting of hazards, and reinforcement of lookout systems. There is great room for improvement in all these areas. According to *Environmental Science and Technology* (2,512,1968), U.S. regulations "do not require vessels to carry sailing directions, Notices to Mariners, and tide tables." Nor are charts of the locations of the more than 7000 oil wells and 1800 miles of pipeline in the Gulf of Mexico available to mariners.

Although the tankers being constructed today are reasonably well-designed, cargo transfer, deballasting, tank draining, and bilge draining features could be further improved to minimize oil losses. Size is also important: supertankers of more than 200,000 tons deadweight capacity may represent so great a damage potential (and so small an economic advantage) that their construction is unwarranted.* Some companies, such as Shell International Marine, Ltd., have stated that they see no advantage in exceeding this size limit; but a year after the sinking of the *Torrey Canyon*, Gulf Oil Corporation continued with plans to build six 300,000-ton tankers in Japanese shipyards.

There are obviously many other kinds of industrial accidents besides oil spills, but few are more complicated to control or have such widespread effects; and some of the lessons learned from them have general applicability. Hindsight is cheap, but both the *Torrey Canyon* and

---

* It has been argued that if tankers are kept small we will need more of them, and consequently there will be more accidents. This might be true, but a small oil spill is comparatively easy to contain and clean up, and unlikely to wreck the ecology of an entire section of coastline. The larger tankers, being difficult to maneuver and slow to stop or turn, may also be more prone to accidents near dangerous coasts and in crowded shipping lanes.

Santa Barbara Channel accidents might have been avoided if there had been some standard compulsory procedure for estimating the accident potential before operations had begun. Too often we ignore the environmental hazards associated with technological and economic "progress." Existing safety regulations and codes never seem to cover the entire scope of industrial operations from raw materials to the distribution (and use) of finished products, nor do they provide the public with meaningful opportunities to examine and delay projects. In an age when every big city is destined to be surrounded by nuclear reactors, and when environmental poisons are produced and shipped in 300,000-ton quantities, these problems need both thought and action to prevent catastrophes. A first step in all countries with an entrenched technology is the complete separation of regulatory from promotional functions. Preferably these should be in separate agencies of government, with the protective and regulatory agencies having an effective veto power over the plans of the others. In the United States, the Environmental Protection Agency represents some progress toward this goal, but it is still too weak (compared with the Atomic Energy Commission, the Departments of Transportation, Commerce, Defense, Agriculture, and Interior, the Federal Power Commission, the Corps of Engineers, the Bureau of Reclamation, and others) and too responsive to the political demands of the executive branch of government (that is, local environmental action groups and informed private citizens have inadequate access to the decision-making process).

Protection of Natural Communities

One way to preserve natural communities is to insulate them from the adverse influences of population and technology by according them some sort of protected status. Before briefly considering several ways of doing this, however, a word of warning is necessary. Officially designated parks, monuments, and wildlife refuges are not necessarily protected. Many government agencies have high-priority rights of eminent domain, and some, like the Atomic Energy Commission and the Department of Defense, exercise these rights in an atmosphere of comparative secrecy. In 1965, for example, these two agencies detonated an underground atomic explosion on Amchitka Island in the middle of the Aleutian Islands National Wildlife Refuge, and subsequently announced and began to carry out plans for five more atomic explosions, including the giant "Cannikan" blast in 1971. This island, one of the last abodes of the sea otter, was thus converted from a wildlife refuge to an atomic proving ground without benefit of democratic review and in spite of the protests of Alaska's governor, Walter J. Hickel (later Secretary of the Interior). Nearly all "protected" land is under continual challenge by a variety of interests, such as Disney Productions with its proposed resort in the Mineral King National Game Refuge (to be serviced via a proposed superhighway cut through Sequoia National Park), the Kennecott Corporation with its proposed open-pit copper mine near Image Lake in the middle of the Glacier Peak Wilderness Area, or the Metropolitan Museum of Art with its nibbles at the irreplaceable park land of Manhattan Island.

There is ample precedent for the creation of new national parks, additions to existing national parks, and designations of wilderness areas by legislative acts, and since these processes are subject to the same pressures already described, there is no need for elaboration. But there are new and exciting opportunities to protect natural communities at the municipal and county level, particularly in suburban areas where the need is greatest. Increasingly, the problems of conserving natural communities, designing livable residences, and providing outdoor recreation facilities have been drawing together. Leadership in this last great attempt to provide a healthful and healthy environment for the urban and suburban dweller has fortunately passed into the hands of a small group of unusually practical and creative men. Names like Ian McHarg, Phillip H. Lewis, Jr., William H. Whyte, and Charles E. Little are not known to the majority of city and suburb residents, who are nevertheless already in their debt.

Every piece of accessible land, public or private, within fifty to a hundred miles of all major cities is in danger of being used for residential or commercial construction by 1985. Thousands of suburban and semirural communities, which were created to provide former city dwellers with peaceful and natural surroundings in which to relax after a hectic day in the city, are being turned into "development slums." The tired commuter often fights traffic in the evening to come "home" to an environment in which the surface area consists of thirty percent asphalt, thirty percent rooftop, thirty percent lawn, and less than ten percent of the kinds of woods and meadows that once made the area beautiful. In addition, the suburbanite must pay exorbitant property taxes so that his municipality can afford to cope with the flooding and erosion caused by the destruction of marshes, swamps, and forests; with the necessity of supplying water, police and fire protection, and waste removal services; and with the overwhelming costs of schools.

Contrary to popular belief, the addition of new residential property to the tax rolls, particularly in development blocs, rarely helps the community economically. Although tax returns increase, the cost of services to be borne by the entire community increases more. Charles E. Little, of New York's Open Space Institute, recounts the story of Closter, New Jersey, which in 1965 wanted to acquire seven parcels of land totaling eighty acres, to be set aside for limited recreational purposes. Acquisition costs were approximately $500,000, and some residents wondered if the town might not be better off by letting the owners sell their property to residential builders. At this point Mayor James E. Carson made some calculations: assuming that the eighty acres could accommodate 160 houses, these houses in turn would contain approximately 200 children to be educated at $720 per pupil per year, for an annual total of $144,000. Additional garbage collection, police services, fire protection, lighting, and other services would cost about $12,000 annually. Thus the total annual increase in municipal costs would be $156,000. Tax returns from these proposed new residences would amount to approximately $100,000, leaving a $56,000 annual deficit to be shared by all residents in the form of permanently increased taxes. On the other hand, if the community bought the land for parks—even assuming no federal or state aid (which they have received)—the land would be completely paid for in ten years, at approximately the same annual cost but with no subsequent expenses except for nominal maintenance costs.

Ecological balances are too delicate and land is too expensive for conservation to proceed haphazardly. Conservation and development must be planned together, and with equal care. Ian McHarg, of the Department of Landscape Architecture and Regional Planning of the University of Pennsylvania, has formulated the following criteria for selecting "open space" in the Philadelphia metropolitan area:

Surface water and waterfront land should be used only for functions that cannot occur elsewhere, including harbors and water-using industries. McHarg estimates that this would consume only one percent of the river area around Philadelphia, leaving the remainder for forestry, agriculture, recreation, and open space adjacent to housing.

The wastes entering streams should be regulated according to the ability of the waterway to absorb pollutants without seriously altering the aquatic flora and fauna.

Marshes must be protected from drainage or filling in order to serve as wildlife reservoirs and flood storage areas.

Floodplains that are under water once every fifty years or more should be closed to all residential and commercial building construction. Recreational, agricultural, and open-space uses and related functions are excepted.

Ground water resources, or aquifers, must be protected by careful management of deep-well injection, sewage disposal, rate of water withdrawal, and similar practices.

Good soil is an irreplaceable asset, slow to form, and like many complex living systems, easily killed. The best agricultural land should be used as such and not be permitted to be developed for other purposes.

Steep slopes (12° or more) erode rapidly when their natural cover is disturbed. This in turn causes siltation of waterways, flooding, failure to replenish aquifers, and destruction of terrestrial and aquatic habitats. Steep slopes should remain completely untouched if unforested, and sparsely developed (less than one house per three acres) if forested.

Forests and woodlands, which are "the major regulators of equilibrium in the water system," which "exercise a profound effect upon climate," and which are "a prime scenic and recreational resource," should be used for forestry, water catchment areas, air purification zones, recreation, and cluster housing restricted to an overall density of one house per acre or less.

McHarg claims studies indicate that if these guidelines were followed in the 3500-square-mile area of Greater Philadelphia, development could proceed normally without upsetting the local ecology or destroying the natural beauty of the region, or adding to the public's economic burden.

Philip H. Lewis, Jr., project director of the monumental Upper Mississippi River Comprehensive Basin Study (Department of Interior), has formulated a different but equally useful set of guidelines for determining which land should be conserved. Lewis and his associates, with the cooperation of conservationists, county agents, and the general public, prepared a "Resource Value Point System" in which hundreds of natural and cultural features of the landscape were characterized and assigned values in terms of their relative importance to recreation and maintenance of environmental quality. These features were then located and charted for a number of areas in the Mississippi Basin and Great Lakes region (for example, Wisconsin; see table, p. 238). According to Lewis, the most striking finding was that 85 to 90 percent of all identified natural and cultural resources could be seen to lie within "environmental corridors" that coincided with topographic corridors delineated by waterways and associated ridges.

Thus, both McHarg and Lewis agree that the key to land acquisition in any regional conservation program is the distribution of water. Only after this has been carefully studied can conservationists and planners decide what land ought to be preserved as open space. If environmental corridors are maintained intact, or nearly so, the result is a network of park land and scenic areas readily accessible to nearly all the population, and which frequently extend, as in the case of Washington, D.C.'s Rock Creek Park, into the heart of the central city.

Once it has been decided what land to acquire, there is the problem of gaining title or control. Few counties or municipalities can readily afford to spend vast sums on land, yet the land must be acquired. In

Some natural and man-made resources inventoried in the Wisconsin study

WATER	Recreational	WILDLIFE
Natural	Ski trails	Bear
	Hiking	Wolf
Waterfalls	Picnic areas	Deer
Bathing beaches	Nature camps	Pheasant
Natural springs, Artesian		Beaver
flows	VEGETATION	Mink
Canoe routes		Ducks
Wild rice areas	*Natural*	Geese
Exceptional islands	Virgin stands (Timber)	Swans
Fish habitat	Rare remnants	Eagles
Chasms	Wildflowers	Great Horned Owls
Trout	Orchards	Ospreys
Catfish		Falcons
	Man-made	Cranes
Man-made	Fire trails and breaks	
Swimming facilities	State forests (existing,	VISUAL QUALITY OF SPACE
Boating facilities, Ramps	potential)	
Boating areas		Enclosed partly by vege-
Harbors of refuge	HISTORICAL AND CULTURAL	tation, partly by topog-
Campsites		raphy
Fish hatcheries	Blacksmith shops	
Mill ponds	Bridges (covered, etc.)	Enclosed by solid and
Reservoirs	Trading posts	open vegetation
	Old forts	
WETLAND	Battlefields	Enclosed by open vege-
	Historical markers	tation
Exceptional wetlands	Museums	
Wildlife observation	Modern mines	Enclosed by open topog-
Wildlife hunting	Ghost towns	raphy
Wildlife preserves	Theaters	
		TOURING FACILITIES
TOPOGRAPHIC	ARCHEOLOGICAL	
		Accommodations
Unique geological forma-	Quarry flint	Hospital
tions	Campsite	Water
	Cornfield	
Caves	Trail	
Exceptional glacial	Historic village sites	
remains	Historic cemetery	
Mineral ore outcroppings	Burial ground	

recent years, in response to this need, a number of organizations and individuals have devised and publicized a whole catalogue of ways in which local governments can acquire land without going bankrupt or alienating large segments of the community. The America the Beautiful Fund of the Natural Area Council, Inc., publishes a pamphlet series called *Aims*, in which such topics as land trusts, grants-in-aid, environmental manpower needs, and even tree-moving machinery are discussed. The Open Space Institute, Inc., has published several reports, including *Stewardship*, a land preservation manual for the private land-owner, and *Challenge of the Land*, by Charles E. Little, a short, practical, and extremely well-written manual "for municipal officials and civic leaders" who want to know the whole range of basic land acquisition techniques, including the political and legal pitfalls that must be avoided. *The Last Landscape*, by William H. Whyte, is a somewhat more theoretical but equally valuable book on the same theme, and there are many others.

A complete account of all current methods of land protection would fill a lengthy volume, but a few of the more common ones can be briefly described. First, direct acquisition by purchase can be financed by bond issues and assisted by federal or state grants. Sources of federal funds in the United States include the Department of Agriculture's "Greenspan" program for purchase of agricultural land to be dedicated to conservation or recreation purposes, or Public Law 566, which provides money for constructing small dams and associated recreational areas. The Department of Commerce may pay up to three-quarters of the cost of parks in certain areas. The Department of the Interior administers conservation funds through its Bureau of Outdoor Recreation. The Open Space Program of the Department of Housing and Urban Development can give matching funds for land purchase. Even the Department of Defense* and the Department of Health, Education, and Welfare can assist in safeguarding land for conservation. In the case of direct land purchase by local governments, the problem seems to be not financing, but presenting the case to the public in a forthright and professional manner.

Second, there is the technique known as "cluster development," in which a residential builder agrees to cluster new homes on smaller-than-normal lots so that part of his tract can be set aside for recreation and conservation. This concept works well only if the local government can decide which acreage should be set aside, and if that acreage

---

* Some of the finest urban and rural landscapes left in the United States are located within the confines of military installations. The Presidio of San Francisco and Fort Lewis in the State of Washington are examples. A few bases now have conservation officers or base agronomists.

is both legally and financially protected in perpetuity. On occasion, cluster development has been used by unscrupulous developers to crowd an excessive number of people onto their land. This is easily avoided by alert city officials; well-managed cluster developments make attractive and viable communities.

Third, many private owners of large tracts of land are willing to donate part of their land to municipalities or to conservation organizations. A variety of perfectly valid motivations are involved, including tax relief, enchancement of the value of their remaining land (because it is now next to a park), and philanthropy. The Open Space Institute estimates that there are approximately 10,000 private owners of "significant open land" in the New York metropolitan region, and a special landowner program has been designed to advise them of the advantages of land donation.

Fourth, there are "easements," in which the owner of land agrees to give permanent protection to some natural feature of his land without surrendering actual ownership. This method has not been very popular, but it has worked well in some cases. In central Florida, the Audubon Society has been able, through the cooperation of many cattle ranchers, to protect bald eagle nesting trees scattered over tens of thousands of acres (although it cannot shield the eagles from the efforts of DDT).

Fifth, municipal zoning such as Westport, Connecticut's Design Development District (DDD), can be used, cautiously, to bring commercial offices and light industry into residential areas, provided attractive structures are built and a significant amount of the company land is set aside as permanent open space. In such an arrangement the participating company benefits by having a good environment for its employees in a setting that will not deteriorate; and the town benefits by both adding to its tax revenues and protecting part of its natural landscape.

Sixth, tracts of land may be purchased by the Nature Conservancy or by similar nonprofit conservation organizations for donation or sale to local, state, or federal agencies as parks, or for protection as private wildlife preserves.

Conservation Law

With the recent successes of environmental lawsuits in a number of countries, conservationists, who are unaccustomed to victory, are apt to see the legal approach to conservation as the answer to all their prayers. Good lawyers are not so easily misled by a few decisions in their favor. The law and the judiciary are valuable tools in the fight to protect endangered communities (and species); like any tools, they have their limitations, and if used sloppily or inappropriately will yield poor results. The law is a precise subject whose rules and traditions are important to its practitioners. It is also a profession that is sensitive in its own slow way to massive and sustained expressions of the public will. Thus the legal efforts of conservationists are and will be successful only when they can convince judges that they are merely asking that well-established criteria and procedures, long used in other areas, now be applied to matters involving the public concern for environmental quality. The United States, which has a rapidly developing body of conservation law, and which needs it badly, seems the best choice as an example for further discussion.

The great value of the law to conservationists is a recent discovery. Indeed the discovery process has been mutual. As the conservationists have begun to learn the strange customs and ways of the courts, judges and lawyers have simultaneously begun to find that, like two Romance languages, conservation and the law share some basic elements that can provide a common ground for understanding. Behind the specialist's fussy details of conservation science and technology and his elusive aesthetic arguments lie working principles such as public trust, irreparable harm, legal obligation, personal damages, and deprivation of legal or constitutional rights—principles with which any legal mind can feel thoroughly at home.

But though there is a common basis for action, it is not a basis for all actions conservationists may desire. It is extremely unlikely, for example, that lawsuits will provide much relief in cases of long-standing abuse, especially if that abuse has heretofore been accepted as part of the way of life, if it is hard to define, and if it would require a major financial or other effort to correct. Mr. Jones may be able to prove that fumes from the expressway that runs past his timber tract are killing and stunting his pine trees, but conservation lawyers are likely to tell him that his best remedy is to replant with yellow poplar; no judge is going to listen seriously to his complaint. It is just not suitable for action under existing law.

In *Defending the Environment*, Michigan law professor Joseph Sax lucidly explains what conservation lawsuits *are* good for: "*Litigation*," he says, is "*a means of access for the ordinary citizen to the process of governmental decision-making*. It is in many circumstances the only tool for genuine citizen participation in the operative process of government." Two points are immediately plain. First, legal actions offer a way, often the only way, to limit and monitor the vast power of semi-autonomous government departments and agencies, including those that are supposed to protect the environment, but don't. Second, the courtroom is best used to prevent or enjoin potentially damaging actions rather than to issue orders to correct or undo damage that has already been sustained. Exceptions to the second rule occur when the damage is recent, easy to correct, and judges can be convinced that defendants willfully ignored the law in their original action.

The great enthusiasm for the courtroom that has taken hold of conservation activists in the United States is a measure of the degree to which government agencies such as the Corps of Engineers, the Departments of Agriculture, Defense, Interior, Transportation, and Commerce, the Federal Power Commission, and the Atomic Energy Commission have ruled their normal operating decisions off limits to concerned private citizens and organizations. It is also a measure of the abuse that has resulted from this unilateral assumption of power. In fact it is the perception of this abuse that has caused the public outcry, and that outcry has certainly not hurt the conservationists in court. Increasingly, judges are willing at least to listen to public complaints about agency steamroller tactics. More significant, environmental lawyers are learning how to use existing laws to protect "public rights." Now that conservation has earned its day in court, new protections are discovered daily in laws that have gathered dust for as much as three quarters of a century.

One recent case exemplifies many of the points just made. Not as dramatic as the successful politico-legal struggle against the Cross-Florida Barge Canal or the unsuccessful international battle against the AEC's "Cannikan" nuclear test on Amchitka Island, this case involved only an acre and a half of an obscure scrap of marsh, which prior to litigation had not even been dignified with a name. The case is officially known as *The United States of America, Plaintiff, v. Major General John C. Baker, Chief of Staff to the Governor, State of New York, Division of Military and Naval Affairs, and Colonel Arthur Sulger, as Post Commander, Camp Smith, Peekskill, New York, Defendants;* more simply the Camp Smith Marsh case.

Camp Smith is a National Guard post on the Hudson River at Peekskill, New York, downstream and on the opposite bank from the U.S. Military Academy at West Point. The Camp is situated at the confluence of Putnam Creek and the Peekskill Bay of the Hudson River, and includes four acres of a predominantly narrow-leaved cattail (*Typha anqustifolia*) marsh, which receives both fresh water from the creek and brackish water from the tidal ebb and flow of this estuarine portion of the river. On or about June 1970, a private contractor began to demolish some old barracks at Camp Smith, prior to erecting new ones. Having been authorized by the post commander, the contractor dumped the rubble from the old barracks into one and a half acres of the marsh and along the shores of the brook, with the intention of filling the area for a parking lot. The rubble, according to subsequent testimony, consisted of "vast quantities" of scrap wood, masonry, boards, tree limbs, factory pallets, bed springs, underbrush, paper, and other items.

If all had gone as such matters usually go, there would now be a new parking lot next to the new barracks at Camp Smith. Today, however, there is no lot, and most of the rubble has been removed at state expense, the rest to be removed later. What Colonel Sulger had no way of knowing at the time, and which eventually upset his straightforward plans for the marsh, was, first, the presence in the area of citizens who were concerned with the preservation of tidal marshes; they included David Seymour, the warden of the Audubon Society's Constitution Marsh Sanctuary opposite West Point, and John Sedgwick, a high school environmental studies teacher in Lakeland, New York. Also presumably unknown to Colonel Sulger was the obscure legal fact that the Camp Smith Marsh, connected to the Hudson by culverts under a highway, might be considered a part of the "navigable waters of the United States," according to a federal anti-pollution statute enacted in 1899.

The Rivers and Harbors Act of 1899 states that parts of the navigable waters of the United States and their tributaries cannot be filled except by permit from the Army Corps of Engineers. The post commander had not requested a permit, although there is no reason to believe that one would necessarily have been denied. This oversight provided grounds for a case. On June 21, 1971, Whitney North Seymour, Jr., the U.S. Attorney for the Southern District of New York, filed a complaint in Federal District Court for a preliminary injunction against continued filling of the marsh, and for removal of the existing fill. The government's case was argued by Assistant U.S. Attorney Ross Sandler.

The case was concise and well-prepared. The government introduced affidavits from four expert witnesses. Leroy MacKenzie, a harbor inspector for the Corps of Engineers, verified the accusation that the marsh had been filled and stated that he had advised Colonel Sulger (in April 1971, after much of the fill had been deposited) of his need for a permit, yet had observed no subsequent change in the filled area. David Seymour, the Audubon warden, testified in general terms to the value of the Hudson River marshlands. E. H. Buckley, senior scientist and plant biochemist with the Boyce Thompson Institute for Plant Research, itemized the specific value of the marsh in terms of converting (via food chains) sewage and waste nutrients from the polluted river into usable marine resources such as fish and ducks, or into food organisms for these animals. Buckley was very explicit:

> To the extent that the river cleans itself the governments of the municipalities, the state and the nation do not have to devote tax dollars for tertiary sewerage treatment. I have estimated on the basis of my detailed studies that an acre of tidal marsh, if thought of as a tertiary sewerage treatment system is worth between $10,000 and $30,000 annually. The Camp Smith Marsh is one of the more valuable tidal marshes of the Hudson River

on a per acre basis. This is true because the Camp Smith Marsh is in a location where it "treats" sewerage nutrients flowing not only down the river but also those flowing up the river from New York City as a result of tidal action.

In addition to this significant and unique bit of testimony, Buckley offered his own services and those of other scientists at Boyce Thompson, free of charge, in supervising both the removal of the fill and any replanting that might be necessary, should the court issue the injunction. He also stated his opinion that the marsh vegetation would not be able to regenerate itself if the fill were left after August 1971. The remaining statement was made by the high school teacher, John Sedgwick. Excerpts from it are quoted as follows:

> Not only is Camp Smith Marsh important as a cornerstone of vital processes in the lower Hudson River; it also has major educational value as a tidal wetland. From an ecological viewpoint the tidal marsh provides the student with a unique self-contained habitat in which to observe a large variety of scientific phenomena. The concept of plant succession and species variation can be dramatically observed at the Camp Smith Marsh. I have led student investigation of this marsh on approximately six occasions and I and my students have inventoried the following plant life. [A description of more than fifty plants, arranged according to micro-habitat, followed.] Student mapping and identification of the vegetation and its zonation provides a productive exercise from which the concepts of plant adaptation and succession can be developed. Students can and have collected and identified many animal forms within the marsh. . . .

Such fish as menhaden, redear sunfish, yellow perch, and banded killifish (a favorite food of the valuable striped bass, which use the estuary as a breeding ground) were listed, as well as reptiles, birds, mammals, insects, shrimp, spiders, crabs, and microscopic animals. The students also observed the nesting and social habits of the dominant marsh bird, the red-winged blackbird; studied bacterial decomposition and peat formation; investigated simple food chains; and "analyzed the chemical and physical character of the water to determine the relationships between such things as temperature or salinity to animal and plant populations." Not surprisingly, Sedgwick concluded his statement by describing the marsh as an "invaluable natural and educational resource."

In response to the federal complaint, the state and the National Guard offered to remove the debris when an engineering batallion had its regular summer exercises the next year, and estimated that the job would take a year. Quicker action was impossible, they claimed, because the state legislature had not authorized funds for reclaiming the marsh. U.S. Attorney Sandler stated that this plan was not acceptable to the plaintiff because of the possibility of irreparable damage to the marsh in the event of delay.

On July 29, 1971, Federal District Judge Morris I. Lasker announced his decision. He found first that the Camp Smith Marsh, as a matter of law, was within the navigable waters of the United States by virtue of its tidal flow, and he agreed with the plaintiff that the Court had jurisdiction under the Rivers and Harbors Act of 1899. Concerning the central question of judicial relief, Judge Lasker stated:

> In the first place, there is no doubt about the value of the area in its original wetlands condition. . . . There are ecological values which are intended to be protected by the Act which confers jurisdiction here and by recent Acts enacted by the Congress which are referred to in the papers of the Government. . . . There is no doubt . . . that the marsh has been damaged by the fill and that if it were to continue in its present condition the damage would be literally irreparable. . . . I find there is no reason to hold a hearing on this subject and the application of the Government for a preliminary injunction is granted.

By late October 1971, the National Guard had satisfactorily completed the first and major stage of marsh reclamation, a week and a half ahead of schedule. Most of the vegetation in the filled area to within fifteen feet of the edges was found to be dead; and E. H. Buckley and his group were preparing to begin controlled replanting, with cattail, of selected portions of the reclaimed area by next spring. Killifish, arriving once again with the tides, were a preliminary indication of how rapidly animal life would be able to respond to the return of marsh vegetation.

The Camp Smith Marsh, October 1971. The marsh is the roughly triangular area bounded by trees (right), the highway (center), and the barracks (foreground). Putnam Creek winds through the marsh to join the Hudson River's Peekskill Bay. The filled portion of the marsh is the oval area adjacent to the barracks; bulldozers are at work removing the fill (see text for further details). (Courtesy U.S. Coast Guard)

The Camp Smith Marsh case makes pleasant reading for those interested in preserving natural communities. Everyone can be reasonably satisfied with the outcome: a much-needed marsh is being restored and scientists will gain valuable information in the process; students will continue to study wetland ecology; the Hudson will be cleansed (although perhaps not so thoroughly as the Augean stables, which it resembles); the Corps of Engineers' harbor inspectors have been vindicated; the State of New York has lost a case but gained a valuable ally in the protection of its marshes; and even the National Guard has

247

suffered little more than a loss of face. To the readers of this book, however, the Camp Smith Marsh case has an additional value as a working example of the uses and limitations of the law in conservation.

In reading any account of the case (and this is even more striking when one has the original documents at hand), it is easy to lose sight of the central issue of the proceedings while examining the lengthy affidavits concerning the value of a marsh. Legally, the important fact was that a part of the "navigable waters" of the United States had been filled without a permit from the Corps of Engineers, *as required by law.* What then was the point of all the testimony about the uses of wet-lands? The answer is that it probably was intended to aid the judge in two ways. First, it led him—an overworked federal judge confronted with many more serious problems—to agree that it would be worth-while to apply and enforce an old law in a way that no one had bothered to do before, namely to protect a tidal marsh. Many conserva-tionists do not realize that judges are not honor bound to listen to all their legitimate complaints and grievances. Conservation lawyers must prepare the ground by first finding a law that has been broken and then by amassing evidence that the violation is not trivial. The second func-tion of the affidavits was to document the need and urgency of remov-ing the fill, a step that goes well beyond issuing an injunction against continued filling. Professor Sax has remarked that judges are reluctant to tell defendants in environmental suits to undo things that have already been done (hence the Rodman Lake drawdown controversy). In the Camp Smith case, according to Judge Lasker's own statement, the plaintiff's witnesses convinced him that there was a better chance of rapid recovery if the fill were removed promptly.

In *Defending the Environment* Sax writes that "the role of courts is not to make public policy, but to help assure that public policy is made by the appropriate entity, rationally and in accord with the aspirations of the democratic process." What Judge Lasker was doing in the marsh controversy was, in a sense, fulfilling the duties of the Corps of En-gineers, whose right to make an administrative decision had been illegally pre-empted by the National Guard post commander. Para-doxically, Judge Lasker was less lenient than the Corps has been in granting other filling permits; he acted as he believed the Corps *should* have acted. This served the dual purpose of righting a wrong and at the same time indicating to the Corps, whose bureaucratic procedures have hitherto kept it semi-autonomous, what questions it ought to ask in future cases involving the filling of tidal marshes, in order to protect the public interest and to carry out its legislative mandate.

One curious statement of the judge inadvertently points out another major function of the courts in today's conservation battles. His legal justification for his decision was, "There are ecological values which are intended to be protected by the Act which confers jurisdiction here [the 1899 law] and by recent Acts enacted by the Congress. . . ." In fact, as Judge Lasker must have known, the 1899 law was drafted long before anyone thought of ecological values, especially values of marshes. In other words, the flexible interpretation that the 1899 Congress cared anything about ecology and the fate of tidal marshes not only conferred jurisdiction on the court but enabled a perceptive judge to translate a growing public pressure and impatience into terms that could have an effect upon the actions of the Corps without involving it in direct controversy. More important, judicial decisions of this sort are a clear, if implicit, way of saying to Congress, "Your existing statutes do not offer the direct environmental protection that the public now demands, but you are on the right track. Make our job easier by writing effective and appropriate laws." For this and other reasons, court cases are often the prelude to legislative action. An example is the *qui tam* legislation recently introduced into Congress, which would enable private citizens and groups to bring suit on behalf of the United States in some cases where there was a suspicion that anti-pollution statutes had been violated, but where the government itself had not taken action.

A final lesson can be extracted from the case of the Camp Smith Marsh. In his decision the judge cited at least four different kinds of value that could be attached to the marsh: educational value, "wildlife" value, economic value as a spawning ground for commercial fish, and a calculated monetary value as a natural sewage treatment facility. Which of these values were most important to the judge? We cannot be sure, but most readers will probably agree that the first two alone might not have won the case.

The laws that must be used to evaluate claims of environmental damage form part of a system that evolved to protect private goods. Private goods always have a monetary value, and this has proven to be a useful common denominator in the courts. Petty and grand larceny are not distinguished by the intentions of the thief or by the nature of the goods stolen, but by the cash value of the missing items. Can the idea of damages in cases involving the environment as a public trust be separated from the question of monetary value? Most advice to conservationists today is to work out monetary values for environmental amenities. No doubt this can and must be done in many cases: there is either the ingenious and legitimate value calculated by E. H. Buckley for a marsh-as-sewage-treatment-plant, or the ingenious but rather shady "recreational value" assigned by the Corps of Engineers when it wants to doctor a failing cost-benefit ratio. But even if we can work out the monetary worth of a scenic vista, how do we convert such ecological coinage as high species diversity (which may be worth the ransom of all life on earth) into dollars, and what do we do with Arizona's commercially worthless but biologically magnificent desert fish? Not long ago the author was privileged to see a full-grown timber rattlesnake minding its own business on a sunny, isolated hillside not far from Manhattan. What is the going price for rattlesnakes undisturbed in their natural habitat? Compromise is fine, but is it compromise or suicide to insist that *all* natural features worth saving be valued as "resources" or not at all? Who would judge the literary worth of a Shakespeare play from a Portuguese translation? Monetary worth is not a suitable symbolic system for representing the true value of some components of the living world. This problem was not created by judges, lawyers, or legislators; it was created by a life style, and the economic system which is the heart of that life style is discussed later.

The report of one small case prosecuted by the government is totally insufficient to convey the magnitude of the upsurge in environmental lawsuits, especially in the private sector. The best illustration is provided by the recent successes and growth of an organization known as the Environmental Defense Fund. First incorporated in 1967, it consisted initially of a handful of concerned lawyers and scientists, the latter mostly biologists at the State University of New York at Stony Brook. Office space was eventually found in a single room above the Stony Brook Post Office. The early fortunes of EDF depended almost entirely upon the talent and energies of two remarkable individuals: Charles F. Wurster, a young organic chemist turned biologist, and Victor Yannacone, a pioneering environmental lawyer with an intuitive grasp of the most complex scientific problems in the realm of ecology. Working together on the now-celebrated Wisconsin DDT hearings (which led to one of the first statewide bans against this chemical), they produced a scientific and legal *tour de force* which has set the pattern for many subsequent cases. By late 1971, after a notable string of legal victories, EDF had grown almost beyond recognition. Wurster was still active in cases concerning insecticides, but Yannacone had left to carry on a private environmental law practice. There were three branch offices of EDF besides the main office in a hundred-year-old farmhouse in East Setauket, New York. Organization business was conducted by twenty-three full-time employees, including eight attorneys and five Ph.D. scientists; the Scientific Advisory Committee of EDF numbered approximately 700 environmental specialists in several countries; and the Legal Advisory Committee was composed of approximately sixty attorneys. Members of both advisory committees, all volunteers, were prepared to provide specialized advice and services or to testify in court, on short notice if necessary. With these resources at its command, the Environmental Defense Fund was simultaneously prosecuting nearly fifty environmental cases throughout the country, and was still expanding in 1972.

Management of Natural Communities

Before a natural community can be managed, its principal elements and their principal interactions must be known. At the least, a managed community should be characterized with respect to species composition, population sizes, and history of fluctuations of these two variables, whenever possible. Errors, false assumptions, and oversimplifications in evaluating community attributes can result in mismanagement and the loss of natural features that should have been preserved.

The following discussion applies primarily to wildlife refuges, national parks and forests, wilderness areas, and other large tracts of land. With the exception of ecologically unusual and fragile communities like the ancient holly forest on Sandy Hook, New Jersey, most small and open-space parcels of land are best managed by limiting recreational and related uses to a reasonable level and by interfering with natural processes only when there is no alternative.

An example of the management problems that stem from application of ecological theory based on conjecture rather than factual data was described in 1964 by Hugh Raup of the Harvard Forest. The Harvard Forest project was started by Harvard University at Petersham, Massachusetts, in 1908; its development plan at that time was based on the prevailing assumption that the "primeval" forests of the pre-Colonial era had been rich and productive and that the surviving forests of twentieth-century New England were sorry remnants of the original forest, still suffering the consequences of early depredations by the European colonists. A guiding corollary of this assumption was that, with proper management, the Harvard Forest could be restored to its former productivity and that it would pay for itself while serving as a model of sustained-yield forestry.

According to Raup the experiment was a complete failure. He says: "At the end of half a century the Harvard Forest, as a demonstration of sustained yield, was a sorry spectacle. It had almost no annual income, and it had lost two-thirds of its capital, due almost entirely to external causes over which it had no control, and which had been unpredictable." Although the economic reasons for this failure are not entirely relevant here, there is a strong indication (as Raup suggests) that the original productivity assumptions based on the concept of a rich primeval American forest were wrong, and that this in turn generated misleading estimates of both the potential productivity of the Harvard Forest and the demand for its lumber on the open market.

Using a variety of methods (many available in 1908), including

The Harvard Forest, an experimental forest originally designed to provide a model system for modern forestry techniques. Its commercial failure has taught us much about the ecology of forests in the Northeast. (Jack J. Karnig)

examination of early historical accounts of the landscape, studies of soils, and analyses of tree ages versus species distribution in existing forests, Raup and his associates have concluded that the pre-Colonial forests were similar in many respects to those relatively undisturbed forests existing today.* "Our natural vegetation in America, even before the coming of Europeans, seems to have lived in a continuing state of major readjustment. Its history of disaster [such as wind and fire] had atomized it, and this I conceive to be one of the greatest blessings we received when we inherited it." Unlike a "fragile ecosystem," this forest was adapted to being destroyed in patches, and therefore suitable for occasional logging. But it was not likely to produce giant old trees in great quantities if left alone for a while.

Thus, in the first decades of this century, the lack of attention to the ecological history of the Harvard Forest community led to two serious management mistakes: first, an overestimate of future productivity; and second, a mistaken emphasis on long-range planning because of the false premise on which some of the early foresters based their understanding of American forest ecosystems. Of course economic return is not the yardstick by which we measure all management efforts in protected areas; nevertheless, the lesson is plain. Ecology was not then and is not yet a fully predictive science; community management, to be successful, must strive to base itself on the maximum amount of ecological data, be responsive to change, not be unduly influenced by rigid ecological theories and models, and utilize the best historical information available.

Good management of natural communities is not synonomous with blanket protection of all species. Occasionally, populations of some species must be thinned to protect the rest of the community. This is especially true of vertebrate herbivores, now that large predators have

* For example, the picture of a damaged forest slowly recovering from Colonial depredations is contradicted by Raup's data gathered from another northeastern forest: "Individual old trees ranging in age up to 300 years were found throughout the forest. . . . Wherever found they matched the species and growth forms around them, thus suggesting that neither the trees nor the sites had changed much during their lifetimes."

been virtually eliminated from most communities. Population regulation techniques can be applied for either or both of two purposes:
keeping particular animal or plant populations at peak productivity
for economic gain, and maintaining populations at optimum size for the
good health of the community. Except when dealing with pests, the
procedure in the two cases is often the same; populations must be kept
at less than their maximum possible density. Optimum population
densities vary with the species and community, and their determination
is a complex process. At a simpler level, many of the changes that
occur in population density can be described by the sigmoid (S-shaped)
population-growth curve (see graph, p. 256), which plays an important
role in the practice of ecological management.

An excellent example of the role of active intervention and management is the rapidly developing agricultural field of "biological control,"
where the "community" may be no more complicated (but hardly
simple!) than a crop plant, a pest of the plant, and a natural enemy of
the pest. C. B. Huffaker and his associates, of the Divisions of Biological Control, University of California at Berkeley and Riverside,
write:

> Biological control is recognized as a substantial means of pest
> *control* even by those who deny that natural enemy action is
> truly *regulating* in nature. Indeed, it is far easier to establish that
> they can *control* their host's densities than that they *regulate*
> those densities. . . . Economically, the question is only academic,
> but we contend that good natural enemies not only act as a
> substantial mortality factor and thereby limit or reduce (control)
> the prey's population size, but they do so in a manner that tends
> to stabilize both their prey's density and their own density.

The case of the cottony cushion scale insect *(Icerya purchasi)*, a serious
pest of California citrus, and its introduced Australian enemy, the
vedalia ladybeetle *(Rodolia cardinalis)*, was discussed earlier (see pp.
91-92). In places where DDT has not been applied, the ladybeetle is
still doing an effective job of controlling the scale insect—an historic
illustration of community management and biological control that has
been working well since 1889.

Examples of the need for active intervention in the protection of

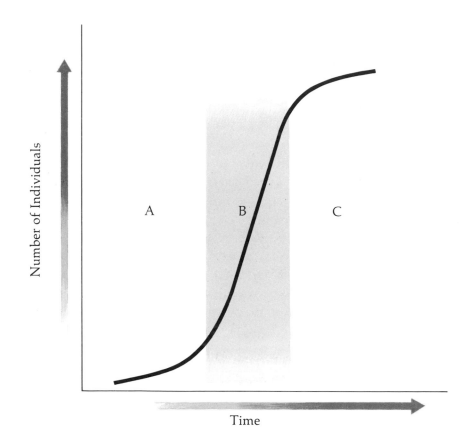

A sigmoid population growth curve. (A) Initial lag phase. Under-utilization of food and shelter resources, danger of population extinction. (B) Rapid (exponential) growth phase. Maximum productivity, optimum utilization of resources. (C) Plateau or stationary phase. Low productivity, high mortality, over-utilization and destruction of food and shelter resources, danger of population crash.

wildlife are numerous. In 1968 the Advisory Board on Wildlife Management, chaired by A. Starker Leopold, recommended to the Secretary of the Interior that:

> The [National Wildlife] refuge system as a whole should be designed and managed to spread migratory waterfowl as evenly as possible throughout the flyways. Excessive concentration, such as the gathering of Canada geese at Horicon Refuge in Wisconsin,

should be avoided or rectified to reduce danger of overkill, crop depredations and epizootic disease. . . . Reducing the intensity of the feeding program would seem to be an initial step in this process, along with regulated hunting on the refuge itself and possible drawdown of water levels.

The extreme form of population control is population elimination. In some kinds of management, particularly for economic gain, simplification of ecosystems by selective elimination of species is practiced. Occasionally this is necessary. It is difficult, for example, to see how wheat could be economically grown and harvested if it were interspersed with other plants in a semi-natural prairie community. Nevertheless, there is debate on the value of many oversimplified communities, including such important ones as single-species tree farms and cattle and sheep ranches.

Other kinds of management involve a minimum of interference with existing communities. It has been pointed out that ecologists like Margalef base their ecological theories on the idea that high species diversity generates stability in a natural community. If one accepts this, it follows that anything that greatly reduces species diversity will induce excessive and possibly ruinous population fluctuations in the remaining species of the community. Conservation policy is clearly delineated within this conceptual framework.

This is a controversial area of theoretical ecology, but for practical purposes it seems best to follow the advice of F. Fraser Darling, a pioneer in wildlife management and conservation:

> We are beginning to see that where there are definite limitations in the environment, such as hard and fast wet and dry seasons, combined with permeable young volcanic soils or senile lateritic earths as in many parts of Africa, it is better to take stock of how the country gets along with its natural communities. . . . Simplification in such conditions produces rapid loss of efficiency in biological activity. . . .
>
> [An] example of projected simplification is in the tropical forests where one school of foresters advises removal of "weed" trees and encouragement of denser stands of the desirable timber trees. To speak of "weed" trees in the beautiful intricacy of the

oldest life form on the planet is sheer arrogance. It is of the very nature of the tropical forest with its thousands of tree species, and characteristic low densities of any one species, to preserve variety and thereby resist change. This community resistance to change is the strength and immunity of the biome to organic catastrophe.

The same statement could be applied not only to monoculture forestry but to agriculture in the humid forested sections of the tropics. Jen-Hu Chang, a geographer at the University of Hawaii, has studied intensively the nature of tropical ecosystems and the problems of tropical agriculture; he concludes,

> In the humid tropics the much-attenuated solar radiation, the persistently high night temperatures, the lack of seasonality, and the excessive rainfall combine in one way or another to reduce the potential photosynthesis and to limit the possibilities of diversified agriculture. [The situation is further complicated by] the intense oxidation and leaching of soils, the lack of nitrogen-fixing legumes, the high cost of fertilizers, the troublesome weed problem, and the prevalence of pests and diseases. . . .

In brief, the potential of agriculture in the humid topics is exceedingly poor.

It is understandable why most people, looking at the lush, verdant growth and teeming animal life of the tropical moist forests, should conclude that the soil and climate would be ideal for growing lumber or food crops. But this is an illusion bred of ignorance. The tropical forest is a marvel of ecological evolution; there is no useful working substitute for it, unlike many temperate zone ecosystems. With a few exceptions, the best management for this four percent of the earth's land surface is protection of the existing community and *conservative* extraction of whatever forest products it offers in its natural state.

Another example of the consequences of altering the species composition of certain natural communities is provided by the substitution of domestic cattle for the savanna herbivores of much of Africa south of the Sahara. The wild ungulates of the dry African savanna are an extremely diverse group, including scores of species from several

Yearly crop of domestic livestock and wild ungulates relative to carrying capacity in similar East African rangelands

Type of range	Animals	Yearly crop (lb/sq. mile)	Stocking rate relative to carrying capacity
Acacia savanna	Cattle, goats, sheep	11,200-16,000	Over
Acacia savanna	Wild ungulates	37,400-90,000	At or under
Moderately managed grass savanna*	Cattle	21,300-32,000	At or slightly over
Acacia-commiphora bushland	Sheep, goats	2,100-8,000	At or over
Acacia-commiphora bushland	Wild ungulates	30,000	At or under

Source: L. M. Talbot, *Publ. I.U.C.N.* N.S., No. 1 (1963) 328.

* Provision of water, fencing, some brush control, dipping, and other disease control.

mammalian orders and ranging in size from the 11.5-pound dik-dik to the 11,500-pound elephant. These species occupy a wide variety of feeding niches, and are therefore not all in competition with each other for food. Unfortunately, conventional European concepts of range management were, until recently, widely adopted in Africa; in vast areas the wild ungulates were removed and replaced with large numbers of cattle, sheep, and goats, all existing on grasses and low plants and unable to use much of the local vegetation for food. In a short time, the original carrying capacity* of many areas was exceeded, plant cover disappeared, carrying capacity declined, livestock died, and dust bowls or baked clay crusts (the hallmark of ecological mismanagement) left thousands of square miles unfit for any human endeavor.

On the other hand, if the native ungulates are kept as part of the community and regularly harvested for meat and other animal products, the results are a much greater total productivity than that provided by cattle, sheep, and goats, without destruction of the habitat (see table above). The meat of most wild ungulates, if cured properly, tastes like beef. As much as a fourth to a half of the total populations of several

* Talbot defines the carrying capacity of an area as "the number of animals of a given size which can be supported for a given period of time by the vegetation growing in that area without adversely affecting the vegetation production."

ungulate species can be harvested annually without a decline in yield. In addition, Lee M. Talbot and associates, authorities on African community management, report that many of Africa's hoofed wild animals offer possibilities for domestication, although, curiously, this has not been done in Africa since the Neolithic period. If estimates are correct, a fifth or more of the African continent that is unfit for other enterprises could be used for "game ranching," thus both conserving and benefiting from the unique character of the savanna community.

There are other wildlife management tools besides the ax or gun; one of the best ways of shaping and manipulating natural communities is by the careful use of fire. Fire is an important component of many ecosystems, and a number of species, like longleaf pine *(Pinus palustris)*

A combination of overgrazing and drought ruined this rangeland in Frio County, Texas. The cattle have no market value. (John McConnell—Courtesy Soil Conservation Service)

Mixed herd of wildebeests and zebras on healthy rangeland, Lake Manyara, Tanzania. Cattle egrets accompany the herd. (Marc and Evelyne Bernheim— Rapho Guillumette)

and sand pine (*Pinus clausa*) in the southeastern United States, are especially adapted to resist it and to profit by its competition-reducing effects. Sand pine, for example, rarely drops its seed cones until they are released by the heat of a strong fire. Even if the parent tree is killed, a new crop of seedlings will quickly spring up in the ashes.

Complete fire protection over a long period of time may cause a drastic change in the local community. One Florida live oak* hammock experimentally shielded from fire since 1936 has been studied by plant ecologist Albert Laessle since 1939. Although the live oaks are still dropping thousands of viable acorns, these are not sprouting. Longleaf

* A live oak is a southern oak that does not lose its leaves in the fall.

Live-oak hammock, Florida Conservation Reserve, Welaka, Florida, May 1942. Protected from fire for seven years. The hammock retains its open aspect, but myrtle oaks are beginning to invade the understory. (Courtesy Albert Laessle)

pines in an adjacent fire-protected area are also not reproducing themselves. In the absence of fire, fire-intolerant trees like the laurel oak (*Quercus laurifolia*) are invading the region. Other trees like the swamp maple (*Rufacer rubrum*) and the swamp red bay (*Tamala pubescens*), normally confined to bayheads or swamps, have appeared; evidently they usually inhabit wet areas not because of a great need for water but because of their lack of resistance to fire. If fire protection is continued, the old community will disappear completely in a few decades.

Fire is often far more useful than complete fire prevention in eco-

The same location in October 1956, after twenty-one years of fire protection. The character of the hammock has completely changed, as fire-sensitive plants take over. The open spaces and light are blocked by the rapidly growing myrtle and laurel oaks, and by thick festoons of Spanish moss (see text). (Courtesy Albert Laessle)

system management. Foresters have known for many years that carefully controlled annual burning in some pine tree farms removes undesirable shrubby vegetation and helps prevent more serious fires from occurring. Some quail hunters in the southern states have refined burning methods to a fine art in order to provide ideal vegetation for maximum bird populations and good hunting. Fire may be even more important in the management of savannas and grasslands. Paul C. Lemon, an ecologist, studied the effects of annual burning on the Nyika Plateau grassland of Malawi, where fires are common. He

263

found that the forage grasses in areas that were burned yearly were much more abundant than in unburned areas, and that the herbaceous legumes that are essential for soil nitrogen metabolism were more numerous after burning. Lemon concluded: "The welfare of herbaceous legumes . . . and of the entire grassland ecosystem may very well depend upon periodic fires. . . . Thus, where it is desirable to encourage the large grazing animals, it seems wise to plan a regimen of regular, if conservative, burning." In other studies it has been found that occasional (but not too frequent) prairie fires are needed to release mineral nutrients that otherwise would remain trapped and unavailable in organic debris.

A final and most attractive example of the potential use of fire in community management has been described by another ecologist, Frederick R. Swan, Jr. In New York state, as in the Middle West, annual fires once maintained a wide diversity of native prairie plants in "oak openings," while areas less exposed to fire were heavily forested with less fire-resistant species of trees and with shade plants. As far east as Long Island, the native grasslands contained at least seventy-one species of woody and herbaceous plants, and probably many more.

European settlement brought fire control and the simultaneous introduction of exotic weeds; grazing by cattle and the plowing of fields also helped to wipe out most of the native plants, which have survived primarily in protected spots such as railroad rights-of-way and steep hillsides. By the turn of the century, agriculture ceased to be profitable in much of New York, and millions of acres of farmland were abandoned. Fire control was largely maintained, however, and the old fields were not recolonized by the majority of the now-scarce native species.

In studies conducted from 1963 to 1966, Swan observed the effects of accidental fires on abandoned fields in south-central New York State. He reports that

> With fire exclusion, poverty grass [*Danthonia spicata*, a fire-sensitive, undesirable native plant] forms a dense mat of twisted leaves which disappears only with the increasing shade of in-

vading trees. Poverty grass fields provide little cover and food for birds and mammals. . . .

Small populations of prairie plants existed in less disturbed areas near some of the fields studied. In some cases, where fields had been accidentally burned twice in the last 20 years, these fire-resistant plants had begun to invade them. Such species included butterfly milkweed (*Asclepias tuberosa*), two species of tick-trefoil (*Desmodium* sp.), two species of bush-clover (*Lespedeza* sp.), lupine (*Lupinus perennis*), New Jersey tea (*Ceanothus americanus*), Indian grass (*Sorghastrum nutans*), and big bluestem (*Andropogon gerardi*).

[In most cases] invasions of fields by these native plants cannot be expected to take place naturally because the plants are now rare.

Swan recommends a combined "program of native plant introduction and prescribed burning" to conserve the remaining native species and to increase the productivity and usefulness of New York's extensive pasture lands and fields.

It should be clear that active intervention is often necessary to preserve natural communities; but this is one of the most difficult aspects of conservation. Nobody can predict, even with sophisticated models and the help of computers, all the results of community management. With the establishment of the migratory waterfowl refuges in the upper Mississippi Valley, most Canada geese stopped migrating to their traditional and entirely adequate wintering grounds south of Illinois. More depressing illustrations of the problems of wildlife management could be cited, but there is no need—the moral is evident: cautious manipulation of ecosystems (especially fragile ecosystems) should always be accompanied and followed by prolonged observation of the flora and fauna; and when in serious doubt, the wisest management is none at all.

It is a truism to say that protected areas should always be large enough to serve their prime recreational, economic, or wilderness function without deterioration of the natural community. A few acres of protected land near Perth, Australia, are quite sufficient (for the moment) to conserve all living individuals of the rare species of sidenecked turtle, *Pseudemydura umbrina*. On the other hand, a 500-acre wilderness area with no visitors would be too small if its purpose was to provide refuge for a wolf pack. A 1200-square-mile national park is also too small if it receives more than two million visitors in a season.

In the case of the hypothetical wolf refuge, the only alternatives would be to enlarge it or to change its prime function. In the case of the national park (Yosemite), enlarging it would be costly and would not solve the basic problem. If we wish to keep the park worth visiting, the total number of visitors will have to be reduced. This could be accomplished in several ways, but the method of advance reservations adopted by the Park Service seems far preferable to financial exclusion based on a high admissions fee. A workable plan to limit automobile traffic without penalizing campers should also be devised. Any such plan consistent with maintenance of park values and standards will not involve building new roads, which would be both inadequate to handle the steadily increasing traffic (new roads attract new traffic) and extremely destructive of wildlife. Instead, relatively unobtrusive transportation systems, such as monorails, offer the best hope for handling park crowds without obliterating what the people come to see.

Where park ecosystems cross national boundaries, international cooperation is essential if the quality and value of the natural area is to be maintained. Political conflicts may make this impossible, but occasionally cooperation is achieved. Two good examples are the Tatra National Park, shared by Czechoslovakia and Poland, and the Waterton-Glacier International Peace Park, astride the Canadian-U.S. border. In both cases joint management is facilitated by the lack of serious international tension; and the character of the mountain range ecosystem in each park makes this cooperative management natural and highly desirable. For example, large carnivores such as bears may follow their usual inclination to roam widely, without incurring unnecessary risks when they stray across an artificial line.

All national parks that successfully contain large wild animals in a self-perpetuating community maintain their integrity by virtue of established or informal usage zones. In Yellowstone Park, only a small fraction of the park area is developed for auto-bound visitors (this part is grossly overcrowded), and the remainder—accessible to hikers—serves as much-needed shelter, forage, and breeding space for the park's celebrated animal populations. There are also large forested areas adjacent to the park.

As another example, Nairobi National Park, five miles from Kenya's largest city, contains lions, rhinos, giraffes, and many other large mammals as well as more than four hundred species of birds. The future existence of this small park is linked in part to the continued free access of its animals to the adjoining few hundred square miles of Masai territory that have in the past been open to them. This kind of zonation, where areas of heavy use border on recovery areas with few visitors, allows respectable numbers of people to enjoy natural communities without destroying them. In the United States, zonation is greatly facilitated by the unwillingness of most tourists to roam more than a few hundred yards from their automobiles.

The dismal failure of the U.S. government's "multiple use" policy, as evidenced in places like Alaska's Admiralty Island, also testifies to the need for clear management priorities and usage zonation when dealing with unspoiled ecosystems. The "multiple use" policy, set forth in Public Law 86-517, urges that National Forest land be used for a variety of purposes simultaneously; thus one area may conceivably be supposed to satisfy mineral, lumber, recreation, and wilderness interests at the same time. Needless to say, first wilderness and then recreation disappear under these conditions.

Not surprisingly, the best examples of the destructiveness of the multiple use approach are seen in the most fragile ecosystems. Since multiple use is based upon the *assumption* that any ecosystem can support all kinds of exploitation simultaneously, there is no serious attempt made to assess the severity and permanence of the damage that results from the policy. In the Chiricahua Mountains of the Coronado National Forest in the American Southwest, the provisions of the Wilderness Act were interpreted to mean that two historic and unobtrusive log cabins should be removed from the wilderness area, but thousands of head of cattle were allowed to remain because of pressure from local ranchers! In these once-magnificent public lands, where private fences now criss-cross the terrain, where the water needs of orchardists and ranchers have lowered the water table nearly beyond the reach of man and vegetation alike, and where erosion and desolation follow the ubiquitous cattle in their unceasing search for the last remaining greenery, the mountain oak–juniper woodlands are being ruined, and the lush desert grasslands have become poor mock-desert wastelands. Such is the thorny fruit of multiple use, the direct opposite of responsible management.

8
Analogues of Natural Communities

But in a sense I do remember different seasons, because all my memories are bound up with things to eat, which varied at different times of the year. Especially the things you used to find in the hedges. In July there were dewberries—but they're very rare—and the blackberries were getting red enough to eat. In September there were sloes and hazel-nuts. The best hazel-nuts were always out of reach. Later on there were beech-nuts and crabapples. Then there were the kind of minor foods that you used to eat when there was nothing better going. Haws—but they're not much good—and hips, which have a nice sharp taste if you clean the hairs out of them. Angelica is good in early summer, especially when you're thirsty, and so are the stems of various grasses. Then there's sorrel, which is good with bread and butter, and pig-nuts, and a kind of wood shamrock which has a sour taste. Even plantain seeds are better than nothing when you're a long way from home and very hungry.

GEORGE ORWELL, *Coming Up for Air*

Not all of man's interactions with nature have been senseless or destructive. Upon occasion people have intentionally or accidentally reshuffled and rearranged the elements of natural communities, making use of evolved relationships between species, and have come up with stable new communities, well suited to coexist with man. Such communities, in a sense man-made as well as man-maintained, can provide some of the values of the original free-living wildlife of a region.

269

The Camargue, a marshland wildlife and botanical reserve at the mouth of the Rhone in southern France. This "subnatural" landscape can be visited only by boat and on horseback. It is a refuge for thousands of egrets, flamingos, Egyptian ibises, and Moroccan storks, as well as beavers and other marsh-dwelling mammals. Hunting is permitted. (Courtesy French Government Tourist Office)

In this book much use is made of the phrase "natural community," a pleasant and convenient enough concept until the time arrives to pay for it with a definition. That time, perhaps somewhat overdue, is now.

The word "natural" makes us think of its opposite, "unnatural," implying that there are two basic kinds of communities in the world: the natural ones, uninfluenced by man, and the unnatural ones, which have been modified by human action. This strict interpretation is no doubt the simplest, but in practice it is useless, since this kind of natural community is now virtually nonexistent. Man has modified everything on earth, if not through direct manipulation of soil, flora, and fauna, then indirectly through changes in the air and water. What

270

is needed is not a dichotomy, natural-unnatural, but a scale running from most natural to least.

Many such schemes of classification have been proposed; one of the best was devised by V. Westhoff, a professor of botany at the Catholic University of Nijmegen, in the Netherlands. He suggests that all regions of the earth fall into one of four categories, as follows:

In natural landscapes the flora and fauna have not been directly disturbed by man. Such landscapes no longer occur in western and central Europe, although they can be found in some uninhabited portions of the globe.

Subnatural landscapes have flora and fauna that have been influenced by man, but not to the extent that species composition or the predominant character and appearance of the community have been modified. Subnatural landscapes occur in Europe and other long-settled regions, but only in the most rugged, sparsely populated areas, such as alpine zones and some marshlands. Part of the mountainous and extreme northern territory of the United States is composed of subnatural landscapes.

Semi-natural landscapes, according to Westhoff's scheme, retain most of the original native elements of the flora and fauna, but the whole appearance and structure of the community has been rearranged by man. The appearance and arrangement of the vegetation are very different from its configuration when undisturbed. Westhoff writes, "In western and central Europe, this type constitutes the greater part of all those areas and biotic communities which are essential for the variety of the landscape and therefore need to be preserved." Included are the less-managed varieties of hayfield and dry pasture, and many other man-modified, partly wild landscapes such as heath, moorland, reed swamp, and hedges (in the European sense; see below).

In cultivated landscapes man has removed many or most of the native species and has introduced others. The aspect of the community is entirely changed.

The word "natural" as it is used in this book generally includes the first two of Westhoff's categories. Critical readers can find exceptions,

The persistence of man-made alterations of the landscape. In this aerial view of part of the Xochimilco-Chalco basin, in Mexico, one can still see traces of Aztec farming methods employed during the fourteenth to sixteenth centuries A.D. In this former marsh, the Aztecs planted maize and greens on long ridges (*chinampas*) built up above the water level. Parallel ditches provided access by canoe and irrigated the crops. From the air, the remains of these ancient "gardens on swamps" appear as a sharply corrugated pattern of parallel lines wherever deep plowing has not destroyed the old *chinampas*. The ridges at the upper left are shown in detail in the following illustration. The top of the photograph is the southeast. (Courtesy Pedro Armillas. Photo by Compañía Mexicana de Aerofoto—© 1971, American Association for the Advancement of Science)

but sometimes a community does not fall neatly into one category or the other.

What I refer to as "analogues of natural communities" are the sorts of highly modified living systems that could be called "semi-natural" or in some cases "cultivated." In areas such as China and Europe, where the land has been continuously subject to the intensely stylized attentions of civilized man for thousands of years, the analogues of

272

natural communities are, as Westhoff points out, the prime reservoirs
of stabilizing diversity. And it is precisely these communities, patiently
sculptured by generations of men over the centuries using a trial-and-
error process that is part of organic evolution—it is these communities
that are now being blotted out by the modern, diversity-destroying
anschluss of production and market efficiency. Here, at least, the conservationist cannot be charged with misanthropy (and the fatuity of
this charge is exposed), since the heaths and hedges and urban parks
are in good measure creations of men. They represent our only evidence
that man can coexist with nature on terms acceptable to him. More
than that, they are the last dwelling places of myriad organisms that
make human life fruitful, rich, and perhaps possible at all.

In many of the oldest managed communities man has actually
brought about local increases in diversity by working with soil and

The old *chinampas* and the parallel ditches are clearly demarcated by differences in vegetation (water-loving weeds now grow in the ditches). Since
the decline of Aztec farming, the *chinampas* have undergone a transition
from a cultivated to a semi-natural landscape. (Courtesy Pedro Armillas—
© 1971, American Association for the Advancement of Science)

vegetation to increase the number of micro-habitats in what may have originally been a uniform environment. This imposed diversity takes work to maintain; a farm pond will fill with mud and weeds if left untended. Moreover, it requires personal, skilled attention; a proper Irish hedge is not best pruned and shaped by chemical sprays and heavy mowing machinery. With this in mind, a series of management rules proposed by Westhoff make excellent sense. Some of them are paraphrased as follows:

The management of a reserve should depart as little as possible from the methods applied formerly.

Intervention should always be gradual, performed on a small scale.

Internal regulation and stability can be increased by careful development of ecological boundary zones based on long-standing human influences within the area.

The more circular the reserve in form and the larger it is in size, the easier it will be to protect it from the threats of external change. This is especially true in landscapes that tend to have a naturally low diversity and monotonous features with widely spaced transition zones.

Management must be responsive to events outside and at the edges of the reserve, taking advantage of contacts that foster diversity, and exerting internal control of vegetation to resist the processes generated by hasty external alterations of the environment.

In summary, wherever man's interactions with nature have been salutary, wherever a cumulative, personal, understanding relationship has been developed with the land over a period of centuries, it is essential to maintain a human presence of the quality to which the community is accustomed and upon which it has become dependent. Any change, either in the direction of neglect and abandonment or towards more intensive, less tailored cultivation, is likely to lead to a loss of local diversity and a deadened environment. Throughout Europe in particular, as man gives way to machine in the countryside, noble landscapes, some of the oldest inherited works of man, are being annihilated in the space of a few weeks or are falling gradually into

Hedgerows in Suffolk, England. (Conway-Scala)

ruin as traditions die. Yet, surprisingly, many educated Europeans still have not realized that there is more to the conservation of nature than the conservation of remote wilderness.

A few examples of successful analogues of natural communities are described in the following pages. Hopefully, no one will read these accounts without thinking of similar possibilities in the bleaker parts of his own environment.

One of the best examples of a man-dependent community of great beauty and great ecologic and economic value is the English hedgerow, which was described by the ecologist Charles S. Elton as "the last really big remaining nature reserve we have in Britain, except for the wild

275

moors and lakes of our northern mountains and the seas around us."
These hedges, unlike the American imitation, are not rows of trimmed
shrubs of a single species used to delineate the margins of suburban
lots. Rather they are complex mixtures of trees, shrubs, flowering and
simple plants, small mammals, song birds, and a host of invertebrates.
They run along country roads and lanes, border fields, and occasionally
extend into urban areas. To many people, they are the essence of
England, the most memorable and distinctive feature of its countryside,
although they are a relatively recent addition, having come into being
largely since the time of Shakespeare. Karel Čapek, the Czech author,
wrote in *Letters from England:* "I have been down in Surrey, and up
in Essex; I have wandered along roads lined with quickset hedges,
sheer quickset hedges which make England the real England, for they
enclose, but do not oppress. . . ."

In addition to their aesthetic value, the hedges make other contributions to the quality of English life. Hedgerows serve as a reservoir for
the vanishing fauna of England, and they preserve plant species that
would otherwise have disappeared, to the detriment of local ecosystems.
According to Elton, one-fifth of Britain's homegrown timber comes
from hedges; they act as windbreaks, retarding evaporation from fields;
and they provide shady areas for domestic animals and hikers. Hedges
are a reservoir for spiders and other natural enemies of insects and
mites that prey on crops. But mainly they are a joy to walk along for
anybody who belongs on earth.

In the United States, the closest approximation to English hedgerows
are the windbreaks planted in the plains states since the dust storms
of the 1930s. Under the aegis of the Forest Service's Shelterbelt Program, more than 18,000 miles of windbreaks were started between
1934 and 1941. These tree belts soon acquire a characteristic associated
flora, which, in turn, provides a habitat for small animals.

Railroad embankments have always been a rich source of wild-
flowers and a haven for rare plant species. Aldo Leopold wrote in *A
Sand County Almanac:* "The outstanding conservator of the prairie
flora, ironically enough, knows little and cares less about such frivoli-
ties: it is the railroad with its fenced right-of-way. Many of these

railroad fences were erected before the prairie had been plowed. Within these linear reservations, oblivious of cinders, soot, and annual clean-up fires, the prairie flora still splashes its calendar of colors, from pink shooting star in May to blue aster in October." Many railroads now spray herbicides to keep plants from overgrowing the tracks. From the point of view of the ecologist, mechanical cutting confined to the immediate strip along the tracks would be better, even though it may be somewhat more expensive.

Superhighways in the United States have traditionally been landscaped with showy trees or planted with grass; but highway architects are beginning to learn how to encourage the more desirable elements of the local wildlife to become established along highway borders. Components of early successional stages grow best on the exposed soils along road shoulders; these include (in the eastern United States) pine, yellow poplar, sweet gum, and birch. The small residents of these communities, such as rabbits and birds, may occasionally be killed by cars, but are rarely dangerous to traffic. Unusual problems are encountered in the maintenance of roadside communities; for example, trees, grasses, and legumes must, in the north, be selected for resistance to the effects of salts (sodium and calcium chloride) spread to combat ice during wintertime. Such complications are generally trivial, however, and the extra trouble is a small price to pay for the absence of billboards and of concrete dyed to look like grass.

Most of the great commercial fisheries of the world are located in the colder oceans, where upwelling currents recycle mineral nutrients, the foundation of all food chains. By contrast, the south temperate and tropical seas are frequently poor in marine life except in shallow coastal waters. Here the intricate structures of coral reefs provide a place for marine plants and animals to live, and support the most elaborate natural communities found in the sea. Unlike the northern fisheries, which are composed of a small number of species, the reef communities contain hundreds of species of fish and a vast assortment of invertebrate and algal forms. Where there are no reefs, the warmer waters of the continental shelf region harbor a relatively sparse fish fauna.

Divers have known for many years that sunken ships attract a number of reef fishes. For several centuries Japanese fishermen have carried this process a step further by deliberately placing rocks in the sea in order to provide a surface of attachment for kelp and other algae, thus supplying food and shelter for fish and crayfish. The success of this technique inspired numerous studies of artificial reef communities. Since 1955 at least nine states and the Virgin Islands have sponsored or encouraged research programs to determine the best construction materials and building methods for artificial reefs. Hawaii and California have been particularly active, and on the east coast the Department of Commerce's Atlantic Marine Laboratory at Sandy Hook, New Jersey, has teams of divers and marine biologists observing artificial reefs in both temperate and tropical waters.

Artificial reefs perform two services exceedingly well: they establish good sport fishing in areas where there was none before, and they provide a constructive way of getting rid of an assortment of junk that only clutters up the environment on land. An artificial reef in the Gulf of Mexico near Galveston, Texas, had the effect of "bringing" good fishing grounds sixteen miles closer to the city. Less than two months after the reef was made, red snapper, grouper, and sand trout took up residence in the damaged concrete pipe sections that formed the reef. In studying its man-made reefs in the Gulf, Alabama has found that not only do individual red snappers become permanent residents of the artificial reefs, but also that they attain a greater average size than inhabitants of nearby natural formations.

Materials used in reef construction include such unlovely items as old automobile tires, chipped building blocks, worn-out ships, broken or damaged concrete pipe, empty oyster shells, old wooden streetcars, building rubble, and stripped used-car bodies. Special concrete "fish houses" seem to be no more attractive to fish than a properly made reef built out of junk. The reefs must be located on a fairly firm bottom and in water sufficiently shallow to transmit light for photo-

Kelp bass swimming inside a car only a few hours after it was "planted" in an artificial reef. An observer takes notes. (Gene Daniels—Black Star)

synthesis and plant growth. Lightweight items should be strung to-gether by cable. The reef components should preferably be of varying size and arranged so as to provide crevices and deep passageways for all sizes of fish. High-profile reefs are better than low ones. The reef should be accurately charted and provided with buoy markers. When periodic biological observations of the reef community are planned, the site should be studied for at least a year before the reef is laid down. Permits for artificial reef construction in U.S. coastal waters are issued by the Army Corps of Engineers.

It is difficult to prove that artificial reefs "make" more fish rather than serve as a gathering point for fish that would otherwise be dif-fusely scattered. Nevertheless, since artificial reefs do represent an increase in plant growth because of their attached algae, it seems likely that some associated fish populations must increase in size. Regardless of which alternative is true in any particular case, these analogues of natural communities are likely to become increasingly important in future years, especially as other human activities—pollution, dredging, filling, overfishing, and similar depredations—begin to threaten the supply of marine fish.

> . . . in Babylon [the United States] there is not really a scarcity of goods, and there is, objectively, no real reason why there can't be people's parks, because the land is available and the where-withal to build such parks is there in abundance. . . . These two questions [the Breakfast for Children Program of Oakland and the People's Park of Berkeley] pose the basic problem that radi-cals have to deal with in Babylon; ultimately, they both pose precisely the same question. It is only because they start from such divergent sources that they give the appearance of being worlds apart. One springs from needs that are obvious and basic, and people can relate to them on that basis, while the other springs from an area that we are not accustomed to looking upon as basic to survival. People can readily relate to the need to eat breakfast, but it is possible that they cannot see the need for a park.
>
> ELDRIDGE CLEAVER, "On Meeting the Needs of the People"

All large cities contain a surprising amount of wildlife, but with a few notable exceptions it is not well integrated into any complex community. Books have been written about the flora and fauna of metropolitan London, Paris, San Francisco, and New York, and sightings of wild animals are still common. Although the giant alligators and caimen of New York's sewer system are mythical, the author is personally acquainted with one thirty-five-pound snapping turtle that lives secretly, and presumably happily, within walking distance of the State House in a major United States city. The wolves, mountain lions, bears, salmon, and oysters that were part of the Manhattan ecosystem prior to its purchase by the Dutch in 1624 are gone, but the red fox, opossum (a new resident), flying squirrel, gray squirrel, muskrat, raccoon, several species of bats, and a host of birds remain.

The most successful nondomesticated species in the city are those whose niches in the wild pre-adapted them behaviorally and physically for life in the human community. These include plants like *Ailanthus* (tree-of-heaven), an introduced species from China, which is an early successional colonizer of disrupted soils and is tolerant of air pollution. Also included are the Norway rat, cockroaches, the rock dove or common pigeon, and the house sparrow. The large size of the urban niche and the paucity of predators have most likely made these animals far more common than they ever were in prehistoric times.

Rats and cockroaches are hardly a good advertisement for the desirability of wildlife (although to millions of ghetto dwellers they represent "nature"); to find a pleasant analogue of a natural community, one must turn away from the creatures that have found a place in the crannies of the human community, and look at the city park. Except in those cases where an unspoiled "environmental corridor" has been allowed to penetrate into the inner city, city parks are highly artificial communities. This is not an implied value judgment; city parks are deemed successful not to the extent to which they duplicate nature, but to the extent to which they allow the urban population to come in contact with some selected salutary features of the natural world. As Jane Jacobs has pointed out in *The Death and Life of Great American*

Ailanthus (tree-of-heaven) growing in Manhattan. This pollution resistant "weed" tree seems to be able to grow anywhere. Its sprouts can even be seen pushing up through small cracks in asphalt and concrete. (John King)

282

"The Ramble," in New York's Central Park (looking westward). A haven for many species of birds, this is one of the wildest places left on Manhattan island. (John King)

283

Cities, open space in the city is not automatically a good thing; a park and the human community around it must be planned and modified with each other in mind: "City parks are not abstractions, or automatic repositories of virtue or uplift, any more than sidewalks are abstractions. They mean nothing [when] divorced from their practical, tangible uses, and hence they mean nothing [when] divorced from the tangible effects on them—for good or for ill—of the city districts and uses touching them." The ideal city park is one where the biological needs of selected trees, shrubs, birds, and other creatures have been satisfied in a way compatible with a maximum diversity of human use. It is difficult to imagine a more challenging problem in wildlife management.

As the human population continues to increase we will turn increasingly for recreation and food to analogues and models of natural communities. In so doing, it is frighteningly easy to forget the real thing—human beings have an extraordinary ability to adapt to inferior environmental conditions. But submerged tires are not the same as a coral reef, and Central Park is not a wilderness area. It would be folly to base all land policy on the doctrine of efficiency; things that have no "use"—like wilderness—may yet have great value. The defect in the systems analysis, cost-benefit approach to complex issues like the fate of natural communities is that we cannot analyze all significant variables; nor do we really know what our future needs, and hence our future priorities, will be. Under these circumstances a dual program of preserving some natural communities in all their diversity and modifying or maintaining the modifications of others is the only policy that makes sense now and maximizes the alternatives available to our descendants.

9

Preservation of Species

There are so many local populations of specific kinds of animals and plants going out of existence in our time that not all can be saved. Conservation resources are strained everywhere, and politicians and philanthropists, whose continued support is needed, soon tire of perpetual alarms. In biblical days, species conservation evidently had a high priority. Noah was instructed: "And of every living thing of all flesh, two of every sort shall thou bring into the ark, to keep them alive with thee; they shall be male and female" (Genesis 6:19). Today, however, there is no ark, and conservationists must decide which threatened populations they will try to preserve and which they must of necessity leave to their fate. Two kinds of biological information are needed in order to make these conservation decisions: knowledge of what fraction of the total gene pool* is threatened and familiarity with the behavior and natural history of the species.

In their discussion of the endangered fishes of the southwestern United States, Minckley and Deacon state that the inclusion in an endangered species list of "peripheral" species ("those represented in a given state or county by an isolated or remnant population peripheral

---

* The total number of genes held by all the individuals of a species; i.e., the sum of genetic information possessed by and defining a species.

to the main body of the gene pool") "seems unwarranted." On the other hand, when small, isolated populations constitute the majority or entirety of a gene pool, as in the case of many of the native fishes of the Southwest, there is justification for acting to conserve them.* If these species are inconspicuous and of no obvious economic significance, it is probably best to group them in some category that has meaning to the layman—such as "Arizona's endangered desert fish"— rather than try to enlist public support for them species by species. Finally, there can be no set rules for making conservation decisions in difficult borderline situations involving races or subspecies, as, for example, the case of the red wolf and coyote. Here, each case should be argued on its own merits.

Some species are far more difficult to protect than others because they are forced by their unique behavior and physiology to occupy some inflexible niche that is particularly vulnerable to the activities of man. The ivory-billed woodpecker is an especially good example of this kind of species. The ivory-bill (*Campephilus principalis*), the largest woodpecker in North America and second largest in the world, formerly inhabited swampy and low-lying forests throughout the southeastern United States. James T. Tanner, author of the best modern account of the bird, has written: "Its large size, striking coloration, ivory-white bill, and curious voice have impressed nearly everyone who has seen it . . . and I, myself, have been impressed by the bird's striking and graceful appearance and the energy and strength of its actions and attitudes." From the early days of this country the ivory-bill has been considered one of the most spectacular of American animals, numerous articles have been written about it, and conservationists have maintained an interest in it; yet for all of this, its decline has been steady. The last fully authenticated sighting of an ivory-bill in the United States was in northern Florida in 1950; a dozen individuals of a slightly smaller race survive in the wildest mountain forests of Oriente Province, Cuba.

---

* It is important to preserve peripheral species when they are part of an isolated and locally unusual community whose scientific, educational, and aesthetic value is high. This holds true even though the peripheral species may be common somewhere else in the world.

Singer Tract, Louisiana, April 1935. Male
ivory-billed woodpecker returning to its nest
to relieve the female, who can be seen pok-
ing her head out of the nesthole. These
birds are probably extinct. (A. A. Allen—
Courtesy National Audubon Society)

There is little doubt that the ivory-bill, never a common bird, fell
victim to its own specialized habitat requirements. Although it in-
habits different kinds of forests containing a variety of tree species, all
of these forests have one thing in common: virgin timber with old
trees. The ivory-bill feeds on wood-boring insects that invade large
dead trees—young, growing trees do not harbor such insects. Because
of these food needs, ivory-bills are far-ranging, seeking out the occasional suitable tree among its healthy neighbors, or looking for local
patches of forest where fire or flood has recently killed a large number
of trees in one place. The birds rarely come near the ground and therefore do not normally take advantage of insects that may inhabit logging
debris. Tanner estimates that a minimum of two and a half to three

square miles of prime untouched habitat is needed to support one pair of ivory-bills.

Throughout the twentieth century there has been a steady loss of virgin forest in the southeast as lumber companies have turned one area after another into comparatively sterile single-species tree farms or have abandoned the clearcut land for cultivation or disuse. By the mid-1930s the best forest that Tanner could find with a reasonable ivory-bill population and suitable for conservation efforts was the giant Singer Tract in Madison Parish, Louisiana, which also contained wolves, panthers, and black bears. Still, despite its obvious suitability as a National Wildlife Refuge, the Singer Tract was completely and recklessly lumbered within a few short years of the publication of Tanner's book.

What kind of conservation effort would be needed now to save the ivory-bill, should remnant populations be uncovered in the United States?* Although the bird is adapted to exist at very low population densities, there would have to be enough individuals left to preserve a semblance of genetic variety. Twenty-five pairs would probably be an absolute minimum figure. This, in turn, would represent a minimum land commitment of seventy-five contiguous square miles of mature lowlands forest, with a surrounding buffer zone of intermediate-quality habitat. Management techniques such as selective cutting of healthy timber and deliberate killing of certain trees in the buffer zone might increase the carrying capacity of the reserve. The entire tract would have to be fully patrolled for poachers. But even if all these provisions could be satisfied, few biologists would be willing to predict the ivory-bill's chances of survival. The probability of allocation of public funds for an ivory-bill wilderness region would thus seem very small, unless other independent reasons for protection of the area could be cited.

It would be hard to find an example of an animal more difficult to protect than the ivory-billed woodpecker, but the conservation litera-

* In recent years there have been unconfirmed reports of sightings of ivory-bills from both the Big Thicket of Texas and Florida, but the likelihood of its survival is not great. The Big Thicket is now experiencing the same fate that befell the Singer Tract.

ture is filled with accounts of other species whose behavior creates similar problems for conservationists.* Clearly, it is difficult to formulate a plan of protection for any creature unless its natural history is known and its environmental niche has been well characterized.

Other kinds of species characteristics may complicate conservation efforts. If a plant or animal is considered injurious or dangerous to man, there is usually an effort made to eradicate it, regardless of its aesthetic, ecological, or historical value and regardless of its present real impact on the human community. If economic or other interests stand to benefit indirectly from the eradication, the anticonservation pressures may be strong. Elton reports that one automobile manufacturer in England advocated the destruction of hedges and that a chemical herbicide company, lobbying for the spraying of roadside meadows, included the wild rose in its list of weeds to be eliminated (the British Nature Conservancy thought differently).

Occasionally an otherwise valuable wild animal does pose a real threat to man. In 1967, within hours of each other, two nineteen-year-old girls camping in different areas of Glacier National Park were killed by grizzly bears. Although there have been previous attacks by bears (mostly by the more common black bears) both in and out of national parks, this grim incident focused attention on the problem. No one will ever know why the first two human killings by grizzly bears in the long history of Glacier National Park took place on the same day; there are, of course, numerous theories. Certainly the nightly feeding of bears at the Granite Park Chalet (causing them to associate humans with food), the lack of proper garbage incineration facilities, and the building of a campground in the middle of a traditional grizzly foraging area did not help create an environment in which humans and bears could mix safely.

Park officials and conservationists were then faced with the need to make a decision about the future management of grizzly bears. One

* One animal that might be even harder to manage on reserves than the ivory-bill is the Siberian tiger. F. E. Warburton estimates that a single pair of Siberian tigers, with cubs, needs at least five hundred square miles of woodland to meet daily food requirements.

alternative was extermination, at least in areas visited by human beings. Most rational and informed people rejected this idea. After the Glacier Park incidents, some angry park visitors demanded to know whether the park was being run for people or for bears—a legitimate question, but double-edged when so many thousands of people visit Glacier Park in order to have the privilege of seeing dangerous wild animals in their native mountain setting.

Conflicts between people and grizzlies can be prevented if proper species management techniques are employed. The major principle of such management is to avoid letting bear and human territories overlap when there is likely to be heavy use by either side. The government agencies that administer our parks and forests have been guilty of near-criminal ineptitude in failing to come to grips with this elementary safety requirement. Instead of installing incinerators that can make garbage unpalatable to bears, personnel have been instructed to capture persistent garbage-seeking bears and transport them elsewhere. Most return promptly, or others take their place. One national monument in Alaska attracts tourists with a brochure that features a photograph of ten brown bears fishing for salmon in a river, thus forcing the over-worked rangers to devote much time and effort to keeping new visitors away from this dangerous spot (which is also outside park boundaries). A safe observation post equipped with wide-field telescopes would eliminate much of the risk in this case. The Park Service has the right to demand that tourists who wish to use remote trails and campsites meet some minimum standard of fitness and experience. This criterion should be enforced. The new policy (adopted after the Glacier National Park killings) of closing any trail or campsite where there has been a bear incident, pending investigation by ranger-naturalists, is sensible and should not be relaxed.

The Forest Service of the U.S. Department of Agriculture, in its insistence on "multiple use," is in the process of needlessly generating in the national forests some of the same kinds of species conservation problems now encountered in the national parks. Admiralty Island, in Alaska's Tongass National Forest, approximately the size of Yellowstone National Park, is probably the richest wilderness area left in

Alaskan brown bear with salmon. Its preservation in parks and refuges poses a real challenge to wildlife management. (Leonard Lee Rue III—Bruce Coleman, Inc.)

North America. It contains sixty-seven streams used by all five species of Pacific salmon and four kinds of trout. There are high densities of mink, otter, beaver, marten, waterfowl, and many other wild animals. There are more bald eagles than in all the other states combined. And there are eight hundred to a thousand grizzly (brown) bears. There are also at least 265,000 acres of good commercial timber land, much of which has been leased for clearcut logging in the best "multiple use" tradition.

According to reports from visitors to Admiralty, logging operations have already resulted in erosion along stream banks, with the loss of

291

salmon runs. Garbage is allegedly sprinkled along logging roads, and illegal hunting of grizzly bears is flourishing. In the light of these accusations, the reply of the Forest Service that only one-third of the island will be logged and that the forest renewal cycle is only a hundred years is not convincing.

The third of the island that will be logged contains the best forests. Moreover, although the spruce may grow back in a hundred years, the contracts negotiated with the lumber companies call for completion of cutting in fifty years or less. In other words, either the lumber firms will cease their Admiralty operations in fifty years to allow regrowth in their original tract or, more likely, they will exert pressure to be allowed to cut in adjacent areas that are now considered commercially unprofitable.

The grizzly bear is not a species that can tolerate multiple use (nor, in this case, is the bald eagle, which does not nest in saplings, or the salmon, which will not spawn in silt-polluted waters). The Forest Service regulations to protect grizzlies and other wildlife on Admiralty, however stringent and well-meaning, are often unenforceable. As the island is exposed to more and more people its bear population will dwindle; in the process there may be more incidents like the ones in Glacier National Park. Priority, not multiple use, is what the grizzly needs. The value to man of knowing that we have enough humanity left to save a few small places for other creatures cannot be translated into economic terms. It has been argued that hunting* on Admiralty would bring more revenue to the state than the pulpwood operations, some of which are foreign-owned. In addition to being economically dubious, this kind of conservation argument is unwise. Short-term economics almost always favor exploitation. The bears of Admiralty Island will be preserved only if the Forest Service decides that in this specific case a population of undisturbed grizzlies is more important to the people of the United States than another commercial timber tract. If they decide otherwise, the euphemism of "multiple use" will fool only the uninformed.

---

* Well-regulated hunting by parties on foot would probably not deplete any of the island's big game populations.

Zoos and Commercial Animal Farms

As open space vanishes and habitats disappear, zoos have been increasingly called upon to preserve homeless species that will breed in captivity. Special facilities, like the Patuxent National Wildlife Center in Maryland, have research programs designed to promote the breeding of endangered species and their ultimate reintroduction to their native habitat. Such programs are only now beginning, but some pilot studies already appear promising.

The masked bobwhite quail *(Colinus virginianus ridgwayi)* was formerly a resident of the southwestern tall grass and mesquite plains from Sonora, Mexico, to southern Arizona east of the Baboquivari Mountains. As overgrazing by domestic cattle destroyed its habitat, its range contracted, and it is now found only in a small area of southern Sonora. An early attempt to establish the quail on a 640-acre replanted reserve west of Tucson, Arizona, met with limited success because of vandalism and winter losses. Two other preservation efforts may be more promising. In one, interested parties from Arizona and Mexico have set aside land and provided a cattle fence to protect a remnant quail population in Sonora. Also, in anticipation that a suitable habitat could be found and maintained in Arizona, a breeding colony of masked quail was started at the Patuxent center. At the request of Senator Mundt of South Dakota, Seymour and James Levy of Tucson provided four pairs of birds; these and others captured in Sonora have now produced a great many offspring which are being returned to suitable habitat in southern Arizona. These quail are the first of a series of native American species to be released in a suitably protected part of their original range after restoration of safe population levels at Patuxent.

Even when species can be bred in captivity, there may be unexpected problems associated with their release, particularly when the captive population is small and the period of captivity extends over several generations of the animal or plant species. Close inbreeding in a small population usually increases the likelihood that harmful recessive genes can combine in an individual to produce undesirable effects. (Of course desirable or neutral recessives may also combine.) The incest taboos of

One fifty-ninth of the world's whooping cranes standing in a pan of water, age three days. This and other endangered species are raised at the United States' Patuxent Wildlife Research Center to preserve a breeding nucleus and to re-stock protected habitats. The whooping crane population is slowly recovering, after reaching an all-time low of fifteen individuals in 1941. Seventeen of these cranes are now at Patuxent; fifteen of them hatched from eggs obtained during four summers from nests in Wood Buffalo National Park, in cooperation with the Canadian Wildlife Service. The wild population has increased in size despite the removal of these eggs; and some of the Patuxent cranes should reach breeding age by 1974. (L. R. Goldman—Courtesy Bureau of Sport Fisheries and Wildlife)

so many human societies are an unconscious acknowledgment of this biological hazard. If the harmful changes are externally slight, they may not be noticed in the supportive and non-selective environment of a zoo. Nevertheless the result will be a population less well equipped to deal with the vicissitudes of a wild existence after release. Although structural changes as the result of inbreeding in zoos are likely to be detected, small gene-controlled alterations in vital behavior patterns may well be overlooked. The inevitable genetic changes that occur in all populations are normally rejected or supported by environmental forces of selection; but most of these forces, such as harshness of climate, scarcity of food, and the presence of predators, are not part of the artificial world of a zoo. Will zoo animals gradually become unsuited for the old life? If so, the endangered animals that are preserved only in zoos will be something less than their wild forebears.

A natural example of this kind of genetic change is provided by those creatures who leave the world of day and night to live in the perpetual blackness of deep caves. Over the course of many generations, cave animals frequently show a reduction or complete loss of

An Aleutian goose, another species raised at Patuxent. Not more than 250 to 300 of these small geese remain in existence. Seventy-five Patuxent-reared individuals were released on Amchitka Island in the spring of 1971. It is not known whether they were affected by the Atomic Energy Commission's "Cannikan" nuclear explosion in the fall of that year. (L. C. Goldman— Courtesy Bureau of Sport Fisheries and Wildlife)

eyes and pigment, not necessarily because these features would be disadvantageous in caves but because random, once deleterious mutations that affect the pigment and eye-forming systems go unchallenged by natural selection. In the outside environment the possessors of these genetic changes would have soon perished; in the cave it does not matter if color and vision are lost. Similarly, in a zoo one can imagine, for example, a small population of a species of captive migratory bird losing its capacity or motivation to migrate after several generations in cages. This tendency might even be accelerated by zoo selection if birds that did *not* become restless in the normal way at migration time fared better in captivity.

Another genetic hazard of "zoo banks" is the reduction of genetic variability associated with small inbred populations. The great advantage of the genetic system used by most animal and plant species is that a "recessive" gene can exist in an individual without exerting its effect if its dominant fellow gene is present also. Only from time to time, when an offspring inherits the same recessive gene from both parents and there is thus no dominant gene present for that trait, will the previously "hidden" recessives exert their effects. This is the genetic basis for many of the individual differences that crop up in any natural population. At any one time only a few gene combinations are highly successful, but the hidden nature of recessives prevents them from being eliminated by natural selection and thus preserves traits that, although not useful at the time, may become valuable if environmental conditions change. When populations are small and inbred, the total gene variety, much of it represented by recessives, decreases drastically. In the process, the population is bound to become less versatile in its capacity to respond to the shifting challenges of the real world. Its survival repertory is diminished. As a practical example, economic botanists have long pointed out that highly inbred plants are often less resistant to epidemic disease than their more variable wild ancestors.*

* A related problem is caused by the careless interbreeding by zoos of animals from different subspecies or races of the same species. Where subspecific differences exist, they may represent adaptations to local environmental peculiarities; cross-breeding will tend to blot out these evolved relationships between popula-

Despite these considerations, it appears that unless there is deliberate selection for some trait, or unless there is consistent brother-sister mating in zoo populations, considerable genetic variability is maintained and genetic change is slow. The Syrian hamsters kept as pets in the United States are derived from a single pair, yet they show great variability in size and coat color. Mutation has evidently restored a great deal of variation that may have been lost. More to the point is the case of the European bison (*Bison bonasus*), whose last wild population was destroyed in Poland's Bialowieza Forest during World War I. Subsequently re-established from a very small number of captive individuals, the Bialowieza herd is thriving, and breeding is proceeding normally. Although there is no way of preventing subtle behavioral and physiological alterations in captive populations, the occurrence and significance of these theoretical results of changes in gene frequencies remain to be tested. The alternative to "zoo bank" preservation of remnant populations—that is, no preservation at all—will certainly be worse in the great majority of cases.

There is no point in returning a zoo-maintained population to its former habitat unless that habitat has been placed under protection in the interim. If this proves impossible, there is always the option of establishing the population in a suitable environment outside its original range. Generally this is a bad idea; most exotic introductions are probably harmful. Nevertheless, they can be considered under certain conditions: when the exotic species has a low reproductive potential or is a big game species that could be easily controlled or removed by hunting, if necessary; when the species can be maintained at a low population density and has a relatively minor impact on its

---

tions and their particular environments. The tiger provides a good example of this. There are several distinct subspecies of tiger, including the Bengal tiger (*Panthera tigris tigris*), the Siberian tiger (*Panthera t. altaica*), the Chinese tiger (*Panthera t. amoyensis*), the Javan tiger (*Panthera t. sondaica*), the Bali tiger (*Panthera t. balica*), and the Sumatran tiger (*Panthera t. sumatrae*). According to the International Union for the Conservation of Nature's *Red Data Book* for mammals, ". . . tigers in captivity are known to be fairly numerous. In the past, however, many zoos have bred tigers with little attention to subspecies so that the average zoo tiger is often an indiscriminate *mixtum compositum*, a creature that never existed in the wild."

ecosystem; when there are no obvious competitor species native to the area of introduction; and when the area of introduction already has a relatively impoverished flora and fauna.

Not all these conditions need be satisfied; introductions are largely a matter of biological common sense. Few could object, for example, to an attempt to save the tiny, attractive, and endangered American bog turtle (Clemmys muhlenbergi) by trying to establish it in bogs of southern Ireland, but no one in his right mind would protect the endangered brown hyena (Hyaena brunnea) by releasing it in New Mexico.

Commercial wild animal farms can relieve much of the economic pressure on rare species, provided they can supply their animal products more cheaply than the exploiters of wild populations are able to do. This has happened with the ostrich, the mink, and others; it could help the alligator, the vicuña, and even some of the spotted cats. Animal farming, however, is a risky and difficult operation. At best, as with domestic animals like cows and chickens, there is the possibility of epidemic disease and other disasters. With wild animals there are additional complications related to peculiarities in their behavior, nutrition, and life cycle.

The Green Turtle

Of all the wild animals currently being commercially farmed, perhaps the most difficult to raise are sea turtles. Of the various kinds of sea turtle, the green or "soup" turtle (Chelonia mydas) is the most valuable to man. An adult green turtle weighing 150-400 pounds provides a large quantity of edible meat, eggs (in the case of females), leather for shoes and handbags, calipee (cartilage) for clear turtle soup, fat for oil, and a lacquered shell for the tourist trade. However, its potential value to man if allowed to rebuild its once-enormous populations is far greater than the profit now being realized on largely frivolous items. There are vast underwater beds of turtle grass and related plants in the shallow parts of tropical oceans, but as marine biologist John Randall has claimed: "At the present time, the utilization of the sea grasses as food by animals, particularly those of economic importance to man, is

European bison in Poland's Bialowieza Forest. These descendants of a few individuals reintroduced to their native habitat are now part of a large thriving herd. (Polish Travel Office—Orbis)

299

negligible." The green turtle and the manatee (sea cow) are the only large edible animals that feed on these grasses, but the manatee, in addition to being more coastal in its distribution, has a low reproductive potential. This leaves the green turtle as the only grazing animal of economic importance that can take advantage of the earth's underwater "grasslands." But this use will never be realized if the green turtle is wiped out by the leather and gourmet food industries. To many, turtle farming seemed the solution to this problem.

Green turtles are strictly marine in nature; only the females leave the water, briefly, at nesting time. The hatchlings, born on tropical beaches, emerge from their nests at night, scramble to the ocean, and disappear in the surf. Until they reach an age of about six months, their whereabouts and habits are unknown. Since tagging of adults has revealed that green turtle nesting beaches and feeding grounds are usually widely separated (by as much as 1500 miles), we assume that during their first months the young turtles are moving toward the areas that will be their feeding grounds, most likely carried passively by the currents. In captivity, young green turtles are carnivorous for the first six to eight months; we can therefore guess that their food source while floating on the surface of the open sea is small invertebrates like those associated with the large floating patches of sargassum seaweed. When the turtles arrive at their shallow-water feeding grounds, they become herbivorous and begin to eat underwater turtle grass (Thalassia). It is at this point that they begin to achieve the bulk of their weight and size.

After reaching maturity, in five to seven years, both males and females return to their birthplace to mate and nest. The females lay approximately one hundred eggs at a time, at twelve-day intervals, two to five times during a summer. They then swim back to their feeding grounds (the males leave earlier). This cycle is repeated at two- or three-year intervals. It is not known how long green turtles live; if they are like their distant relatives, the giant land tortoises, they may live more than a hundred years. Once they are full-grown, only sharks are likely to injure them; such injuries are probably not common.

Green turtles are easily overexploited because of their habit of congregating at specific beaches to nest. Although widely dispersed at different feeding grounds, all green turtles of the western Caribbean and Gulf of Mexico, for example, return to one beach—Tortuguero, Costa Rica—at breeding time. Similarly, nearly all green turtles that feed in coastal waters off the bulge of Brazil are born and nest at Ascension Island in the mid-Atlantic. At the great majority of nesting beaches there is no protection for the species, and the rapidly expanding populations of coastal peoples take virtually all the eggs. (A few turtle beaches, such as Tortuguero, are now partially protected—most are not.) The nesting females are also killed, sometimes for their meat, but more often for their valuable and easily portable calipee and hide. Since the nesting process lasts more than an hour, and since sea turtles leave an enormous track in the sand, a few poachers on a beach at night can easily find and kill every turtle that comes out of the sea to nest. But there is little more safety for the turtles in the water. Harpooners in small boats are active near the nesting beaches, and if a turtle manages to return to its feeding ground, fisherman with nets await it there. During the past four hundred years the green turtle populations of the warmer oceans have been reduced from tens of millions to a few thousand individuals.

The two main problems facing a commercial turtle farmer can be deduced from a knowledge of the life history of *Chelonia*. During their early carnivorous phase the small green turtles can be fed ground or chopped fish (inexpensive "trash fish" species can be used) or an assortment of commercial animal foods made from animal products. When the turtles weigh several pounds, after six to eight months, they are willing to eat vegetable food. Although they will continue to eat ground fish indefinitely, it is totally uneconomical to raise livestock on animal products. The easiest way to provide vegetable food is to fence a sizable shallow-water area that contains a good stand of turtle grass. This creates additional problems. Underwater fencing is expensive, difficult to maintain, and easily damaged by storms. Sea turtles kept in this kind of enclosure are likely, sooner or later, to escape. If an enclosed bay is fenced across a narrow neck, the fence acquires a heavy growth of seaweed that impedes the tidal flow necessary to keep the bay water (with its dense animal population) clean and also necessary to prevent the area from filling up with silt washed off the land by rain. Furthermore, a few thousand rapidly growing green turtles will soon denude even a moderately large area of its turtle grass. Land-grown vegetable foods could be used; this would obviate the necessity of having unusually large pens. However, it is not known whether any nutritionally acceptable crop could be grown in the sandy, salty soils found near most tropical places that would be otherwise suitable for raising green turtles. Machines to harvest and collect turtle grass are another possibility now in the developmental stage.

The second problem that must be solved is replenishing the supply of young turtles. No existing rookery can tolerate the annual loss of thousands of eggs or hatchlings for even one commercial farm. It has been argued that since the natural mortality of the tiny hatchlings must approach ninety-nine percent, the eggs taken can be "replaced" by the release of a few hundred pen-raised yearlings a year later. In a sense this is true, but since there is no evidence that these herbivorous yearlings are motivated or physiologically equipped to travel safely to the feeding grounds a year late, nor that they are still capable of "learning" the route if necessary, these released turtles cannot be considered an acceptable substitute for the thousands that are taken.

Of course it is conceivable that green turtles could be bred at a turtle farm and the wild populations left alone. But, even if we avoid the still unanswered questions of whether green turtles will breed consistently in captivity and whether the females will use the beaches provided as nesting sites, there is still an overwhelming difficulty facing the turtle farmer. He will need, at the very least, 20,000 eggs per year, the produce of approximately fifty females. Since the turtles will probably nest only every two or three years, this means a total of nearly 150 females will have to be kept on hand. Another twenty-five to fifty adult males will be required. In other words, any turtle farmer who does not intend to parasitize natural nesting grounds will have to keep and maintain more than 60,000 pounds of adult sea turtles. Clearly, the only easy solution to this problem (and a possible solution to the problem of feeding the young turtles) is to turn them loose on turtle

Samuel Nixon, an Audubon game warden, holds a three-year-old, sixty-pound green turtle raised at the Caribbean Conservation Corporation's experimental nonprofit turtle farm, Great Inagua, Bahamas. Turtles do not reach sexual maturity until they are about six years old. (Courtesy David W. Ehrenfeld)

303

grass flats near the farm and hope they will stay. (Marked turtles escaping from commercial pens in Key West, Florida, have been known to return to their own Nicaraguan feeding grounds.) If this is done, new difficulties will be encountered. Will the turtles nest on nearby beaches? How can the turtles and nests be protected from poachers? How can the young turtles be harvested economically?

When we add to everything already mentioned the usual hazards of disease, egg and infant mortality, hurricanes, and other dangers, the labors of Hercules seem easy in comparison to turtle farming. However, turtle farming may yet have some promise if the young-adults and adults can be induced to stay and eventually breed near the farm without being penned, and if the projects can free themselves from dependence on natural nesting grounds. Even if turtle farms fail commercially, they may still prove useful on a government- or foundation-subsidized basis as a way of circumventing the usual high hatchling mortality associated with the first six months of life in the wild. In this case the turtle farm would be increasing the world population of green turtles by releasing healthy six-month-old animals in large numbers, but would not necessarily be able to harvest enough adults to pay for operations during the first one or two decades.

The problem of green turtle conservation is extremely complex; it involves economics, international law, national policy, local customs, and the physiology and behavior of the animal itself. Consequently, no single approach is likely to resolve the difficulty. In such a situation, it is wise to consider all the conservation alternatives. Turtle farming has been attempted by various individuals and groups for at least a half-century, with no great commercial success (although the first large-scale project with adequate financial backing did not begin until 1968). There are however, other ways of conserving sea turtles. Between 1960 and 1969, Archie Carr, director of the Caribbean Conservation Corporation, airlifted a total of several hundred thousand Costa Rican hatchlings to protected former nesting beaches in many Caribbean countries. The U.S. Navy provided an amphibious plane and crew for these operations, and the Costa Rican government has protected part of the Tortuguero nesting beach. It is perhaps too early to tell

whether nesting colonies have been re-established in any of the transplantation sites, although there has been a marked increase in young-
adult green turtles seen in Florida Bay near an Everglades Park beach
where Costa Rican turtles were released. In Sarawak, Professor Tom
Harrisson has helped develop another kind of conservation technique:
the nesting beaches there are controlled by a Turtles Board, which
fully protects the females and conserves a portion of the eggs in a
hatchery. Nevertheless, the Sarawak green turtle population is declining, in part because of excessive hunting of adult turtles throughout
the South China Sea. At several South American nesting beaches, Peter
Pritchard, with financial assistance from the World Wildlife Fund,
introduced a modified version of the egg-protection scheme employed
at Sarawak. Instead of setting aside a small fraction of the eggs, nearly
all were "purchased" from the natives at the nesting beach. This highly
successful conservation venture not only protected the eggs but allowed the local Indian populations to be economically independent of
turtle meat and eggs as a source of food. Unfortunately, egg purchasing
is too costly to be continued indefinitely at any locality; it is strictly a
stopgap procedure.

Turtle farming, transplantation of eggs and hatchlings, and egg
protection will probably be inadequate by themselves to reverse the
effects of overexploitation. International agreements will be needed
to prevent the extinction of the species. Any such agreements, to be
effective, will have to regulate all activities pertaining to the taking
of turtles (and eggs), including fishing in international waters. A large
number of governments will have to participate, and enforcement will
be difficult. Yet enforcement might be unnecessary if the provisions
of the agreement could be extended to limit manufacture, distribution,
and sale of turtle products, especially in the consumer nations—the
United States, Great Britain, West Germany, and Japan. In the world
of economically valuable but endangered species it is demand, ultimately, that is the arbiter of supply, and the relationship is always
inverse. Ironically, there is not one current turtle product that could
not be replaced by a cheaper and less damaging substitute: clear turtle
soup with sherry is good, but hardly a mainstay of world nutrition,

even that of the rich who consume it; if the vanishingly small possibility that turtle eggs enhance fertility and libido proves true, then
they are about as useful in areas of population explosion as a seven-
year drought—if not, chicken eggs will do; turtle leather is usually
dyed and glossed to look exactly like plastic, so why not use plastic?
and turtle oil has not been proven any more beneficial to the complexion than bacon drippings, or other animal fats—*if* grease is good
for the complexion at all.

It is probably unfair to pick an example of wild-animal farming that
is so complex and problem-ridden and then confuse the issue with
mention of other kinds of conservation techniques. In fact it would
have been easier to write a brief description of an ostrich farm. But
the kind of conservation victory represented by ostrich farms, although
real and worthwhile, is misleading because it is out of context. The
context of conservation is the sum of man's activities in the world, and
in the light of this context the saving of a species by inclusion in a
refuge or by propagation in a zoo or animal farm seems sadly transitory in these times. Unless conservation operates at a global level with
full involvement in all aspects of the conduct of human life, it will be
an anachronistic and unsuccessful endeavor.

Promising and Successful Protection Efforts

Although biological difficulties stand in the way of conserving some
species, others respond more readily to specific protection measures,
occasionally even in the midst of a deteriorating environment. A few
brief samples of promising or already successful results follow; most
of the information was obtained from the *Newsletter* of the Council

Turtle nesting beach, Tortuguero, Costa Rica. A solitary female green turtle
slowly returns to the sea in the early morning after a late night's nesting emergence. This beach is now partially protected, but elsewhere the huge tracks
of these ponderous creatures enable poachers to find them quickly, usually
before they have had a chance to lay their eggs. (Courtesy David W. Ehrenfeld)

of Europe, which surveys numerous regional and national reports.

Both the Soviet Union and Denmark have designated arctic reserves to protect the endangered musk ox (*Ovibos moschatos*), one on the island of Wrangel, the other a national park in the northern half of East and North Greenland.

It is now a criminal offense to hunt polar bears, Ussuri tigers, Kamchatka beavers, mountain antelopes, Middle-Asian gazelles, bustards, flamingos, and egrets in the Soviet Union. Populations of Ussuri tigers, elks, Saiga antelopes, and flamingos are reported to be in a recovery phase, each having previously neared extinction.

The wild boar (*Sus scrofa*) population in Estonia has increased from three to four hundred in 1955 to approximately 5000 in 1971.

In Poland, the elk (*Alces alces*), which nearly disappeared after World War II, now numbers over six hundred and is re-extending its range to the west and northeast.

Six to ten lynxes (*Lynx lynx*) have been seen on the Dübener moor north of Leipzig; others have been observed in various parts of Saxony. It is not known where these particular animals came from. The lynx is fully protected in these regions of East Germany. Like other big cats, the lynx seems able to maintain itself at remarkably low population densities and to recover rapidly if given the chance.

Brown bears (*Ursus arctos*) in Scandanavia, once nearly wiped out, are doing well under protection: in Finland they have stablized at a population of 150; in Sweden the more than 400 bears are increasing in number and extending their range southward. Another predator, the lynx, is also faring better in Scandanavia, although the wolf and wolverine are either extinct or nearly so throughout the peninsula.

The Hudsonian godwit (*Limosa haemastica*), a formerly common shore bird, breeds in the Canadian Northwest Territories and winters from Brazil to Tierra del Fuego. Much reduced by hunting, it is now increasing again thanks to protection in the northern part of its vast range.

Other examples of successfully protected species range from the trumpeter swan in the U.S. Midwest to various reef animals in Australia. Lest the reader become euphoric, he should be aware that the kind of optimistic reports just cited are scarce and growing relatively

A musk ox bull. Musk oxen now have Arctic reserves set aside for them by the Soviet Union and Denmark. (Leonard Lee Rue III—Bruce Coleman, Inc.)

scarcer amidst the flood of news about species in trouble. Moreover, they emanate mostly from areas such as Europe, where conservation traditions among stable human populations are not only strong, but where all the truly fragile species disappeared many centuries ago, leaving more adaptable kinds behind to hold the semi-natural fort against the frequent excesses of man. Elsewhere, in much of Africa, in Central and South America, in Oceania, in parts of Asia, and especially in the Indian subcontinent, the preservation of species is only the beginning of a dream.

10
Conclusions

The Dangers

Because of our extensive alteration of the physical world and our
failure to conserve the communities and species that constitute our
biological environment, mankind has begun to experience locally the
first warning signs and symptoms of a global ecological deterioration.
I have grouped the main dangers that lie ahead in three broad categories.

Buffers are chemical solutions (of a weak acid or base and its salt,
in water) that are capable of counteracting the increase in acidity or
alkalinity that normally occurs when a strong acid or alkali (base) is
added to water. It is a characteristic of buffers that they work well up
to a point: before this point is reached they can resist and neutralize
the effects of small successive additions of acid or alkali, to the extent
that hardly any change can be observed in the buffered solution. But

311

if the buffer capacity of the solution is exceeded, even by a tiny amount of added acid or alkali, then the measurable acidity or alkalinity of the solution changes abruptly and drastically, as if the buffer weren't there at all.

Certain physical and biological systems in the natural world act in a way that is roughly analogous to this property of buffer solutions. They can tolerate a reasonable amount of manipulation or abuse without showing much evidence of serious damage, but when the limits of their ability to buffer external influences is exceeded, they deteriorate rapidly. Unlike the change in buffer solutions, however, this deterioration may be irreversible. Several examples of this "buffer effect" follow.

Populations of many organisms are adapted to survive fairly large fluctuations in their numbers of individuals, but for some of these populations there is a critical point. When the number of individuals falls below this critical level, intraspecies relationships are markedly altered and the population decline continues to extinction.

Soils are also capable of adjusting to a wide variety of physical and biotic fluctuations. However, when bad agricultural or building practices or improper lumbering operations occur, the soil may give way. Erosion and chemical changes of soils can be self-accelerating processes, particularly in the tropics, and these changes may occur with comparative speed after several years of mismanagement.

Finally, the organic pollution of lakes offers another example of the buffer effect. Pollution with organic wastes first causes gradual eutrophication in lakes that have a large volume of water to dilute the pollutants. This is usually characterized by an increase in single-celled organisms such as diatoms, algal flagellates, and bacteria, with a corresponding increase in ciliates and other zooplankton (animal plankton) that consume these organisms. Although the species composition of the community may change, there are still many fish, invertebrates, and other organisms living in the lake. But if pollution continues or increases there eventually comes a time when the microflora characteristic of early pollution is replaced by green algae such as *Chlorella* and blue-green algae such as *Microcystis*, neither of which will support a large zooplankton population. As the zooplankton population dwindles, some kinds of fish—at the other end of the food chain—also become scarce. Meanwhile, the algae pile up against the leeward shore in rotting masses, the toxins of the blue-green algae kill farm animals, birds, and still more fish, and the deoxygenation caused by the algal decay further reduces the flora and fauna of the lake. Here again, although pollution may have been going on for years with no gross observable effects, these final changes, irreversible in the course of a lifetime, often occur with drastic suddenness.

There is no way of telling with certainty how significant the buffer effect will turn out to be with respect to global environmental parameters. We do not know, for example, how the oceans, upon which we depend for food and oxygen renewal, will respond to a continued influx of waste materials, whether there will be signs of change that will warn up to stop in time, or whether we will be lulled to catastrophe by the false promise of an infinite capacity to absorb pollutants. If the latter is a more accurate respresentation of the true situation, conventional pollution-monitoring systems will be of little use, and only a fundamental breakthrough in our understanding of oceanic ecosystems would enable us to predict the danger point.

> Oh, a sleeping drunkard
> Up in Central Park,
> And a lion-hunter
> In the jungle dark,
> And a Chinese dentist,
> And a British queen—
> All fit together
> In the same machine.
> Nice, nice, very nice;
> Nice, nice, very nice;
> Nice, nice, very nice—
> So many different people
> In the same device.
>
> KURT VONNEGUT, JR.,
> Cat's Cradle

In 1958 LaMont Cole coined the word "ecosphere." By this he meant "the largest possible ecosystem: namely, the sum total of life on earth together with the global environment and the earth's total resources." His reason for inventing this word was that it describes a functional entity, a unit, whose myriad interdependent elements, including the inorganic environment, are bound together in part by photosynthesis, respiration, and other fundamental metabolic activities of plants and animals.

In any such functional unit it is impossible to isolate and contain the effects of a major change in one of the components. Readjustments take place throughout the system, and there may be no way of knowing what these will be. Flood control in California mountains may destroy coastal plain redwood communities. On a grander scale, the continued use of combustion engines and fossil fuels by an expanding population, and the continued destruction of forests and green space may, via the "greenhouse effect," cause worldwide climatic changes and the flooding of coastal cities.

Another example of unforeseen ramifications of disturbances in ecosystems concerns the destruction of Pacific coral reefs by the sea star (*Acanthaster planci*). Richard H. Chesher of the University of Guam has reported that since 1967, large sections of the reefs around Guam, Palau, Truk, Rota, Johnston Island, Wake, and other islands, as well as parts of the Great Barrier Reef of Australia, have been killed by this predatory starfish. The situation is serious, for when the reef is gone, the islands lose both their fisheries and their main protection against wave erosion. Although the reasons for the sudden proliferation of starfish can only be guessed at, Chesher points out that the larvae of the starfish are normally eaten by the filter-feeding corals, resulting presumably in a natural equilibrium. But when man kills parts of reefs by blasting and dredging, the larvae are provided with fresh, safe surfaces on which to settle. When they mature, they kill adjacent reef areas, produce more successful larvae, and the population of starfish spirals out of control. Other theories postulate that starfish predators have been destroyed by insecticides or that sea star population explosions occur as part of a natural cycle which has nothing to do with the activities of man. The recent spontaneous subsidence of the sea star population explosion in Hawaii only deepens the mystery.

On the positive side, the encouragement and growth of Rocky Mountain beaver populations has been found to smooth the annual fluctuations in the run-off of water to the southwestern desert below. The effects of beaver dams and ponds on stream flow are easy to comprehend, but this is a doubly exceptional example: changes in one part of the ecosphere often have unforeseen or remote ramifications, and these are rarely as beneficial to the environment of man and nature as beaver dams. The few examples listed above are of situations we think we somewhat understand; the ones we do not even recognize may prove the greater danger.

The many factors that tend to reduce the diversity of the earth's species and natural communities have been discussed throughout this book; it is the consequences of loss of diversity that concern us here. Some individuals would prefer a simpler planet. As late as 1967, an American corporation advertised that the conversion of virgin forests to tree farms was in part a public service because "most virgin forests are already doomed. They're waging a constant, losing battle against disease, insects and wildlife. . . . But when [we cut] a stand of trees, it's like gardening on a grand scale. New seedlings are planted and grown under the best possible conditions. Excess undergrowth is thinned. Protective sprays and fertilizers are applied. The result is a healthier, more abundant forest." What they did not add is that the single-species forest, if it replaced a diverse hardwood stand, is also very monotonous, that it supports an impoverished fauna of animals and birds, that nobody knows whether it will last more than three or four cutting cycles, and that it is suspected by many ecologists of being potentially susceptible, like the banana plantations of Central America, to uncontrollable parasitic infestations. (What would the equivalent of a chestnut blight or dutch elm disease do to a monoculture forest?) It has, in short, all the potential hazards of any truncated, oversimplified ecosystem.

What the proponents of simplification fail to comprehend is the ominous uncertainty of their schemes. Forest ecosystems cannot be freeze-dried or stored on microfilm to be reconstituted in case of emergency. What if tree farms begin to fail in the twenty-first century, and there are no sizeable natural forest communities left in some of the climatic and soil regions? The prospect of vast blighted zones choked with weeds and scarred by erosion is more than a Wellsian fantasy. In the marshes, the prairies, the deserts, and even the oceans, as well as the forests, the spectre of the irrevocable loss of the diversity that stabilizes the ecosphere and makes it habitable and pleasant threatens all species, including man.

The thread that unites these three dangers is the lack of scientific predictability that characterizes all our interactions with ecosystems. There is danger primarily because of our ecological ignorance. In a more restricted context, Hugh Raup has given the best advice for dealing with these realities of existence:

> I propose that we should plan ahead only so far as we can see with some degree of precision, and then readjust our plans at frequent intervals. We can be assured that there will never be enough facts available to give these plans any finality, and that we shall always be making judgments based upon probabilities. At every point of decision we will make use of whatever knowledge and measurement of value we can acquire, testing each for relevance to the point at issue as it relates to the frame of reference existing at the time.

If we add two injunctions—to conserve variety in order to preserve the options available to future generations, and to place the burden of justification on those who advocate disruptive actions—we have acceptable guidelines for management of the natural amenities of our planet.

The Sources of the Problem

While the biological life of the planet is eroded away and conservation policies are blocked, it is an exercise in paranoia to search for scapegoats—there are so many of them everywhere. Yet only by identifying the sources of the problem is it possible to devise solutions. Many of the principal causes of conservation failure are described below.

The economic success of modern nations is often judged and possibly dictated by their growth rates. When the Gross National Product goes up a little, economists fidget and smile reassuringly, but when it goes up more, they laugh. The Gross National Product is the monetary value of goods and services produced by a country in one year. If it goes up, that usually means more goods produced or more services rendered, or both. This in turn means an increase in the consumption of raw materials or, in some cases, an increase in the population (which provides and accepts services), or both. In communist countries there are similar measures of economic health that are based on the value of goods and services produced.

How long can economic expansion continue, and is there any theoretical limit to economic growth? Obviously, the response will vary for different countries, but in general the answers seem to be that economic expansion cannot continue indefinitely if it happens in the traditional way, and that it will be limited by exhaustion of mineral resources or destruction of the biological environment (including destruction by war or war production)—whichever comes first. Of these two limiting factors, the first is at least capable of analysis.

Walter R. Hibbard, Jr., formerly of the U.S. Bureau of Mines, has warned: "The needed materials which can be recovered by known methods at reasonable cost from the earth's crust are limited, whereas their rates of exploitation and use obviously are not. This situation cannot continue." It is true that we have not yet started to mine our wastes, but even if we are able to recover large quantities of iron from assorted scrap, some metals, such as silver and mercury, are largely nonreclaimable. One-third of our silver, for example, is used (and therefore lost) in the manufacture of photographic films and papers. Nevertheless, it does seem that by economies and substitutions combined with new prospecting and mining techniques we ought to be able to postpone the inevitable raw materials crisis at least until the end of the twentieth century.

In the case of the destruction of the natural world, the period of grace seems shorter and the prospects more gloomy. Economic expansion is too closely linked to the growth of population and technology. The only way man can avoid wrecking his environment is to find out how many people and machines the earth can support in something approaching an equilibrium condition, and then limit their numbers to these calculated levels. But it is likely that this would mean, even now, a gradual reduction in the earth's population and a cutback in many industries. Clearly, until we can uncouple the concept (and reality) of economic health from the process of economic expansion, until we can disassociate "progress" from "growth," there will be no effective conservation.

Herman Daly, an economist, has written:

> Production is a deplorable activity made necessary by the fact that wealth wears out or is used up, and must be replaced. It is not the increase of production, but the increase of capital stock which makes us rich. The social and economic implications of minimizing rather than maximizing production are decidedly radical. Ecological conservatism breeds economic radicalism.
>
> In the past growth has been a solvent for sticky income problems. . . . The result of zero growth would be mass unemployment. Since production is minimized, the demand for factors, including labor, will be less.

Rather than abandon the idea of zero production growth, Daly counsels a radical economic solution in terms of a revised system for distributing income and wealth. This, he admits, would place an unprecedented strain on our "moral resources."

I agree with Daly; at the same time I cannot help but look for ways to soften the economic blow. Perhaps a little hope emerges from a closer examination of the things produced by "production." Although precise, quantitative figures would be difficult to come by, it is clear that various products have very different labor/pollution ratios. (In this ratio, labor refers to the time spent by persons involved in the extraction of raw materials, production, distribution, and sales of the product; and pollution refers to all pollution "costs" associated with extraction of raw materials, production, distribution, use, and ultimate disposal of the product.) Many modern products have a very low ratio (relatively little labor and much pollution)—the best (worst) example that comes to mind is the snowmobile.

The main ingredient of a snowmobile, by weight, is steel, whose manufacture consumes fossil fuel and usually pollutes large quantities of water. Subsequent manufacture of the parts does the same. The assembly of a snowmobile is not particularly destructive of the environment, but its use more than makes up for this. Consuming gasoline and oil, frightening and driving away wildlife, wrecking winter vegetation, and accelerating erosion, a snowmobile in action is pure pollution. On the other hand, the labor involved in making a snowmobile is not proportionately high; most of the manufacturing steps are heavily automated.

At the other extreme in terms of the labor/pollution ratio are such disparate items as guitars and computers. The guitar in use pollutes not at all (unless it is badly played), and as we have seen, computer pollution can be reduced by economies in paper consumption. Both require much human labor to produce, far more than the relatively small pollution costs associated with their manufacture (this is crudely verified by their extremely high value per pound of weight, in a society where hand labor is very expensive). Both computers and guitars can be produced in such a way that the laborers who make them can take pride in their craft. Lewis Mumford, in *The Pentagon of Power*, quotes a "sad little tale" passed on to him by Dennis Gabor, a British professor of engineering and Nobel laureate:

> I heard that IBM-France had made a remarkable experiment. In their great factory at Corbeil-Essonnes they made a break with division of labor. One technician completed a sizeable element of a computer, using hundreds of tools, tested it himself, and *signed it*, like an artist! I heard also that the gain in interest and the

development in intelligence of these workmen was fabulous. Thereupon I wrote an enthusiastic letter to IBM-France and asked to visit them. I got a crestfallen letter, that "until now it was indeed like this—but their new factory will be fully automated!"

"IBM," writes Mumford, "was plainly not concerned with increasing *human* intelligence or giving back to machine workers the quality of life that once was fostered by the higher crafts."

If the rat race of perpetual expansion were to end, dehumanizing efficiency would no longer be at a premium and we could *afford* to make more items with a high labor/pollution ratio. Although some of the radical economic changes that Professor Daly writes about would still be necessary, the threat of mass unemployment in "the steady state" need not ever materialize if we plan wisely.

Today many political decisions affecting conservation are made by municipal, county, or state governments; these decisions involve zoning regulations, local pollution control ordinances, park policies, waste disposal, and similar actions. It is, however, at the local level that government seems most inadequate and incompetent to deal with conservation problems. Too often the quality of local government is poor, with cumbersome, archaic charters, conflicting and inadequate laws, uncertain financial and political ties with higher governmental agencies, and a dreary procession of uneducated, lackluster officials often drawn from the most exploitative segment of society and heavily in debt for campaign expenses. Problems are judged only according to the business ethic—if no orthodox solution is forthcoming, decisions are postponed until the next administration. The disposition of land is decided by realtors; the regulation of industry is managed by industrialists. It was funny when Dickens lampooned it a century ago; it is far from funny now.

Local governments are needed as a counterweight to centralized control, but something must be done to improve their quality. Perhaps the social and economic upgrading of local political offices would help.

Why should the mayor of a city with a population of 50,000 individuals not be as well paid and socially esteemed as the president of a medium-sized corporation? If part-time county commissioners were paid the same high fee as expert industrial consultants, more experts in government might serve, part-time, as county commissioners. The increase in salaries could hardly cost more than the current price of bad government.

Federal regulatory agencies are certainly necessary to monitor and control activities that transcend the geographical limits of local agencies. There is, however, a fundamental paradox inherent in their very existence. At one extreme, we must acknowledge the importance of both an "overview" and the possibility of coordinated response in the face of large-scale change. At the other extreme, we cannot deny that monolithic, massive decision-making can stifle the creative diversity of local response and invention, which is our best hope of finding and testing the right answers to numerous complex problems. How to achieve coordination, how to use the considered advice of experts, how to plan in an orderly and non-piecemeal fashion without losing all local influence and trampling on alternative plans is a terribly knotty problem. We need large regulatory agencies, but we must find many ways of leaving them open and accessible from "below," while shielding them from the powers of the central government and massive corporations or (in communist countries) industrial-bureaucratic complexes. Agencies that are evaluating or formulating long-range plans or major innovations must be made "inefficient," relatively slow, and conservative, and they should have multiple channels rather than a single chain of hierarchical authority, to prevent the bullish mistakes of big management from intruding in the china shop of our biological world. But this can only be done *provided the agencies cannot be circumvented during their deliberations* by the innovators, the designers, the builders, the managers, and the forces of "progress." When quicker responses or day-by-day management is needed, the agency or part of an agency, can be more efficient but should remain accessible to the public. In no case should the same agency have both a promotional and a regulatory function: in the United States, the Federal Power Commission and the Atomic Energy Commission conspicuously violate this rule.

> *The world is not so governed from above that private and social interest always coincide. It is not so managed here below that in practice they coincide. It is not a correct deduction from the Principles of Economics that enlightened self-interest always operates in the public interest. Nor is it true that self-interest generally is enlightened; more often individuals acting separately to promote their own ends are too ignorant or too weak to attain even these.*   JOHN MAYNARD KEYNES, *The End of Laissez-Faire*

The greatest barrier to the implementation of a strong and unified conservation policy is the difficulty of protecting those parts of the public domain that have traditionally been exploited by private interests. Both Keynes and later Hardin have explained that there is no logically consistent reason why an individual, corporation, or nation acting in self-interest should voluntarily abstain from exploiting the public domain even when the result will be certain destruction of the valuable features of that domain. Hardin, in fact, goes somewhat farther in "The Tragedy of the Commons" by asserting that it is usually damaging to private interests (at least in the short run) to act for the collective good as far as the commons are concerned. Of the many examples of this paradox already given, the commercial extermination of the blue whale and self-extermination of the whaling industry is the most striking.

If private interests cannot be expected to protect the public domain, then external regulation by public agencies, governments, or international authorities is needed. If that regulation is effective, the commons will be managed to provide the maximum *sustained* yield of natural products, which in turn will ultimately maximize the sum total of the profits for the various interests that rely on the commons. This concept, simple in theory, is difficult to put into practice.

In a book entitled *The Common Wealth in Ocean Fisheries*, Francis T. Christy, Jr., and Anthony Scott examine three suggested methods of protecting overexploited fisheries, a classic example of the "commons":

Sacrifice the freedom of the seas and assign exclusive fishing rights for a specific area to a particular nation or consortium of nations.

Allow free entry into all fishing areas, but establish some absolute quota or limit to the catch of each nation.

Internationalize the fishery, with all the details concerning which vessels will be allowed to fish and which methods and equipment will be used being regulated by a control authority. The only "rights" of the member nations would be to a proportionate share in the regulated total catch or to an equity in the profits of the fishery.

Each protection scheme has its limitations; moreover, there are a large number of possible permutations and combinations of the three, and therefore Christy and Scott wisely refrain from advocating any one in particular. Nevertheless, from the restricted point of view of the problem of the commons, it does seem possible to make some value judgments.

The first method, exclusive use, only transfers the public domain problem to a smaller stage, as various interests compete within each assigned territory. Even if there is regulation by individual nations, it is likely to be piecemeal; in the oceans, this makes little biological sense.

The second method, the quota system, is theoretically attractive but easily crippled by international political and economic squabbles. The difficulty is that the absolute size of the catch itself is subject to international negotiation, as each country, in competition with its fellows, argues for a larger quota. Countries that have quotas too small to enable them to fish at a profit may have to abandon their rights to the fishery, sell their quota at a loss to some other country, or may elect to ignore the quota altogether. The whaling treaty is an example of the latter.

The third method, internationalization, may be the best of the three. Here the participating nations can fight over the size of their proportionate share in the fishery without affecting the actual management decisions. This is a flexible system, permitting rapid adjustments to ecological change. It is also efficient since the fishing authority would be free to buy its labor and capital in the cheapest markets and to bargain effectively for the highest price for its products. The Pribilof Island fur seal treaty is an example: wildlife management decisions were effectively insulated from international political pressures by an agreement which stipulated only the *percentage distribution* of the proceeds of the catch. The wildlife managers, freed from commercial pressure to kill as many seals as possible, could take advantage of a convenient characteristic of seal behavior, the tendency for males to accumulate harems at breeding time. Since a harem may contain forty females, only the strongest and most ferocious males ever get a chance to breed. The rest are surplus, eating squids and fish that might otherwise go to nursing females, and not reproducing themselves. It is primarily these young bachelor bulls that are harvested; and the enormous increase in fur seal populations, from an estimated low of 132,000 in 1910 to nearly 2,000,000 in 1964, is proof of the wisdom of the policy. The late Ernest P. Walker, author of the great work *Mammals of the World*, described this as "one of the finest examples of conservation in action." Unfortunately, except for the Canadian-United States treaty protecting migratory birds, there is no other successful international agreement along the lines of Christy and Scott's third suggestion.

All "solutions" to the problem of public domain involve subdividing and apportioning the commons in some way. When the commons refers to some kind of natural resource, it is probably sufficient to separate the functions of resource management and apportionment of profits, as in the case of an internationalized fishery. When the commons refers, however, not to a material resource but to a previously unregulated activity such as adding to the world's stock of children, the hazard to collective interests is equally great, but the remedies are much further away.

In the preface to his book *Ulendo*, Archie Carr writes: ". . . the way the world is changing, how do we know what will seem pleasant to people a thousand years from now? . . . People can be made not just to live shoulder-to-shoulder in tiers, but to enjoy living that way." Adaptability to changing environments is a useful quality in a nomadic and curious creature like man, but it can be a deadly trap when the changing environments are themselves man-made. It can lead to acceptance of deteriorating living conditions, to a breakdown, in effect, of the feedback that is essential for maintenance of environmental quality control.

The essence of the problem was stated by Francis N. Ratcliffe, writing in *The Australian Quarterly:*

> . . . The changes which conservationists worry about, and which the practice of conservation is designed to prevent, take place a little too slowly for the ordinary man to appreciate, although horribly fast in terms of historical time. Most people find it hard to conjure up a detailed picture of a situation or scene as it was ten years before; and yet one must be able to do this in order to appreciate the extent and nature of progressive change. Steady deterioration, in fact, tends to be accepted uncritically.

This problem is at its worst in the urban New World, where nothing seems to last long enough to become a permanent part of the public image of the countryside because nothing is valued so much as newness. Claude Lévi-Strauss has pointed out that the "cycle of evolution" of large American cities is very rapid, but this is now also true of all areas within a distance of one to two hours' drive from a large city. Change is expected and accepted: the fact that so much change, from the central city to the national park, is for the worse, is only recorded as a vague awareness or a confused recollection by the majority of people.

One way to make people aware of slow deterioration is to keep some of the former landscapes around for comparison. In Boston, it may have been the contrast between the greatness of Louisburg Square and Faneuil Hall, on the one hand, and the drab "modern" office buildings in Scollay Square on the other, that made the city fathers accept an unconventional plan for the superb new City Hall built in the late 1960s. In Maine, the existence of a squalid horror like Route 1 south of Belfast, side-by-side with the unrivaled scenery of Acadia and Baxter Parks, may help conservationists argue against hasty commercialization.

Perhaps county or district conservators skilled in photography would be of use, particularly if they were provided with attractive, centrally located exhibit halls in which to show the history of the area. Certainly, the officials of the Sierra Club must have had something like this in mind when they began to publish their magnificent photographic records of vanishing landscapes.

There is a more direct and forceful way of making people aware of deteriorative change and at the same time preventing that change. A hint of this emerging technique appeared in John Sedgwick's testimony at the Camp Smith Marsh hearings. A critical factor in the U.S. Attorney's success in this case was that the marsh had been biologically and ecologically described and inventoried *before* its partial destruction, so that various witnesses could testify reliably about its value without having studied it themselves prior to the damage. The marsh was *known* in terms of its relationship to the local landscape and ecosystem, and that knowledge was contributed by Sedgwick's high school students.

It is impossible to protect any community, whether semi-natural surburban or totally wild, unless it has been at least partially characterized. The concept of an "ecological inventory," even in cities, is of immense value, and is beginning to grow in popularity. These inventories must be minutely and carefully done, including identification and mapping of *all* trees and shrubs in the inventory area (with a statement about condition of health) and identification and less precise mapping of smaller vegetation types (with special attention paid to native plants of any size). Birds can be identified, counted, and associated with specific local habitats; small mammals can be live-trapped and released after identification; reptiles, amphibians, fish, invertebrates (especially insects and spiders), and even microscopic life can be included in the inventory.

As might be guessed, this kind of inventory is beyond the capacity of one single person to perform, especially because it should be repeated every year. Members of garden clubs and amateur naturalists can take part; but in general this is a job for the high schools. Science teachers can be trained to supervise this sort of study; the financial investment in books and equipment is comparatively small. The benefits, on the other hand, are potentially enormous. Most obvious is the knowledge and awareness gained of the local ecosystem, making it likely that destructive "development" plans will be noticed and questioned before they are implemented. Of equal importance are the benefits for the participating students. In the United States (which the author knows best) most students suffer from the fact that they are virtually worthless to their community and to themselves until the age of seventeen or later. The adolescent years are drone years—no doubt many social ills originate in this unreasonable prolongation of childhood irresponsibility. Science fairs, "junior" equivalents of adult organizations, and similar make-work schemes are often miserable failures because they are transparent and fraudulent attempts to hide this real lack of meaning in the lives of adolescents. All villages, towns, and communities need ecological inventories; interested high school students, who are likely to be nearing the peak of their learning capacity, are the persons to entrust with this genuinely important job; both the wild and the human community will be well served. Furthermore, those students who never again have formal training in biology will still be vastly more informed and appreciative of their natural environment than were their parents; and those who are attracted to a career in ecology or related fields will find out about their interest and ability at a conveniently early age, and will provide a vital and growing profession with much-needed manpower. Finally, but not least significant, this is an activity in which the work and the advantages for both sexes can and should be entirely equal.

People have a remarkable ability to avoid confronting unpleasant facts, and the problems of conservation are very unpleasant. History has conspired in a number of countries to aid and abet these processes of rationalization, denial, and hero worship.

In the United States, the Soviet Union, Australia, and all other large industrialized nations that have recently had a frontier, there is a myth, which goes something like this: "This is a big country with a lot of open space in it. The people are all crowded together in the cities, but if you fly across the country by jet you see nothing but trees, rocks, and empty land. There's plenty of room for more people, more houses, more factories and businesses if we spread them out properly. Even if we make a few mistakes, there is always more land."

This widespread misconception, which Ratcliffe terms the "Big Country Mystique," is as outmoded as butter churns and flintlock rifles, but it stubbornly persists. The amount of unpopulated open space left is greatly exaggerated; the amount of unruined unpopulated space is far less. Things have changed since the days of the frontier. Not only does suburban sprawl fill the interstices between many cities, but as one might expect, the best sites for cities already have cities on them. There is no need, however, to rest the case on this argument. The amount of unpopulated open space left is irrelevant. The ecological resources of all developed countries are already strained to the breaking point. They can hardly be strained less by an added burden of people and their accoutrements, no matter what the spatial arrangements of new population centers may be.

> *Ah, my child, if you wish to overturn the world by striving to set a little more happiness in it, you have only to remain in your laboratory here, for human happiness can only spring from the furnace of the scientist.*   EMILE ZOLA, *Paris*

> *Students are beginning to doubt that Galileo, Watt, and Edison have contributed as much and as lastingly to human advancement and happiness as Socrates, Lao-tze, and Francis of Assisi.*
> RENÉ DUBOS, *So Human An Animal*

> *The older I get, the less I care about science and the more about nature.*   ARCHIE CARR (in a letter to the author)

When the Big Country Mystique fails and the ecological facts of life threaten to push their way into the public consciousness, there is always someone who tries to frighten them back with the spectre of science. Scientism, the belief that the methods of science and technology can be used to solve all problems, including those of the humanities and social sciences, has waxed strong since the days of

Zola, fed by the great twentieth-century developments in physics, chemistry, biology, and engineering. With respect to conservation, scientism is expressed as the optimistic faith that the most challenging problems concerning population control, pollution, exhaustion of resources, food production, protection of species, and similar questions will be overcome by scientific-technologic discoveries or applications yet to be made. Among scientists, many of whom believe in scientism, this faith is occasionally sustained by the idea that if the public and big business wanted to, they could easily extricate the country from its ecological predicament by spending large sums of money on appropriate technological research and development.

Apart from the philosophical objections to scientism and its corollaries, one way to counter this kind of argument is to point out that, in scientific terms, the bulk of the data would not appear to support the hypothesis. Science and technology have a long history of creating ecological problems; their record for solutions that do not in themselves generate more problems is less than impressive.

Laymen do not seem to realize that scientists and engineers are human, and have human egos. (In fact, some scientists and engineers themselves do not like to acknowledge this.) Their expectations of these specialists are frighteningly naive. Indeed, the postponement of immediate gratification that goes along with the years of study needed for a scientific or technical advanced degree is often sustained by an ego-serving promise of power that has little to do with the real needs of the world. In the year 1590 or thereabouts, at the dawn of a new age, Christopher Marlowe had Doctor Faustus utter a prophetic warning:

> O, what a world of profit and delight,
> Of power, of honor and omnipotence
> Is promised to the studious artisan [expert]!
> All things that move between the quiet poles
> Shall be at my command . . .

Perhaps the extraordinarily long period of childhood dependence among human beings fosters the commonplace notion that there is always someone stronger and wiser to take care of things; but what-ever the origin of this belief, we can no longer let it blind us to the Faustian element in science and technology. Experts are no more likely to be wicked than anyone else; they are not less likely to be wicked, either. It is a strange kind of self-deception that enables a person to stand among the high-powered automobiles, chemical insecticides, thermonuclear bombs, napalm, and nerve gas and look to science and technology for salvation. Science does have a major role to play in the future of conservation; many aspects of that role have been indicated in this book. Nevertheless, science will need careful guidance and supervision from other disciplines; and even given the best of circum-stances, the outcome of its efforts will remain for some time beyond the reach of scientific prediction.

The promise of technologists is, as it has been for more than a cen-tury, that a new miracle age is just over the horizon. "You don't want to go back to the old life, with all its inconveniences?" they ask, as if the more deadly inconveniences of our present state were but a small price to pay for tomorrow's mechanically perfect bliss, with its total automation, decision-making by computer, and perpetual (if boring) life. But those who fear rather than welcome this paradise are fright-ened by a shadow. The question is not whether the miracle age will come to pass—it will not—but rather what will be left of the natural world when the mess of the present and the next twenty to thirty years is finally cleaned up and the last skirmishes and rear-guard actions have been fought. Technology has become preposterous; it is as viable now as the dodo was in 1681, with one difference—the dodo became extinct quietly and without hurting anybody; most of the debris it left behind has been safely confined in a few drawers of the Ashmolean and British Museums. What is required of us now is not more hero-worship of technology, but a careful appraisal and a selection of those of its inventions that are really worth salvaging and developing.

The Good Life

In wildness is the preservation of the world.
HENRY DAVID THOREAU, *Walking*

A reverence for the natural world was one of the first signs of man's humanity and has been an important feature of many societies. Throughout the Old and New Stone Ages this attitude flourished, and it was a vital part of the great Mediterranean and Oriental civilizations that followed. In Greece, before the Roman conquests, the land was alive with spirits; every grove was filled with the presence of protective deities, every stream and mountain was personified and respected by the people who lived nearby. But the rise of western Christianity, with its Judeo-Christian doctrine of an exclusive relationship between man and God, largely rejected this special regard for nature; in so doing it set the stage for the global ecological disaster that threatens to culminate in our century.

The dominant theme of Occidental culture is embodied in the word "progress," a concept that has been remarkably sacrosanct until now. One trouble with progress, apart from its effects on the ecosphere, is, paradoxically, its animal mindlessness; in the excitement of change there is neither time nor apparent need to do what humans are uniquely capable of—to make plans for the future. Progress discourages independent speculation about goals and meanings. There is never time to ask the question, "What do we want?" except in the most immediate and material sense. Yet this question must be asked at this time—and answered—if it is not already too late. Either nationally or internationally the world's peoples will have to define what the good life is, and then must reconcile this ideal with the closest approximation that the earth can provide on a sustained basis.

In any consideration of the good life we must first evaluate the prevailing Western ethic. The historian Lynn White, Jr., has stated the problem well:

> I personally doubt that disastrous ecologic backlash can be avoided simply by applying to our problems more science and more technology. . . . Both our present science and our present

technology are so tinctured with orthodox Christian arrogance toward nature that no solution for our ecologic crisis can be expected from them alone. Since the roots of our trouble are so largely religious, the remedy must also be essentially religious, whether we call it that or not. We must rethink and refeel our nature and destiny. The profoundly religious, but heretical, sense of the primitive Franciscans for the spiritual autonomy of all parts of nature may point a direction.*

Since these words were written in 1967, they have been widely discussed, with the majority of scientists (but not all) branding them as impractical, idealistic and hopelessly pastoral—all three adjectives being epithets in this age of technology. I rely on the preceding chapters of this book to defend the holistic view against such attacks, regardless of whether the view is expressed as pastoralism, spirituality, or ecological theory. The mechanomorphic faith in progress and technology is considered practical and hard-nosed by its proponents; but the facts do not bear them out. The belief in progress is a religion cloaked in a shroud of "objectivity," and like the Aztec rites of old, human sacrifice is at the heart and center of its ceremonial practice.

Several writers have seen through the disguises of the religion of progress and have traced the notion back through history; none, however, has followed it so far or characterized it so brilliantly as Lewis Mumford. He finds that although our science and technology and the refinements of our present economic systems have aspects of newness, and although our immense capacity for ecological damage is new, the mechanistic, self-subordinating, power-worshipping kind of society in

---

* Not surprisingly, the organized Judeo-Christian religions of today have been, officially at least, blind to the holistic view of the natural world and thoroughly unwilling to accept a limited, life-sized image of man and his place in the world. Where it existed, the primitive Franciscan tradition of oneness with nature has been all but obliterated; the image of St. Francis seen in the magnificent paintings of Giotto, always in the midst of trusting birds and animals, is in majestic contrast to the spirit of the twentieth century, when one can find Franciscan monasteries whose barracks-like buildings stand surrounded by treeless, manicured lawns with not even a bird feeder in evidence. Among contemporary Judeo-Christian religious groups, few besides the Jehovah's Witnesses would appear to have formulated a holistic and balanced philosophy of man in relation to his environment (see *Awake!*, April 22, 1971).

which we find ourselves is at least as old as the Pyramid Age in Egypt and Mesopotamia. Even so, not every society in history has been enslaved by what Mumford calls the "pentagon of power"*—nor is every society today as deeply in its thrall as ours—and this is the basis of Mumford's hope. Indeed some cultures, scattered throughout historical time, have been able to guide and channel the natural anthropocentrism, the ego, of man away from fulfillment in the pursuit of power, and toward fulfillment in the good life.

Ironically, today the nations best suited to grapple with the problem of the good life may be those that we refer to as "underdeveloped." Most of these poorer nations still have the chance to control technology before it masters them, and many of them, such as India, China, and Indonesia, still have at least the remnants of cultural and religious traditions that teach man to live in peace with nature. But even though we may have more difficulty, the industrialized countries, especially the United States, will have to move toward the same goal, for the sake of everyone who lives on the planet.

The only justification of the Western ideal of progress has been that it promotes man's comfort and well-being; but if we look dispassionately at the results of a century of progress, we find nearly all men anxious and alone. Technology, masquerading as an end rather than a means, has unnecessarily moved man away from nature, and in so doing has moved him away from himself. Even if there were no ecological crisis, conservation would still have its most important mission before it: preserving wilderness for those human beings who are fortunate enough to know now that it is part of them and that they enjoy it, and also for those in the future who may learn to use technology in a way that does not subvert the human heritage. Carr must have had something like this in mind when he said: "The real reason for saving tuataras is so people can continue to sing them out of their holes."

---

* The basic ingredient of the "Power Complex" is power itself (from animal labor to nuclear power); this is supported by political power, property, productivity, profit, and publicity. So intricate and subtle an idea deserves reading in its original context; see Mumford in "Suggested Readings."

> . . . *despair is only for those who see the end beyond all doubt.*
> J. R. R. TOLKIEN, *The Lord of the Rings*

I have been told, by people who have read the preceding pages in manuscript, that there is a great deal of depressing information in them. No doubt this is true; an honest and balanced account of the facts of conservation in the 1970s does not make encouraging reading. Similarly, although possible solutions or at least rational approaches to problems are offered throughout the book, and especially in this chapter, I have provided no grand synthesis of cures, no magical liniment for the aches and pains of beleaguered nature. Nor should I: to expect simple solutions, to deny the immense complexity of our dilemma, is to be part of the dilemma and incapable of coping with it.

Does all this make me an optimist or a pessimist? The reader is entitled to know after many pages of "objective" scientific writing— miles of words with scarcely a hint of the first person singular. This question is easy to answer, but it is the wrong question; genuine, hundred-percent pessimists are very rare and they do not write books about conservation. So maybe the question should be rephrased to read, "What is there to make conservationists optimistic?"

There seem to be three possible reasons for optimism about the future of life on earth. First, there is what we might call *simple* or *rational* optimism, based on the analytic judgment that things are actually getting better. Such optimism is now very uncommon among ecologists and other environmental scientists, many of whom believe that some kind of vast and unprecedented global "break" or "discontinuity" is coming within the next ten to forty years. There are exceptions. René Dubos, who describes himself as a "despairing optimist," writes: "One of the most hopeful signs of our period is the extent of soul-searching among scientists and sociologists concerning the nature of the scientific enterprise and the urgency to rededicate it to worthwhile social goals." But one suspects that there is something more behind Dubos' optimism than this insubstantial and ghostly glimmer of positive change.

The second source of optimism is human nature; most human natures contain optimism because it is useful in sustaining life. Fraser Darling has remarked that "We could not continue unless we were congenitally in some measure optimists and we could not make the forward movements we did unless we were pessimists as well." In other words, a personality containing a blend of optimism and pessimism has an evolutionary advantage. In this vein, Paul Ehrlich, the most vocal catastrophist among modern ecologists, has wondered why he bothers to participate in so many traditional conferences and planning sessions concerning a future that he feels is bound to be total chaos. His answer is, "Maybe I just can't keep myself scared." Partly for this reason, some of Ehrlich's colleagues have referred to him as "not an optimist but the most cheerful of pessimists." Surely this kind of optimism is present in all conservationists; it is not, however, likely to be very reassuring to the reader who wants something more real.

The third possible reason for optimism, shared by this author and some others, is deceptively similar to the second. In brief, it is the hope in supra-rational factors which are, by definition, unknowable. This is not equivalent either to superstitious faith or to mysticism. It is an acknowledgement that the future course and events of life, the most complex and diverse set of interacting phenomena in a complex universe, are well beyond the predictive abilities of man. It is, justly, an ecologist's optimism. Dubos, who at times seems to accept the approach of catastrophe, has pointed out that "The original Greek word *catastrophe* meant a sudden change of course, an overturn not necessarily associated with disaster." Although, as we saw, he speculates about what might bring such a benign catastrophe to pass, he does not really claim to predict a specific chain of events. This kind of optimism can also be found in the writings of Mumford: "We must allow, when we consider the future, for the possibility of miracles, on the grounds developed by Charles Babbage in the *Ninth Bridgewater Treatise* and by James Clerk Maxwell in his famous letter on singular points. By a miracle we mean not something outside the order of nature but something occurring so infrequently and bringing about such a radical change that one cannot include it in any statistical prediction." Of course, as Mumford indicates, *singular points* can as easily be devastating as favorable in their effects—but then there is a difference between a qualified optimism and the blind faith that everything will be all right.

Whatever their expectations of the future, men must think and then act. During this possibly last, fey surge of population and technology it may be futile to think of perfecting a still-embryonic system for the conservation of life on earth; however, in the absence of reliable prophecy, both the optimist and pessimist can agree that there is no other human endeavor more worth the effort.

References Cited

Chapter 1

Amerasinghe, Hamilton S., in M. T. Farvar *et al.*, *Environment* 13(8), 10 (1971).

Darling, F. Fraser, *A Herd of Red Deer* (Garden City, N.Y.: Doubleday, Anchor Books, 1964).

Glacken, Clarence J., in *Man's Role in Changing the Face of the Earth*, W. L. Thomas, Jr., ed. (Chicago: University of Chicago Press, 1956).

Kesteven, G. L., *Science* 160, 857 (1968).

Chapter 2

Athwal, D. S., *Quarterly Review of Biology* 46, 1 (1971).

Brown, L. R., *Science* 158, 604 (1967).

Chittenden, H. M., *Transactions of the American Society of Civil Engineers* 62, 245 (1909).

Commoner, B., Corr, M., and Stamler, P. J., *Environment* 13(3), 2 (1971).

Dansereau, P., *Biogeography* (New York: Ronald Press, 1957).

Elton, C. S., *The Ecology of Invasions by Animals and Plants* (London: Methuen, 1958).

Frankel, O. H., in *Genetic Resources in Plants—Their Exploration and Conservation*, O. H. Frankel and E. Bennett, eds. (Oxford: Blackwell, 1970).

Iltis, H., personal communication.

Klein, D. R., *Science* 173, 393 (1971).

Leopold, A. Starker, and Leonard, J. W., *Audubon* 68, 176 (1966).

Margalef, R., *American Naturalist* 97, 357 (1963).

337

————, *Perspectives in Ecological Theory* (Chicago: University of Chicago Press, 1968).

Odum, E., *Fundamentals of Ecology* (Philadelphia: Saunders, 1971).

Paddock, W. C., *BioScience 20*, 897 (1970).

Partington, W., *Florida Naturalist 41*(2B), (1968).

Pfeiffer, E. W., and Westing, A. H., *Environment 13*(9), 2 (1971).

Sauer, C. O., in *Environ/Mental*, P. Shepard and D. McKinley, eds. (Boston: Houghton Mifflin, 1971).

Schmitt, W. R., *Annals of the New York Academy of Sciences 118*, 645 (1965).

Spilhaus, A., *Science 159*, 710 (1968).

Tatum, L. A., *Science 171*, 1113 (1971).

Yarwood, C. E., *Science 168*, 218 (1970).

Chapter 3

Abelson, P. H., *Science 161*, 113 (1968).

Blegvad, H., *Proceedings of the United Nations Conference on the Conservation and Utilization of Resources VII*, 51 (1951).

Carr, A., *National Geographic Magazine 131*, 133 (1967).

Chiapetta, J., *Audubon 70*, 30 (1968).

Epstein, S. S., and Taylor, F. B., *Science 154*, 261 (1966).

Ferguson, F. A., *Environmental Science and Technology 2*, 188 (1968).

Graham, J. B., Rubinoff, I., and Hecht, M. K., *Proceedings of the National Academy of Sciences 68*, 1360 (1971) (material about sea snakes).

Katzer, M. F., and Pollack, J. W., *Environmental Science and Technology 2*, 341 (1968).

King, W., *Florida Naturalist 41*, 99 (1968).

Lapp, R. E., *The New York Times*, Dec. 12, 1971, Sect. 4, p. 11.

Laycock, G., *The Alien Animals* (Garden City, N.Y.: Natural History Press, 1966).

MacArthur, R. H., and Connell, J. H., *The Biology of Populations* (New York: Wiley, 1966).

MacClean, D. C., et al., *Environmental Science and Technology 2*, 444 (1968).

Nicholson, H. P., *Science 158*, 871 (1967).

Odum, H. T., *A Tropical Rain Forest* (Washington, D.C.: U.S. Atomic Energy Commission, 1970).

Patrick, R., *Purdue University Engineering Extension Series 87*, 325 (1954).

Pryde, P. R., *Environment 13*(9), 16 (1971).

Smith, J. E., ed., *"Torrey Canyon" Pollution and Marine Life* (Cambridge: Cambridge University Press, 1968).

Sullivan, W. T., and Evans, R. L., *Environmental Science and Technology 2*, 194 (1968).

Van den Bosch, R., *Natural History Magazine*, Dec. 1971.
Wurster, C. F., Jr., and Wingate, D. B., *Science 159*, 979 (1968).

Chapter 4

Florence, R. G., *Ecology 46*, 52 (1965).
Hodge, F. W., *Business and Economic Dimensions 1*(4), 1 (1965).
Proxmire, Hon. W., *Congressional Record* (Senate), Aug. 23, 1965.
Robinson, B., *Science 160*, 833 (1968).
Stone, E. C., and Vasey, R. B., *Science 159*, 157 (1968).

Chapter 5

American Zoologist 7(2), 233 (1967) (articles on wolves).
Carr, A., *Handbook of Turtles* (Ithaca, N.Y.: Cornell University Press, 1952).
Conway, W. G., *Animal Kingdom 73*(3), 18 (1968).
Cott, H. B., *Transactions of the Zoological Society of London 29*(4), 211 (1961).
————, reported in *New Scientist*, Oct. 3, 1968, p. 9.
Eimerl, S., and DeVore, I., *The Primates* (New York: Time, Inc., 1965).
Hillaby, J., *Animal Kingdom 70*, 143 (1967).
Lagler, K., *American Midland Naturalist 29*, 257 (1943).
Leopold, A., *A Sand County Almanac* (New York: Oxford, 1966).
Lerman, J. C., *Science 160,* 251 (1968).
Lévi-Strauss, C., *The Savage Mind* (Chicago: University of Chicago Press, 1966).
McIlhenny, E. A., *The Alligator's Life History* (Boston: Christopher, 1935).
Minckley, W. L., and Deacon, J. E., *Science 159*, 1424 (1968).
Quaintance, C. W., *Science 161*, 520 (1968).
Schaller, G. B., *Audubon 70*(3), 80 (1968).
Sherwood, G., *Audubon 73*(6), 72 (1971).
Talbot, L. M., *A Look at Threatened Species* (published for the International Union for the Conservation of Nature by the Fauna Preservation Society, 1960).
Williams, G. C., *Adaptation and Natural Selection* (Princeton, N.J.: Princeton University Press, 1966).

Chapter 6

Ruud, J. T., *Norsk Hvalfangst Tidende*, June 1950.
Small, G., *The Virtual Extinction of an Extraterritorial Pelagic Resource— The Blue Whale* (doctoral dissertation, Columbia University, 1968).
————, *The Blue Whale* (New York: Columbia University Press, 1971).

Watt, K. E. F., *Ecology and Resource Management* (New York: McGraw-Hill, 1968).

Chapter 7

Blake, J., *Science 164*, 522 (1969).
Chang, Jen-hu, *The Geographical Review 58* (3), 333 (1968).
Darling, F. F., *British Ecological Society Jubilee Symposium*, a supplement of the *Journal of Ecology 52* and the *Journal of Animal Ecology 33* (Oxford: Blackwell, 1964), p. 39.
Darnay, A. J., Jr., *Environmental Science and Technology 3*, 328 (1969).
Hardin, G., *Science 162*, 1243 (1968).
Harkavy, O., Jaffe, F. S., and Wishik, S. M., *Science 165*, 367 (1969).
Huffaker, C. B., Messenger, P. S., and DeBach, P., in *Biological Control*, C. B. Huffaker, ed. (New York: Plenum, 1971).
Katzer, M. F., and Pollack, J. W., *Environmental Science and Technology 2*, 341 (1968).
Laessle, A., *Quarterly Journal of the Florida Academy of Sciences 21*(1), 101 (1958).
Lemon, P. C., *Ecology 49*, 316 (1968).
Leopold, A. Starker, *et al.*, *Audubon 70*(3), 8 (1968).
Lewis, Philip H., Jr., *Regional Design for Human Impact* (Kaukauna, Wis.: Thomas, 1969).
Little, C. E., *Challenge of the Land* (New York: Open Space Institute, 1968).
McHarg, I., in *Taming Megalopolis 1*, H. W. Eldredge, ed. (Garden City, N.Y.: Doubleday, Anchor Books, 1967).
Mayer, J., *Daedalus 93*(3), 830 (Summer 1964).
Raup, H., *British Ecological Society Jubilee Symposium* (see Darling, above), p. 19.
Swan, F. R., Jr., *Proceedings of the West Virginia Academy of Science 39*, 251 (1967).
Talbot, L. M., *et al.*, *The Meat Production Potential of Wild Animals in Africa* (Farnam Royal, England: Commonwealth Agricultural Bureaux Technical Communication No. 16, 1965).

Chapter 8

Čapek, K., *Letters from England* (London: Geoffrey Bles, 1925).
Cleaver, E., *Ramparts 8*(3), 34 (1969).
Elton, C. S., *The Ecology of Invasions by Animals and Plants* (London: Methuen, 1958).
Jacobs, J., *The Death and Life of Great American Cities* (New York: Random House, Vintage, 1961).
Leopold, A., *A Sand County Almanac* (New York: Oxford), 1966.

Unger, I., *Artificial Reefs*, adapted by E. C. Bolster (American Littoral Society Special Publication No. 4: Highlands, N.J., 1966).

Westhoff, V., *New Scientist*, April 16, 1970, p. 108.

Chapter 9

Elton, C. S., *The Ecology of Invasions by Animals and Plants* (London: Methuen, 1958).

Minckely, W. L., and Deacon, J. E., *Science 159*, 1424 (1968).

Olsen, J., *Sports Illustrated 30*, 36 (1969) (about grizzly bear incident in Glacier Park).

Randall, J. E., *Ecology 46*, 255 (1965).

Tanner, J. T., *The Ivory-Billed Woodpecker* (New York: Dover, 1966).

Chapter 10

Chesher, R. H., *Science 165*, 280 (1969).

Christy, F. T., and Scott, A., *The Common Wealth in Ocean Fisheries* (Baltimore: Johns Hopkins, 1965).

Cole, LaMont C., *Scientific American*, April 1958, p. 83.

Daly, H., *The New York Times*, October 14, 1970.

Darling, F. F., Ehrlich, P., et al., in *A Conversation on Population, Environment, and Human Well-Being* (Washington, D.C.: The Conservation Foundation, 1971).

Dubos, R., *Reason Awake: Science for Man* (New York: Columbia University Press, 1970).

Hibbard, W. R., Jr., *Science 160*, 143 (1968).

Lévi-Strauss, C., *Tristes Tropiques* (New York: Atheneum, 1963).

Mumford, L., in *Man's Role in Changing the Face of the Earth*, W. L. Thomas, Jr., ed. (Chicago: University of Chicago Press, 1956).

Ratcliffe, F. N., *The Australian Quarterly 40*(1), 1 (1968).

Raup, H., *British Ecological Society Jubilee Symposium* (see Chapter 7, Darling, above), p. 19.

Walker, E. P., *Mammals of the World II* (Baltimore: Johns Hopkins, 1964).

White, L., Jr., *Science 155*, 1203 (1967).

Suggested Readings

I have made no attempt to provide a complete list of readings; consequently many good books that might have been included will not be found here. The books that are listed, however, amply cover the subject of conservation; and I believe them to be of uniformly high quality.

Chapter 1

Bade, W. F., *The Life and Letters of John Muir* (Boston: Houghton Mifflin, 1924). The quality of Muir's prose is commensurate with his vision and his feeling for the natural world.

Clepper, Henry, ed., *Origins of American Conservation* (New York: Ronald Press, 1966). A book of readings by twentieth-century conservationists, mostly of the forestry–wildlife management school. Contains much historical information.

Nash, Roderick, ed., *The American Environment: Readings in the History of Conservation* (Reading, Mass.: Addison-Wesley, 1968). A well-selected and well-edited collection of writings by nineteenth- and twentieth-century environmentalists.

Van Doren, Mark, ed., *Travels of William Bartram* (New York: Dover, 1955; paperback). This eighteenth-century description of the natural splendors of the American southeast can be considered a principal source of the holistic and wilderness conservation themes in both England and the United States.

343

Chapter 2

Brown, Lester R., and Finsterbusch, Gail W., *Man and His Environment: Food* (New York: Harper & Row, 1972). The production of food, past, present, and future. A careful discussion of land use patterns, new food technologies, and the impact of agriculture on the earth's eco-systems. However, there is little consideration of the loss of crop diversity.

Elton, Charles S., *The Ecology of Invasions by Animals and Plants* (London: Methuen, 1958). A modern ecological classic which is also delightful to read. The concluding chapters constitute a prophetic essay on the value of biological diversity.

Kormondy, Edward J., *Concepts of Ecology* (Englewood Cliffs, N.J.: Prentice-Hall, 1969). A good beginning text on ecology at the college level. Paperback and concise.

Leopold, Aldo, *A Sand County Almanac* (New York: Oxford, 1966). The modern conservation bible. Simply and elegantly written by the pioneer of game management. Contains the "land ethic."

Marine, Gene, *America the Raped—The Engineering Mentality and the Devastation of a Continent* (New York: Simon and Schuster, 1969). A hard and unflattering look at the earth-movers, by a radical en-vironmentalist.

Odum, Eugene, *Ecology* (New York: Holt, Rinehart & Winston, 1963). Simi-lar to Kormondy.

————, *Fundamentals of Ecology* (Philadelphia: Saunders, 1971). The best of the general ecology texts. Written for college and graduate students.

Shepard, Paul, and McKinley, Daniel, eds., *Environ/Mental* (Boston: Hough-ton Mifflin, 1971). A book of readings, as imaginatively selected as its title suggests. The essays are not all of the same quality, but this is still perhaps the finest of the many books of its type.

Teal, John, and Teal, Mildred, *Life and Death of the Salt Marsh* (Boston: Atlantic–Little, Brown, 1969). The ecology, in depth, of a valuable ecosystem, and how it is being destroyed. A compelling and very readable case history.

Chapter 3

Benarde, M. A., *Our Precarious Habitat* (New York: Norton, 1970). Much information about pollution, with reference primarily to public health rather than other ecological effects.

Brown, Tom, *Oil on Ice* (San Francisco: Sierra Club, 1971). The story of the North Slope oil rush and its present and future impact on the Alaskan wilderness. Interesting, but skimpy in ecological detail.

Carson, Rachel, *Silent Spring* (Boston: Houghton Mifflin, 1962). An historic little book about the many side effects of insecticides; it ended the permissive, polluted slumber of the western world. Still very much worth reading. Impressively documented.

Hynes, H. B. N., *The Biology of Polluted Waters* (Liverpool: Liverpool University Press, 1960). Certainly the best book for the non-specialist about water pollution. Hynes, a noted expert on British and North American streams, is remarkably lucid with this difficult subject, and his English is a delight to read. Contains nothing on radioactive wastes.

Rose, Steven, ed., *CBW: Chemical and Biological Warfare* (Boston: Beacon Press, 1969). A collection of essays, mostly by research chemists, physicists, biologists, and physicians, on such subjects as "defoliants," "psychedelics," and "napalm." Accurate, non-hysterical, well-researched, and frightening.

Chapter 4

Maass, Arthur, *Muddy Waters: The Army Engineers and the Nations Rivers* (Cambridge: Harvard University Press, 1951). The Corps of Engineers is changing, but not fast enough to enable us to forget this book.

Van Doren, Mark, ed., *Travels of William Bartram* (see above, Chapter 1). Bartram's descriptions of southern Georgia and northern Florida inspired Coleridge and Wordsworth to create some of their finest poetry, including Coleridge's "Kubla Khan." His knowledge of natural history was immense, and his understanding of nature truly ecological.

Chapter 5

Errington, Paul L., *Of Predation and Life* (Ames, Iowa: Iowa State University Press, 1967). The case for predators, by a biologist who began by trapping them and ended by studying them.

Fisher, James, Simon, Noel, and Vincent, Jack, *Wildlife in Danger* (New York: Viking Press, 1969). A fascinating if disturbing account, with illustrations, of virtually all of the animals and plants known to be endangered by 1969. Very accurate. By the compilers of the *Red Data Books* of the International Union for the Conservation of Nature.

Greenway, James C., Jr., *Extinct and Vanishing Birds of the World* (New York: Dover, 1967; paperback). No longer up to date, but still the starting point for reading about extinctions caused by man.

National Geographic Society, *Vanishing Peoples of the Earth* (Washington; D.C., 1968). An important aspect of the loss of natural diversity.

Ziswiler, Vinzenz, *Extinct and Vanishing Animals* (New York: Springer-Verlag, 1967). A good little paperback that analyzes the process of extinction and provides both ideas and information about it.

Chapter 6

Scheffer, Victor B., *The Year of the Whale* (New York: Scribner's, 1969). Good natural history presented as good literature. This book is about sperm whales (also endangered), but it will help the reader understand all whales.

Small, George L., *The Blue Whale* (New York: Columbia University Press, 1971). A scholarly and fact-filled discussion of blue whales and the whaling industry. The short-sightedness and greed so clearly exposed in this book would be hard to believe in a work of fiction.

Chapter 7

Commoner, Barry, *The Closing Circle* (New York: Knopf, 1971). Technology as the villain of "the environmental crisis." Ecologically sound. Contains interesting thoughts on the economics of pollution. A book of major importance, which should be read with *Population, Resources, Environment* (see below).

Darling, F. Fraser, and Milton, John P., eds., *Future Environments of North America* (Garden City, N.Y.: Natural History Press, 1966). The report of a conference held in 1965 by the Conservation Foundation; successor to *Man's Role in Changing the Face of the Earth* (see below). Good sections on habitat management, economics, regional planning, etc.

Ehrlich, Paul, and Ehrlich, Anne, *Population, Resources, Environment* (San Francisco: Freeman, 1972). Overpopulation as the villain of "the environmental crisis." A better-documented *Population Bomb*. The latest but hopefully not the last word on the ramifications of the population explosion, particularly with respect to resources; also a good discussion of population control. Should be read with *The Closing Circle* (see above).

Hardin, Garrett, ed., *Population, Evolution, and Birth Control* (San Francisco: Freeman, 1969). A collection of essays: from Aristotle and Malthus to Boulding and the Paddocks. Includes "The Tragedy of the Commons." Well-selected, but omits the important dissenting opinions of Jean Mayer about world food supplies.

McHarg, Ian L., *Design with Nature* (Garden City, N.Y.: Natural History Press, 1969). A beautifully constructed book, with magnificent maps and pictures as well as McHarg's flowing English. Much fascinating material on urban design.

Mumford, Lewis, *The City in History* (New York: Harcourt, Brace and World, 1961). One of Mumford's greatest works. The best way to understand what cities are, and how they arrived at their present condition. Can be read in conjunction with Jacobs (see *Suggested Readings*, Chapter 8).

National Academy of Sciences–National Research Council, *Resources and Man* (San Francisco: Freeman, 1969). Report of a committee chaired by geologist Preston Cloud. Excellent information on world resources, including minerals, food from the land, food from the sea, energy, etc.

Sax, Joseph, *Defending the Environment: A Strategy for Citizen Action* (New York: Knopf, 1970). A thoughtful and interesting book on U.S. environmental law. The detailed case histories make absorbing reading; the "morals" seem to follow almost of their own accord.

Thomas, William L., Jr., ed., *Man's Role in Changing the Face of the Earth* (Chicago: University of Chicago Press, 1956). Report of an international symposium held in 1955. This 1100-page volume does justice to the memory of George P. Marsh and to the vast scope of the subject. The fifty-three contributors include Carl Sauer, Clarence Glacken, Alexander Spoehr, Pierre Teilhard de Chardin, Marston Bates, and Lewis Mumford.

Whyte, William H., *The Last Landscape* (Garden City, N.Y.: Doubleday, 1968). The preservation of open space in and near cities, with an emphasis on suburban design.

Chapter 8

Anderson, Edgar, *Plants, Man and Life* (Berkeley and Los Angeles: University of California Press, 1969; paperback). A classic account of the evolving relationship between man and plants, including both crop plants and weeds.

Bennett, George W., *Management of Artificial Lakes and Ponds* (New York: Reinhold, 1962). Practical ecology, as its title indicates.

Brainerd, John W., *Nature Study for Conservation* (New York: Macmillan, 1971). An amazing compendium of information on understanding and managing land, from garden plots to wilderness areas. For those who are tired of too much theory and too little practical advice, this is the ideal book.

Evans, Howard Ensign, *Life on a Little-Known Planet* (New York: Delta, 1970; paperback). The planet is Earth, and the subjects of this delightful book are the familiar but generally unknown insects about us. Evans is a noted entomologist, a skilled writer, and as his readers know, an effective conservationist.

Geertz, Clifford, *Agricultural Involution: The Processes of Ecological Change in Indonesia* (Berkeley: University of California Press, 1968). An ecological anthropologist describes how man and the environment interact, for better or worse, in Indonesia. A careful study of the ways in which regional ecology and agricultural customs can limit the carrying capacity of the land for man.

Hickling, C. F., *Fish Culture* (London: Faber, 1971). Another practical book;

it contains everything one might want to know about the raising of fish for food, including fish ponds, fish culture in rice fields, and fish culture in running water and seawater. Not intended as light reading.

Hoskins, W. G., *The Making of the English Landscape* (Harmondsworth, Eng.: Pelican, 1970; paperback). The unique character of the English landscape is seen as the result of human intervention from pre-Roman times. Hoskins demonstrates the importance of history in furthering ecological understanding.

Jacobs, Jane, *The Death and Life of Great American Cities* (New York: Vintage, 1961). She demonstrates that diversity is as important to urban man as it is to "natural" ecosystems.

Kieran, John, *A Natural History of New York City* (Boston: Houghton Mifflin, 1959). A surprising number and variety of creatures are still part of the urban environment.

Sauer, Carl O., *Agricultural Origins and Dispersals: The Domestication of Animals and Foodstuffs* (Cambridge, Mass.: Massachusetts Institute of Technology Press, 1969; paperback). Written by a great geographer who predicted, a third of a century ago, many of our present-day environmental problems. Extremely interesting and very clearly written. Should be read with Anderson (see above).

White, Gilbert, *The Natural History of Selborne* (London: Oxford, 1937; modern edition). First published in 1789, this book comprises the Reverend White's poems and letters about his observations of animal and plant life in his parish of Selborne in Hampshire. A testimonial not only to White's genius, but to an age and place in which man and nature could easily be viewed as one.

Chapter 9

Carr, Archie, *So Excellent a Fishe: A Natural History of Sea Turtles* (Garden City, N.Y.: Natural History Press, 1967). Neither Carr's style nor his knowledge of natural history is surpassed by any contemporary biologist. In no other book are the problems of the preservation of species so thoroughly explored. Superb reading.

Darling, F. Fraser, *A Herd of Red Deer* (Garden City, N.Y.: Doubleday, Anchor Books, 1964; paperback). Darling was one of the first to make clear, in this long-celebrated account of two years spent watching the red deer of the Scottish highlands, that the protection of a species depends on an intimate knowledge of its behavior.

Hediger, H., *Wild Animals in Captivity* (New York: Dover, 1964; paperback). The problems of keeping wild animals in zoos, and the lessons learned from long experience. Rich in anecdotes; very pleasant reading. By Europe's greatest zoo-keeper.

Chapter 10

Carr, Archie, *Ulendo: Travels of a Naturalist In and Out of Africa* (New York: Knopf, 1964). Carr's perception of nature is so clear and strong that in following him on his East African journeys the reader can experience the destruction of wilderness as a personal loss.

Dubos, René, *So Human an Animal* (New York: Scribner's, 1968). This book by a distinguished bacteriologist and human ecologist cuts through the false promises of scientism and technology to examine the real physical and spiritual needs of man.

Ellul, Jacques, *The Technological Society* (New York: Knopf, 1965). Technology analyzed as the driving force in our society, by one of the strongest critics of "progress." Profound and often somewhat complex.

Gabor, Dennis, *Innovations: Scientific, Technological and Social* (London: Oxford, 1970). Intended for laymen and scientists, this hundred-page book is a list of major inventions that are probably about to be made. Unlike some others who have played this game, Gabor, a Nobel Laureate in physics, comments on the social and environmental impact these inventions are likely to have.

Glacken, Clarence J., *Traces on the Rhodian Shore* (Berkeley and Los Angeles: University of California Press, 1967). The place of nature in western thought from ancient times to the end of the eighteenth century. A fine source book on this difficult subject.

Mumford, Lewis, *The Pentagon of Power* (*The Myth of the Machine*, Vol. II) (New York: Harcourt Brace Jovanovich, 1970). Technology in the context of history. Repetitious and overly speculative, but it explains the incredible destructiveness of our society and times better than any other work of non-fiction. All conservation reading should start with this book.

Thoreau, Henry David, *The Maine Woods* (New York: Crowell, 1961; paperback). When you forget what conservation is about, Thoreau reminds you.

Tolkien, J. R. R., *The Lord of the Rings*, 3 vols. (London: George Allen & Unwin, 1954). People either dislike these books or find them overwhelmingly rich in imagery, character delineation, and philosophic content; there seems to be no middle ground. Although Tolkien cautions against specific allegorical interpretations, it would be foolish not to see *The Lord of the Rings* as, in part, a parable of the ending of the natural world, grim, sad, thoroughly modern, and realistic despite the superficially happy conclusion and the fairy-tale format. I view it as the most powerful, if indirect, writing on the human implications of conservation.

Vonnegut, Kurt, Jr., *Cat's Cradle* (New York: Dell, 1965; paperback). A very funny book about the end of the world. Vonnegut understands that the wisdom and maturity of man are not commensurate with his powers.

Periodicals

Audubon. The National Audubon Society: New York (bimonthly). Broad coverage of conservation topics; careful reporting and fine writing. Best photography of any comparable magazine.

BioScience. American Institute of Biological Sciences: Washington, D.C. (monthly). A general biological journal with frequent articles on ecology, environmental quality, and conservation; also political comment and news. Mainly for persons with biological training.

Conservation Directory. National Wildlife Federation: Washington, D.C. (annual). A listing of private and governmental organizations, agencies, and officials concerned with natural resource use and management. Complete and very useful.

Consumer Reports. Consumers Union of U.S., Inc.: Mount Vernon, N.Y. (monthly). Contains occasional reports on consumer products that may have an adverse effect on the environment or on public health.

Daedalus. American Academy of Arts and Sciences: Boston (quarterly). Leading experts from all fields write scholarly articles on problems of world significance. Often contains important material on population and technology.

Environment (formerly *Scientist and Citizen*). Committee for Environmental Information: St. Louis, Missouri (ten issues per year). Tough, uncompromising articles about environmental pollution, intended for the layman. Carefully reviewed by an advisory board of distinguished scientists. Very readable.

National Geographic Magazine. National Geographic Society: Washington, D.C. (monthly). Often contains articles on vanishing peoples, wildlife, and natural communities. Excellent photographs and maps. Well researched.

Natural History. American Museum of Natural History: New York (monthly). Often includes semi-popular articles on conservation topics by noted biologists. An enjoyable magazine of high quality.

Nature in Focus: Bulletin of the European Information Centre for Nature Conservation. Council of Europe: Strasbourg (quarterly); and *Newsletter.* Council of Europe: London (bi-monthly). Excellent sources of information about conservation, especially in Europe. Good on political-legal aspects.

New Scientist. New Science Publications: London (weekly). A general science news magazine for scientists and educated laymen. British orientation, but the news and review articles will interest U.S. readers. Much on pollution and conservation; very high quality.

Oryx. Fauna Preservation Society: London (quarterly). Comprehensive survey of world conservation news, plus general articles on conservation and related biological subjects.

Red Data Books (five volumes at present). International Union for the Conservation of Nature: Morges, Switzerland. The central listings and descriptions of the endangered mammals, birds, reptiles and amphibians, fish, and flowering plants of the world. Brought up to date at frequent intervals by supplements. The major source of information about endangered animals; however, non-inclusion in these lists does not necessarily mean that a species is safe. Should be available in every public library.

Annual Report of the Smithsonian Institution Center for Short-Lived Phenomena. Cambridge, Mass. Brief accounts, with sources, of all the major (and some minor) fish kills, oil spills, insect irruptions, earthquakes, volcanic eruptions, and the like, for the preceding year. Inexpensive and very complete.

Sports Illustrated. Time Inc.: Chicago (weekly). Often contains well-written and informative articles which reflect the conservation consciousness of hunters and fishermen.

The New York Times. New York (daily). Very complete and detailed newspaper coverage of environmental and conservation topics. Has a useful index service.

Index

353